Student Solutions Manual for

COLLEGE MATHEMATICS II

Custom Edition

PATRICIA FOARD

Edited by Brian K. Saltzer

Taken from
Student Solutions Manual by Patricia Foard for
Algebra & Trigonometry, Second Edition, by Robert Blitzer

PEARSON
Custom
Publishing

PEARSON
Prentice
Hall

Taken from:

Student Solutions Manual
by Patricia Foard
for *Algebra & Trigonometry*, Second Edition
by Robert Blitzer
Copyright © 2004 by Pearson Education, Inc.
Published by Prentice Hall
Upper Saddle River, New Jersey 07458

This special edition published in cooperation with Pearson Custom Publishing.

Printed in the United States of America

10 9 8 7 6 5

ISBN 0-536-81378-7

BA 999231

BK

Please visit our web site at *www.pearsoncustom.com*

PEARSON CUSTOM PUBLISHING
75 Arlington Street, Suite 300, Boston, MA 02116
A Pearson Education Company

Contents

From: *Student Solutions Manual for Algebra and Trigonometry,* Second Edition by Patricia Foard

Chapter 1

Check Point Exercises

1. **a.** A 30° angle lies in quadrant I and is shown in the following graph.

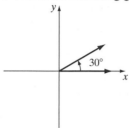

  b. A 210° angle is a positive angle. It has a counterclockwise rotation of 180° followed by a counterclockwise rotation of 30°. The angle lies in quadrant III and is shown in the following graph.

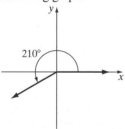

  c. A –120° angle is a negative angle. It has a clockwise rotation of 90° followed by a clockwise rotation of 30° The angle lies in quadrant III and is shown in the following graph.

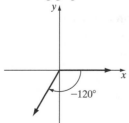

  d. A 390° angle is a positive angle. It has a counterclockwise rotation of 360°, one complete rotation, followed by a counterclockwise rotation of 30°. The angle lies in quadrant I and is shown in the following graph.

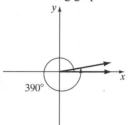

2. **a.** For a 400° angle, subtract 360° to find a positive coterminal angle.
$400° – 360° = 40°$

  b. For a –135° angle, add 360° to find a positive coterminal angle.
$–135° + 360° = 225°$

3. **a.** $\theta = 78°$
Complement $= 90° – 78° = 12°$
Supplement $= 180° – 78° = 102°$
For a 78° angle, the complement is a 12° angle and the supplement is a 102° angle.

  b. $\alpha = 150°$
For the angle's complement, we consider subtracting 150° from 90°. The difference is negative. Because we use only positive angles for complements, a 150° angle has no complement. It does, however, have a supplement.
Supplement $= 180° – 150° = 30°$
The supplement of a 150° angle is a 30° angle.

4. The radian measure of a central angle is the length of the intercepted arc, *s,* divided by the circle's radius, *r*. The length of the intercepted arc is 42 feet: *s* = 42 feet. The circle's radius is 12 feet: *r* = 12 feet. Now

use the formula for radian measure to find the radian measure of θ.

$$\theta = \frac{s}{r} = \frac{42 \text{ feet}}{12 \text{ feet}} = 3.5$$

Thus, the radian measure of θ is 3.5

5. a. $60° = 60° \cdot \frac{\pi \text{ radians}}{180°} = \frac{60\pi}{180} \text{ radians}$

$= \frac{\pi}{3} \text{ radians}$

b. $270° = 270° \cdot \frac{\pi \text{ radians}}{180°} = \frac{270\pi}{180} \text{ radians}$

$= \frac{3\pi}{2} \text{ radians}$

c. $-300° = -300° \cdot \frac{\pi \text{ radians}}{180°} = \frac{-300\pi}{180} \text{ radians}$

$= -\frac{5\pi}{3} \text{ radians}$

6. a. $\frac{\pi}{4} \text{ radians} = \frac{\pi \text{ radians}}{4} \cdot \frac{180°}{\pi \text{ radians}}$

$= \frac{180°}{4} = 45°$

b. $-\frac{4\pi}{3} \text{ radians} = -\frac{4\pi \text{ radians}}{3} \cdot \frac{180°}{\pi}$

$= -\frac{4 \cdot 180°}{3} = -240°$

c. $6 \text{ radians} = 6 \text{ radians} \cdot \frac{180°}{\pi \text{ radians}}$

$= \frac{6 \cdot 180°}{\pi} \approx 343.8°$

7. The formula $s = r\theta$ can only be used when θ is expressed in radians. Thus, we begin by converting 45° to radians. Multiply by $\frac{\pi \text{ radians}}{180°}$.

$45° = 45° \cdot \frac{\pi \text{ radians}}{180°} = \frac{45}{180}\pi \text{ radians}$

$= \frac{\pi}{4} \text{ radians}$

Now we can use the formula $s = r\theta$ to find the length of the arc. The circle's radius is 6 inches : $r = 6$ inches. The measure of the central angle in radians is $\frac{\pi}{4} : \theta = \frac{\pi}{4}$. The length of the arc intercepted by this central angle is

$s = r\theta = (6 \text{ inches})\left(\frac{\pi}{4}\right) = \frac{6\pi}{4} \text{ inches} \approx 4.71 \text{ inches.}$

8. We are given ω, the angular speed.
$\omega = 45$ revolutions per minute
We use the formula $v = r\omega$ to find v, the linear speed. Before applying the formula, we must express ω in radians per minute.

$\omega = \frac{45 \text{ revolutions}}{1 \text{ minute}} \cdot \frac{2\pi \text{ radians}}{1 \text{ revolutions}}$

$= \frac{90\pi \text{ radians}}{1 \text{ minute}} \text{ or } \frac{90\pi}{1 \text{ minute}}$

The angular speed of the propeller is 90π radians per minute. The linear speed is

$v = r\omega = 1.5 \text{ inches} \cdot \frac{90\pi}{1 \text{ minute}} = \frac{135\pi \text{ inches}}{\text{minute}}$

The linear speed is 135π inches per minute, which is approximately 424 inches per minute.

Exercise Set 1.1

1. $90° < 145° < 180°$
quadrant II

3. $-100° + 360° = 260°$
$180° < 260° < 270°$
quadrant III

5. $362° - 360° = 2°$
$0° < 2° < 90°$
quadrant I

7. obtuse
$(90° < \theta < 180°)$

9. straight
$$\left(\frac{1}{2} \text{ rotation}\right)$$

11. 135° is a positive angle. It has a counter-clockwise rotation of 90° followed by a counterclockwise rotation of 45°. The angle lies in quadrant II and is shown in the following graph.

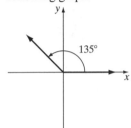

13. −150° is a negative angle. It has a clockwise rotation of 90° followed by a clockwise rotation of 60°. The angle lies in quadrant III and is shown in the following graph.

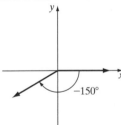

15. 420° is a positive angle. It has a counter-clockwise rotation of 360°, one complete rotation, followed by a counterclockwise rotation of 60°. The angle lies in quadrant I and is shown in the following graph.

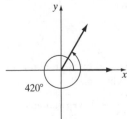

17. −90° is a negative angle. It has a clockwise rotation of 90°. The angle is a quadrantal angle and is shown in the following graph.

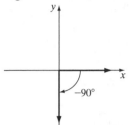

19. $395° - 360° = 35°$

21. $-150° + 360° = 210°$

23. $-45° + 360° = 315°$

25. 52°
Complement = $90° - 52° = 38°$;
Supplement = $180° - 52° = 128°$

27. 37.4°
Complement = $90° - 37.4° = 52.6°$;
Supplement = $180° - 37.4° = 142.6°$

29. 111°
Since subtracting 111° from 90° is negative, there is no complement.
Supplement = $180° - 111° = 69°$

31. $\theta = \dfrac{s}{r} = \dfrac{40 \text{ inches}}{10 \text{ inches}} = 4 \text{ radians}$

33. $\theta = \dfrac{s}{r} = \dfrac{8 \text{ yards}}{6 \text{ yards}} = \dfrac{4}{3} \text{ radians}$

35. $\theta = \dfrac{s}{r} = \dfrac{400 \text{ centimeters}}{100 \text{ centimeters}} = 4 \text{ radians}$

37. $45° = 45° \cdot \dfrac{\pi \text{ radians}}{180°}$

$\qquad = \dfrac{45\pi}{180} \text{ radians}$

$\qquad = \dfrac{\pi}{4} \text{ radians}$

39. $135° = 135° \cdot \dfrac{\pi \text{ radians}}{180°}$

$\qquad = \dfrac{135\pi}{180} \text{ radians}$

$\qquad = \dfrac{3\pi}{4} \text{ radians}$

41. $300° = 300° \cdot \dfrac{\pi \text{ radians}}{180°}$

$\qquad = \dfrac{300\pi}{180} \text{ radians}$

$\qquad = \dfrac{5\pi}{3} \text{ radians}$

43. $-225° = -225° \cdot \dfrac{\pi \text{ radians}}{180°}$

$\qquad = -\dfrac{225\pi}{180} \text{ radians}$

$\qquad = -\dfrac{5\pi}{4} \text{ radians}$

45. $\dfrac{\pi}{2} \text{ radians} = \dfrac{\pi \text{ radians}}{2} \cdot \dfrac{180°}{\pi \text{ radians}}$

$\qquad = \dfrac{180°}{2}$

$\qquad = 90°$

47. $\dfrac{2\pi}{3} \text{ radians} = \dfrac{2\pi \text{ radians}}{3} \cdot \dfrac{180°}{\pi \text{ radians}}$

$\qquad = \dfrac{2 \cdot 180°}{3}$

$\qquad = 120°$

49. $\dfrac{7\pi}{6} \text{ radians} = \dfrac{7\pi \text{ radians}}{6} \cdot \dfrac{180°}{\pi \text{ radians}}$

$\qquad = \dfrac{7 \cdot 180°}{6}$

$\qquad = 210°$

51. $-3\pi \text{ radians} = -3\pi \text{ radians} \cdot \dfrac{180°}{\pi \text{ radians}}$

$\qquad = -3 \cdot 180°$

$\qquad = -540°$

53. $18° = 18° \cdot \dfrac{\pi \text{ radians}}{180°}$

$\qquad = \dfrac{18\pi}{180} \text{ radians}$

$\qquad \approx 0.31 \text{ radians}$

55. $-40° = -40° \cdot \dfrac{\pi \text{ radians}}{180°}$

$\qquad = -\dfrac{40\pi}{180} \text{ radians}$

$\qquad \approx -0.70 \text{ radians}$

57. $200° = 200° \cdot \dfrac{\pi \text{ radians}}{180°}$

$\qquad = \dfrac{200\pi}{180} \text{ radians}$

$\qquad \approx 3.49 \text{ radians}$

59. $2 \text{ radians} = 2 \text{ radians} \cdot \dfrac{180°}{\pi \text{ radians}}$

$\qquad = \dfrac{2 \cdot 180°}{\pi}$

$\qquad \approx 114.59°$

61. $\dfrac{\pi}{13} \text{ radians} = \dfrac{\pi \text{ radians}}{13} \cdot \dfrac{180°}{\pi \text{ radians}}$

$\qquad = \dfrac{180°}{13}$

$\qquad \approx 13.85°$

63. $-4.8 \text{ radians} = -4.8 \text{ radians} \cdot \dfrac{180°}{\pi \text{ radians}}$

$\qquad = \dfrac{-4.8 \cdot 180°}{\pi}$

$\qquad \approx -275.02°$

65. $r = 12$ inches, $\theta = 45°$
Begin by converting 45° to radians, in order to use the formula $s = r\theta$.

$45° = 45° \cdot \dfrac{\pi \text{ radians}}{180°} = \dfrac{\pi}{4} \text{ radians}$

Now use the formula $s = r\theta$.

$$s = r\theta = 12 \cdot \frac{\pi}{4} = 3\pi \text{ inches} \approx 9.42 \text{ inches}$$

67. $r = 8$ feet, $\theta = 225°$

Begin by converting 225° to radians, in order to use the formula $s = r\theta$.

$$225° = 225° \cdot \frac{\pi \text{ radians}}{180°} = \frac{5\pi}{4} \text{ radians}$$

Now use the formula $s = r\theta$.

$$s = r\theta = 8 \cdot \frac{5\pi}{4} = 10\pi \text{ feet} \approx 31.42 \text{ feet}$$

69. 6 revolutions per second

$$= \frac{6 \text{ revolutions}}{1 \text{ second}} \cdot \frac{2\pi \text{ radians}}{1 \text{ revolutions}} = \frac{12\pi \text{ radians}}{1 \text{ seconds}}$$

$$= 12\pi \text{ radians per second}$$

71. First, convert to degrees.

$$\frac{1}{6} \text{ revolution} = \frac{1}{6} \text{ revolution} \cdot \frac{360°}{1 \text{ revolution}}$$

$$= \frac{1}{6} \cdot 360° = 60°$$

Now, convert 60° to radians.

$$60° = 60° \cdot \frac{\pi \text{ radians}}{180°} = \frac{60\pi}{180} \text{ radians}$$

$$= \frac{\pi}{3} \text{ radians}$$

Therefore, $\frac{1}{6}$ revolution is equivalent to 60° or $\frac{\pi}{3}$ radians.

73. The distance that the tip of the minute hand moves is given by its arc length, s. Since $s = r\theta$, we begin by finding r and θ. We are given that $r = 8$ inches. The minute hand moves from 12 to 2 o'clock, or $\frac{1}{6}$ of a complete revolution. The formula $s = r\theta$ can only be used when θ is expressed in radians. We must convert $\frac{1}{6}$ revolution to radians.

$$\frac{1}{6} \text{ revolution} = \frac{1}{6} \text{ revolution} \cdot \frac{2\pi \text{ radians}}{1 \text{ revolution}}$$

$$= \frac{\pi}{3} \text{ radians}$$

The distance the tip of the minute hand moves is

$$s = r\theta = (8 \text{ inches})\left(\frac{\pi}{3}\right) = \frac{8\pi}{3} \text{ inches}$$

$$\approx 8.38 \text{ inches.}$$

75. The length of each arc is given by $s = r\theta$. We are given that $r = 24$ inches and $\theta = 90°$. The formula $s = r\theta$ can only be used when θ is expressed in radians.

$$90° = 90° \cdot \frac{\pi \text{ radians}}{180°} = \frac{90\pi}{180} \text{ radians}$$

$$= \frac{\pi}{2} \text{ radians}$$

The length of each arc is

$$s = r\theta = (24 \text{ inches})\left(\frac{\pi}{2}\right) = 12\pi \text{ inches}$$

$$\approx 37.70 \text{ inches.}$$

77. Recall that $\theta = \frac{s}{r}$. We are given that $s = 8000$ miles and $r = 4000$ miles.

$$\theta = \frac{s}{r} = \frac{8000 \text{ miles}}{4000 \text{ miles}} = 2 \text{ radians}$$

Now, convert 2 radians to degrees.

$$2 \text{ radians} = 2 \text{ radians} \cdot \frac{180°}{\pi \text{ radians}} \approx 114.59°$$

79. Recall that $s = r\theta$. We are given that $r = 4000$ miles and $\theta = 30°$. The formula $s = r\theta$ can only be used when θ is expressed in radians.

$$30° = 30° \cdot \frac{\pi \text{ radians}}{180°} = \frac{30\pi}{180} \text{ radians}$$

$$= \frac{\pi}{6} \text{ radians}$$

$$s = r\theta = (4000 \text{ miles})\left(\frac{\pi}{6}\right) \approx 2094 \text{ miles}$$

To the nearest mile, the distance from A to B is 2094 miles.

81. Linear speed is given by $v = r\omega$. We are given that $\omega = \dfrac{\pi}{12}$ radians per hour and $r = 4000$ miles. Therefore,

$$v = r\omega = (4000 \text{ miles})\left(\frac{\pi}{12}\right)$$

$$= \frac{4000\pi}{12} \text{ miles per hour}$$

$$\approx 1047 \text{ miles per hour}$$

The linear speed is about 1047 miles per hour.

83. Linear speed is given by $v = r\omega$. We are given that $r = 12$ feet and the wheel rotates at 20 revolutions per minute.
20 revolutions per minute

$$= 20 \text{ revolutions per minute} \cdot \frac{2\pi \text{ radians}}{1 \text{ revolution}}$$

$$= 40\pi \text{ radians per minute}$$
$$v = r\omega = (12 \text{ feet})(40\pi)$$

$$\approx 1508 \text{ feet per minute}$$

The linear speed of the wheel is about 1508 feet per minute.

85.–95. Answers may vary.

97.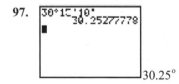
30.25°

99.
30° 25'12"

101. A right angle measures 90° and

$$90° = \frac{\pi}{2} \text{ radians} \approx 1.57 \text{ radians}.$$

If $\theta = \dfrac{3}{2}$ radians $= 1.5$ radians, θ is smaller than a right angle.

103. $s = r\theta$
Begin by changing $\theta = 26°$ to radians.

$$26° = 26° \cdot \frac{\pi}{180°} = \frac{13\pi}{90} \text{ radians}$$

$$s = 4000 \cdot \frac{13\pi}{90}$$

$$\approx 1815 \text{ miles}$$

To the nearest mile, Miami, Florida is 1815 miles north of the equator.

Section 1.2

Checkpoint Exercises

1. Use the Pythagorean Theorem, $c^2 = a^2 + b^2$, to find c.
$a = 3, \ b = 4$

$$c^2 = a^2 + b^2 = 3^2 + 4^2 = 9 + 16 = 25$$

$$c = \sqrt{25} = 5$$

Referring to these lengths as opposite, adjacent, and hypotenuse, we have

$$\sin\theta = \frac{\text{opposite}}{\text{hypotenuse}} = \frac{3}{5}$$

$$\cos\theta = \frac{\text{adjacent}}{\text{hypotenuse}} = \frac{4}{5}$$

$$\tan\theta = \frac{\text{opposite}}{\text{adjacent}} = \frac{3}{4}$$

$$\csc\theta = \frac{\text{hypotenuse}}{\text{opposite}} = \frac{5}{3}$$

$$\sec\theta = \frac{\text{hypotenuse}}{\text{adjacent}} = \frac{5}{4}$$

$$\cot\theta = \frac{\text{adjacent}}{\text{opposite}} = \frac{4}{3}$$

2. Apply the definitions of these three trigonometric functions.

$$\csc 45° = \frac{\text{length of hypotenuse}}{\text{length of side opposite } 45°}$$

$$= \frac{\sqrt{2}}{1} = \sqrt{2}$$

$$\sec 45° = \frac{\text{length of hypotenuse}}{\text{length of side adjacent to } 45°}$$

$$= \frac{\sqrt{2}}{1} = \sqrt{2}$$

$$\cot 45° = \frac{\text{length of side adjacent to } 45°}{\text{length of side opposite } 45°}$$

$$= \frac{1}{1} = 1$$

3.

$$\tan 60° = \frac{\text{length of side opposite } 60°}{\text{length of side adjacent to } 60°}$$

$$= \frac{\sqrt{3}}{1} = \sqrt{3}$$

$$\tan 30° = \frac{\text{length of side opposite } 30°}{\text{length of side adjacent to } 30°}$$

$$= \frac{1}{\sqrt{3}} = \frac{1}{\sqrt{3}} \cdot \frac{\sqrt{3}}{3} = \frac{\sqrt{3}}{3}$$

4. $\tan \theta = \dfrac{\sin \theta}{\cos \theta} = \dfrac{\dfrac{2}{3}}{\dfrac{\sqrt{5}}{3}}$

$$= \frac{2}{3} \cdot \frac{3}{\sqrt{5}} = \frac{2}{\sqrt{5}}$$

$$= \frac{2}{\sqrt{5}} \cdot \frac{\sqrt{5}}{\sqrt{5}} = \frac{2\sqrt{5}}{5}$$

$$\csc \theta = \frac{1}{\sin \theta} = \frac{1}{\dfrac{2}{3}} = \frac{3}{2}$$

$$\sec \theta = \frac{1}{\cos \theta} = \frac{1}{\dfrac{\sqrt{5}}{3}} = \frac{3}{\sqrt{5}}$$

$$= \frac{3}{\sqrt{5}} \cdot \frac{\sqrt{5}}{\sqrt{5}} = \frac{3\sqrt{5}}{5}$$

$$\cot \theta = \frac{1}{\tan \theta} = \frac{1}{\dfrac{2}{\sqrt{5}}} = \frac{\sqrt{5}}{2}$$

5. We can find the value of cos_ by using the Pythagorean identity.

$$\sin^2 \theta + \cos^2 \theta = 1$$

$$\left(\frac{1}{2}\right)^2 + \cos^2 \theta = 1$$

$$\frac{1}{4} + \cos^2 \theta = 1$$

$$\cos^2 \theta = 1 - \frac{1}{4}$$

$$\cos^2 \theta = \frac{3}{4}$$

$$\cos \theta = \sqrt{\frac{3}{4}} = \frac{\sqrt{3}}{2}$$

6. a. $\sin 46° = \cos(90° - 46°) = \cos 44°$

b. $\cot \dfrac{\pi}{12} = \tan\left(\dfrac{\pi}{2} - \dfrac{\pi}{12}\right)$

$$= \tan\left(\frac{6\pi}{12} - \frac{\pi}{12}\right)$$

$$= \tan \frac{5\pi}{12}$$

7.

Scientific Calculator Solution			
Function	**Mode**	**Keystrokes**	**Display** (rounded to four places)
a. sin 72.8°	Degree	72.8 SIN	0.9553
b. csc 1.5	Radian	1.5 SIN 1/x	1.0025

Graphing Calculator Solution			
Function	**Mode**	**Keystrokes**	**Display** (rounded to four places)
a. sin 72.8°	Degree	SIN 72.8 ENTER	0.9553
b. csc 1.5	Radian	(SIN 1.5) x^{-1} ENTER	1.0025

8. Because we have a known angle, an unknown opposite side, and a known adjacent side, we select the tangent function.

$$\tan 24° = \frac{a}{750}$$

$$a = 750 \tan 24°$$

$$a \approx 750(0.4452) \approx 334$$

The distance across the lake is approximately 334 yards.

9. $\tan\theta = \dfrac{\text{side opposite}}{\text{side adjacent}} = \dfrac{14}{10}$

Use a calculator in degree mode to find θ.

Scientific Calculator	Graphing Calculator
TAN⁻¹ (14 ÷ 10) ENTER	TAN (14 ÷ 10) ENTER

The display should show approximately 54. Thus, the angle of elevation of the sun is approximately 54°.

Exercise Set 1.2

1. $c^2 = 9^2 + 12^2 = 225$

$c = \sqrt{225} = 15$

$\sin\theta = \dfrac{\text{opposite}}{\text{hypotenuse}} = \dfrac{9}{15} = \dfrac{3}{5}$

$\cos\theta = \dfrac{\text{adjacent}}{\text{hypotenuse}} = \dfrac{12}{15} = \dfrac{4}{5}$

$\tan\theta = \dfrac{\text{opposite}}{\text{adjacent}} = \dfrac{9}{12} = \dfrac{3}{4}$

$\csc\theta = \dfrac{\text{hypotenuse}}{\text{opposite}} = \dfrac{15}{9} = \dfrac{5}{3}$

$\sec\theta = \dfrac{\text{hypotenuse}}{\text{adjacent}} = \dfrac{15}{12} = \dfrac{5}{4}$

$\cot\theta = \dfrac{\text{adjacent}}{\text{opposite}} = \dfrac{12}{9} = \dfrac{4}{3}$

3. $a^2 + 21^2 = 29^2$

$a^2 = 841 - 441 = 400$

$a = \sqrt{400} = 20$

$\sin\theta = \dfrac{\text{opposite}}{\text{hypotenuse}} = \dfrac{20}{29}$

$\cos\theta = \dfrac{\text{adjacent}}{\text{hypotenuse}} = \dfrac{21}{29}$

$\tan\theta = \dfrac{\text{opposite}}{\text{adjacent}} = \dfrac{20}{21}$

$\csc\theta = \dfrac{\text{hypotenuse}}{\text{opposite}} = \dfrac{29}{20}$

$\sec\theta = \dfrac{\text{hypotenuse}}{\text{adjacent}} = \dfrac{29}{21}$

$\cot\theta = \dfrac{\text{adjacent}}{\text{opposite}} = \dfrac{21}{20}$

5. $10^2 + b^2 = 26^2$

$b^2 = 676 - 100 = 576$

$b = \sqrt{576} = 24$

$\sin\theta = \dfrac{\text{opposite}}{\text{hypotenuse}} = \dfrac{10}{26} = \dfrac{5}{13}$

$\cos\theta = \dfrac{\text{adjacent}}{\text{hypotenuse}} = \dfrac{24}{26} = \dfrac{12}{13}$

$\tan\theta = \dfrac{\text{opposite}}{\text{adjacent}} = \dfrac{10}{24} = \dfrac{5}{12}$

$\csc\theta = \dfrac{\text{hypotenuse}}{\text{opposite}} = \dfrac{26}{10} = \dfrac{13}{5}$

$\sec\theta = \dfrac{\text{hypotenuse}}{\text{adjacent}} = \dfrac{26}{24} = \dfrac{13}{12}$

$\cot\theta = \dfrac{\text{adjacent}}{\text{opposite}} = \dfrac{24}{10} = \dfrac{12}{5}$

7. $21^2 + b^2 = 35^2$

$b^2 = 1225 - 441 = 784$

$b = \sqrt{784} = 28$

$\sin\theta = \dfrac{\text{opposite}}{\text{hypotenuse}} = \dfrac{28}{35} = \dfrac{4}{5}$

$\cos\theta = \dfrac{\text{adjacent}}{\text{hypotenuse}} = \dfrac{21}{35} = \dfrac{3}{5}$

$\tan\theta = \dfrac{\text{opposite}}{\text{adjacent}} = \dfrac{28}{21} = \dfrac{4}{3}$

$\csc\theta = \dfrac{\text{hypotenuse}}{\text{opposite}} = \dfrac{35}{28} = \dfrac{5}{4}$

$\sec\theta = \dfrac{\text{hypotenuse}}{\text{adjacent}} = \dfrac{35}{21} = \dfrac{5}{3}$

$\cot\theta = \dfrac{\text{adjacent}}{\text{opposite}} = \dfrac{21}{28} = \dfrac{3}{4}$

9. $\cos 30° = \dfrac{\text{length of side adjacent to } 30°}{\text{length of hypotenuse}}$

$= \dfrac{\sqrt{3}}{2}$

11. $\sec 45° = \dfrac{\text{length of hypotenuse}}{\text{length of side adjacent to } 45°}$

$\qquad = \dfrac{\sqrt{2}}{1} = \sqrt{2}$

13. $\tan \dfrac{\pi}{3} = \tan 60°$

$\qquad = \dfrac{\text{length of side opposite } 60°}{\text{length of side adjacent to } 60°}$

$\qquad = \dfrac{\sqrt{3}}{1} = \sqrt{3}$

15. $\sin \dfrac{\pi}{4} - \cos \dfrac{\pi}{4} = \sin 45° - \cos 45°$

$\qquad\qquad = \dfrac{1}{\sqrt{2}} - \dfrac{1}{\sqrt{2}} = 0$

17. $\tan \theta = \dfrac{\sin \theta}{\cos \theta} = \dfrac{\frac{8}{17}}{\frac{15}{17}} = \dfrac{8}{15}$

$\csc \theta = \dfrac{1}{\sin \theta} = \dfrac{1}{\frac{8}{17}} = \dfrac{17}{8}$

$\sec \theta = \dfrac{1}{\cos \theta} = \dfrac{1}{\frac{15}{17}} = \dfrac{17}{15}$

$\cot \theta = \dfrac{\cos \theta}{\sin \theta} = \dfrac{\frac{15}{17}}{\frac{8}{17}} = \dfrac{15}{8}$

19.

$\tan \theta = \dfrac{\sin \theta}{\cos \theta} = \dfrac{\frac{1}{3}}{\frac{2\sqrt{2}}{3}} = \dfrac{1}{2\sqrt{2}}$

$\qquad = \dfrac{1}{2\sqrt{2}} \cdot \dfrac{\sqrt{2}}{\sqrt{2}} = \dfrac{\sqrt{2}}{4}$

$\csc \theta = \dfrac{1}{\sin \theta} = \dfrac{1}{\frac{1}{3}} = \dfrac{3}{1} = 3$

$\sec \theta = \dfrac{1}{\cos \theta} = \dfrac{1}{\frac{2\sqrt{2}}{3}} = \dfrac{3}{2\sqrt{2}}$

$\qquad = \dfrac{3}{2\sqrt{2}} \cdot \dfrac{\sqrt{2}}{\sqrt{2}} = \dfrac{3\sqrt{2}}{4}$

$\cot \theta = \dfrac{\cos \theta}{\sin \theta} = \dfrac{\frac{2\sqrt{2}}{3}}{\frac{1}{3}} = \dfrac{2\sqrt{2}}{1} = 2\sqrt{2}$

21. $\sin^2 \theta + \cos^2 \theta = 1$

$\left(\dfrac{6}{7}\right)^2 + \cos^2 \theta = 1$

$\dfrac{36}{49} + \cos^2 \theta = 1$

$\cos^2 \theta = 1 - \dfrac{36}{49}$

$\cos^2 \theta = \dfrac{13}{49}$

$\cos \theta = \sqrt{\dfrac{13}{49}} = \dfrac{\sqrt{13}}{7}$

23. $\sin^2 \theta + \cos^2 \theta = 1$

$$\left(\frac{\sqrt{39}}{8}\right)^2 + \cos^2\theta = 1$$

$$\frac{39}{64} + \cos^2\theta = 1$$

$$\cos^2\theta = 1 - \frac{39}{64}$$

$$\cos^2\theta = \frac{25}{64}$$

$$\cos\theta = \sqrt{\frac{25}{64}} = \frac{5}{8}$$

25. $\sin 37° \csc 37° = \sin 37° \cdot \dfrac{1}{\sin 37°} = 1$

27. $\sin^2\theta + \cos^2\theta = 1$

$\quad \sin^2\dfrac{\pi}{9} + \cos^2\dfrac{\pi}{9} = 1$

29. $\quad 1 + \tan^2\theta = \sec^2\theta$

$\quad 1 + \tan^2 23° = \sec^2 23°$

$\quad\qquad\qquad 1 = \sec^2 23° - \tan^2 23°$

31. $\sin 7° = \cos(90° - 7°) = \cos 83°$

33. $\csc 25° = \sec(90° - 25°) = \sec 65°$

35. $\tan\dfrac{\pi}{9} = \cot\left(\dfrac{\pi}{2} - \dfrac{\pi}{9}\right)$

$\qquad\quad = \cot\left(\dfrac{9\pi}{18} - \dfrac{2\pi}{18}\right)$

$\qquad\quad = \cot\dfrac{7\pi}{18}$

37. $\cos\dfrac{2\pi}{5} = \sin\left(\dfrac{\pi}{2} - \dfrac{2\pi}{5}\right)$

$\qquad\quad = \sin\left(\dfrac{5\pi}{10} - \dfrac{4\pi}{10}\right)$

$\qquad\quad = \sin\dfrac{\pi}{10}$

39.

Scientific Calculator Solution			
Function	**Mode**	**Keystrokes**	**Display** (rounded to four places)
sin 38°	Degree	38 [SIN]	.6157

Graphing Calculator Solution			
Function	**Mode**	**Keystrokes**	**Display** (rounded to four places)
sin 38°	Degree	[SIN] 38 [ENTER]	.6157

41.

Scientific Calculator Solution			
Function	**Mode**	**Keystrokes**	**Display** (rounded to four places)
tan 32.7°	Degree	32.7 [TAN]	.6420

Graphing Calculator Solution			
Function	**Mode**	**Keystrokes**	**Display** (rounded to four places)
tan 32.7°	Degree	[TAN] 32.7 [ENTER]	.6420

43.

Scientific Calculator Solution			
Function	**Mode**	**Keystrokes**	**Display** (rounded to four places)
csc 17°	Degree	17 [SIN] [1/x]	3.4203

Graphing Calculator Solution			
Function	**Mode**	**Keystrokes**	**Display** (rounded to four places)
csc17°	Degree	(| [SIN] 17 |) [x⁻¹] [ENTER]	3.4203

45.

Scientific Calculator Solution			
Function	**Mode**	**Keystrokes**	**Display** (rounded to four places)
$\cos\dfrac{\pi}{10}$	Radian	[π] ÷ [10] [=] [COS]	.9511

Graphing Calculator Solution			
Function	**Mode**	**Keystrokes**	**Display** (rounded to four places)
$\cos\dfrac{\pi}{10}$	Radian	[COS] (| π ÷ 10 |) [ENTER]	.9511

47.

Scientific Calculator Solution			
Function	**Mode**	**Keystrokes**	**Display** (rounded to four places)
$\cot \dfrac{\pi}{12}$	Radian	π ÷ 12 ▯ TAN 1/x	3.7321

Graphing Calculator Solution			
Function	**Mode**	**Keystrokes**	**Display** (rounded to four places)
$\cot \dfrac{\pi}{12}$	Radian	(TAN (π ÷ 12)) x^{-1} ENTER	3.7321

49. $\tan 37° = \dfrac{a}{250}$

$a = 250 \tan 37°$

$a \approx 250(0.7536) \approx 188$ cm

51. $\cos 34° = \dfrac{b}{220}$

$b = 220 \cos 34°$

$b \approx 220(0.8290) \approx 182$ in.

53. $\sin 23° = \dfrac{16}{c}$

$c = \dfrac{16}{\sin 23°} \approx \dfrac{16}{0.3907} \approx 41$ m

55.

Scientific Calculator	Graphing Calculator	Display (rounded to the nearest degree)
.2974 $\boxed{\text{SIN}^{-1}}$	$\boxed{\text{SIN}^{-1}}$ .2974 $\boxed{\text{ENTER}}$	17

If $\sin \theta = 0.2974$, then $\theta \approx 17°$.

57.

Scientific Calculator	Graphing Calculator	Display (rounded to the nearest degree)
4.6252 $\boxed{\text{TAN}^{-1}}$	$\boxed{\text{TAN}^{-1}}$ 4.6252 $\boxed{\text{ENTER}}$	78

If $\tan\theta = 4.6252$, then $\theta \approx 78°$.

59.

Scientific Calculator	Graphing Calculator	Display (rounded to three places)
.4112 $\boxed{\text{COS}^{-1}}$	$\boxed{\text{COS}^{-1}}$ .4112 $\boxed{\text{ENTER}}$	1.147

If $\cos\theta = 0.4112$, then $\theta \approx 1.147$ radians.

61.

Scientific Calculator	Graphing Calculator	Display (rounded to three places)
.4169 $\boxed{\text{TAN}^{-1}}$	$\boxed{\text{TAN}^{-1}}$ .4169 $\boxed{\text{ENTER}}$	.395

If $\tan\theta = 0.4169$, then $\theta \approx 0.395$ radians.

63. $\tan 40° = \dfrac{a}{630}$

$a = 630 \tan 40°$

$a \approx 630(0.8391) \approx 529$

The distance across the lake is approximately 529 yards.

65. $\tan\theta = \dfrac{125}{172}$

Use a calculator in degree mode to find θ.

Scientific Calculator	Graphing Calculator
125 $\boxed{\div}$ 172 $\boxed{=}$ $\boxed{\text{TAN}^{-1}}$	$\boxed{\text{TAN}^{-1}}$ $\boxed{(}$ 125 $\boxed{\div}$ 172 $\boxed{)}$ $\boxed{\text{ENTER}}$

The display should show approximately 36. Thus, the angle of elevation of the sun is approximately 36°.

67. $\sin 10° = \dfrac{500}{c}$

$c = \dfrac{500}{\sin 10°} \approx \dfrac{500}{0.1736} \approx 2880$

The plane has flown approximately 2880 feet.

69. $\cos\theta = \dfrac{60}{75}$

Use a calculator in degree mode to find θ.

Scientific Calculator	**Graphing Calculator**
60 ÷ 75 = COS⁻¹	COS⁻¹ (60 ÷ 75) ENTER

The display should show approximately 37. Thus, the angle between the wire and the pole is approximately 37°.

71.–81. Answers may vary.

83.

θ	0.4	0.3	0.2	0.1	0.01	0.001	0.0001	0.00001
$\cos\theta$	0.92106	0.9553	0.98007	0.995004	0.99995	0.9999995	0.999999995	1
$\dfrac{\cos\theta-1}{\theta}$	−0.19735	−0.149	−0.09965	−0.04996	−0.005	−0.0005	−0.00005	0

$\dfrac{\cos\theta-1}{\theta}$ approaches 0 as θ approaches 0.

85. In a right triangle, the hypotenuse is greater than either other side. Therefore both $\dfrac{\text{opposite}}{\text{hypotenuse}}$ and $\dfrac{\text{adjacent}}{\text{hypotenuse}}$ must be less than 1 for an acute angle in a right triangle.

87. a. Let a = distance of the ship from the lighthouse.

$\tan 35° = \dfrac{250}{a}$

$a = \dfrac{250}{\tan 35°} \approx \dfrac{250}{0.7002} \approx 357$

The ship is approximately 357 feet from the lighthouse.

b. Let b = the plane's height above the lighthouse.

$\tan 22° = \dfrac{b}{357}$

$b = 357\tan 22° \approx 357(0.4040) \approx 144$

$144 + 250 = 394$

The plane is approximately 394 feet above the water.

Section 1.3

Checkpoint Exercises

1. We need values for *x, y,* and *r.* Because $P = (4,-3)$ is a point on the terminal side of θ, $x = 4$ and $y = -3$. Furthermore,

$$r = \sqrt{x^2 + y^2} = \sqrt{4^2 + (-3)^2} = \sqrt{16 + 9}$$
$$= \sqrt{25} = 5$$

Now that we know *x, y,* and *r,* we can find the six trigonometric functions of θ.

$$\sin \theta = \frac{y}{r} = \frac{-3}{5} = -\frac{3}{5}$$

$$\cos \theta = \frac{x}{r} = \frac{4}{5}$$

$$\tan \theta = \frac{y}{x} = \frac{-3}{4} = -\frac{3}{4}$$

$$\csc \theta = \frac{r}{y} = \frac{5}{-3} = -\frac{5}{3}$$

$$\sec \theta = \frac{r}{x} = \frac{5}{4}$$

$$\cot \theta = \frac{x}{y} = \frac{4}{-3} = -\frac{4}{3}$$

2. a. $\theta = 0° = 0$ radians
   The terminal side of the angle is on the positive *x*-axis. Select the point $P = (1,0)$: $x = 1, y = 0, r = 1$
   Apply the definitions of the cosine and cosecant functions.

   $$\cos 0° = \cos 0 = \frac{x}{r} = \frac{1}{1} = 1$$

   $$\csc 0° = \csc 0 = \frac{r}{y} = \frac{1}{0}, \text{ undefined}$$

   b. $\theta = 90° = \frac{\pi}{2}$ radians
   The terminal side of the angle is on the positive *y*-axis. Select the point $P = (0,1)$: $x = 0, y = 1, r = 1$
   Apply the definitions of the cosine and

cosecant functions.

$$\cos 90° = \cos \frac{\pi}{2} = \frac{x}{r} = \frac{0}{1} = 0$$

$$\csc 90° = \csc \frac{\pi}{2} = \frac{r}{y} = \frac{1}{1} = 1$$

c. $\theta = 180° = \pi$ radians
   The terminal side of the angle is on the negative *x*-axis. Select the point $P = (-1,0)$: $x = -1, y = 0, r = 1$
   Apply the definitions of the cosine and cosecant functions.

   $$\cos 180° = \cos \pi = \frac{x}{r} = \frac{-1}{1} = -1$$

   $$\csc 180° = \csc \pi = \frac{r}{y} = \frac{1}{0}, \text{ undefined}$$

d. $\theta = 270° = \frac{3\pi}{2}$ radians
   The terminal side of the angle is on the negative *y*-axis. Select the point $P = (0,-1)$: $x = 0, y = -1, r = 1$
   Apply the definitions of the cosine and cosecant functions.

   $$\cos 270° = \cos \frac{3\pi}{2} = \frac{x}{r} = \frac{0}{1} = 0$$

   $$\csc 270° = \csc \frac{3\pi}{2} = \frac{r}{y} = \frac{1}{-1} = -1$$

3. Because $\sin \theta < 0$, θ cannot lie in quadrant I; all the functions are positive in quadrant I. Furthermore, θ cannot lie in quadrant II; $\sin \theta$ is positive in quadrant II. Thus, with $\sin \theta < 0$, θ lies in quadrant III or quadrant IV. We are also given that $\cos \theta < 0$. Because quadrant III is the only quadrant in which cosine is negative and the sine is negative, we conclude that θ lies in quadrant III.

4. Because the tangent is negative and the cosine is negative, θ lies in quadrant II. In quadrant II, *x* is negative and *y* is positive. Thus,

$$\tan \theta = -\frac{1}{3} = \frac{y}{x} = \frac{1}{-3}$$

$x = -3, y = 1$
Furthermore,

$$r = \sqrt{x^2 + y^2} = \sqrt{(-3)^2 + 1^2} = \sqrt{9 + 1} = \sqrt{10}$$

Now that we know x, y, and r, we can find $\sin\theta$ and $\sec\theta$.

$$\sin\theta = \frac{y}{r} = \frac{1}{\sqrt{10}} = \frac{1}{\sqrt{10}}\cdot\frac{\sqrt{10}}{\sqrt{10}} = \frac{\sqrt{10}}{10}$$

$$\sec\theta = \frac{r}{x} = \frac{\sqrt{10}}{-3} = -\frac{\sqrt{10}}{3}$$

5. a. Because $210°$ lies between $180°$ and $270°$, it is in quadrant III. The reference angle is $\theta' = 210° - 180° = 30°$.

b. Because $\dfrac{7\pi}{4}$ lies between $\dfrac{3\pi}{2} = \dfrac{6\pi}{4}$ and $2\pi = \dfrac{8\pi}{4}$, it is in quadrant IV. The reference angle is

$$\theta' = 2\pi - \frac{7\pi}{4} = \frac{8\pi}{4} - \frac{7\pi}{4} = \frac{\pi}{4}.$$

c. Because $-240°$ lies between $-180°$ and $-270°$, it is in quadrant II. The reference angle is $\theta = 240 - 180 = 60°$.

d. Because 3.6 lies between $\pi \approx 3.14$ and $\dfrac{3\pi}{2} \approx 4.71$, it is in quadrant III. The reference angle is $\theta' = 3.6 - \pi \approx 0.46$.

6. a. $300°$ lies in quadrant IV. The reference angle is $\theta' = 360° - 300° = 60°$.

$$\sin 60° = \frac{\sqrt{3}}{2}$$

Because the sine is negative in quadrant IV, $\sin 300° = -\sin 60° = -\dfrac{\sqrt{3}}{2}$.

b. $\dfrac{5\pi}{4}$ lies in quadrant III. The reference angle is $\theta' = \dfrac{5\pi}{4} - \pi = \dfrac{5\pi}{4} - \dfrac{4\pi}{4} = \dfrac{\pi}{4}$.

$$\tan\frac{\pi}{4} = 1$$

Because the tangent is positive in quadrant III, $\tan\dfrac{5\pi}{4} = +\tan\dfrac{\pi}{4} = 1$.

c. $-\dfrac{\pi}{6}$ lies in quadrant IV. The reference angle is $\theta' = \dfrac{\pi}{6}$.

$$\sec\frac{\pi}{6} = \frac{2\sqrt{3}}{3}$$

Because the secant is positive in quadrant IV, $\sec\left(-\dfrac{\pi}{6}\right) = +\sec\dfrac{\pi}{6} = \dfrac{2\sqrt{3}}{3}$.

Exercise Set 1.3

1. We need values for x, y, and r. Because $P = (-4, 3)$ is a point on the terminal side of θ, $x = -4$ and $y = 3$. Furthermore,

$$r = \sqrt{x^2 + y^2} = \sqrt{(-4)^2 + 3^2} = \sqrt{16 + 9} = \sqrt{25} = 5$$

Now that we know x, y, and r, we can find the six trigonometric functions of θ.

$$\sin\theta = \frac{y}{r} = \frac{3}{5}$$

$$\cos\theta = \frac{x}{r} = \frac{-4}{5} = -\frac{4}{5}$$

$$\tan\theta = \frac{y}{x} = \frac{3}{-4} = -\frac{3}{4}$$

$$\csc\theta = \frac{r}{y} = \frac{5}{3}$$

$$\sec\theta = \frac{r}{x} = \frac{5}{-4} = -\frac{5}{4}$$

$$\cot\theta = \frac{x}{y} = \frac{-4}{3} = -\frac{4}{3}$$

3. We need values for x, y, and r. Because $P = (2, 3)$ is a point on the terminal side of θ, $x = 2$ and $y = 3$. Furthermore,

$$r = \sqrt{x^2 + y^2} = \sqrt{2^2 + 3^2} = \sqrt{4 + 9} = \sqrt{13}$$

Now that we know x, y, and r, we can find the

six trigonometric functions of θ.

$$\sin\theta = \frac{y}{r} = \frac{3}{\sqrt{13}} = \frac{3}{\sqrt{13}} \cdot \frac{\sqrt{13}}{\sqrt{13}} = \frac{3\sqrt{13}}{13}$$

$$\cos\theta = \frac{x}{r} = \frac{2}{\sqrt{13}} = \frac{2}{\sqrt{13}} \cdot \frac{\sqrt{13}}{\sqrt{13}} = \frac{2\sqrt{13}}{13}$$

$$\tan\theta = \frac{y}{x} = \frac{3}{2}$$

$$\csc\theta = \frac{r}{y} = \frac{\sqrt{13}}{3}$$

$$\sec\theta = \frac{r}{x} = \frac{\sqrt{13}}{2}$$

$$\cot\theta = \frac{x}{y} = \frac{2}{3}$$

5. We need values for x, y, and r. Because $P = (3, -3)$ is a point on the terminal side of θ, $x = 3$ and $y = -3$. Furthermore,

$$r = \sqrt{x^2 + y^2} = \sqrt{3^2 + (-3)^2} = \sqrt{9+9}$$
$$= \sqrt{18} = 3\sqrt{2}$$

Now that we know x, y, and r, we can find the six trigonometric functions of θ.

$$\sin\theta = \frac{y}{r} = \frac{-3}{3\sqrt{2}} = \frac{-1}{\sqrt{2}} \cdot \frac{\sqrt{2}}{\sqrt{2}} = -\frac{\sqrt{2}}{2}$$

$$\cos\theta = \frac{x}{r} = \frac{3}{3\sqrt{2}} = \frac{1}{\sqrt{2}} \cdot \frac{\sqrt{2}}{\sqrt{2}} = \frac{\sqrt{2}}{2}$$

$$\tan\theta = \frac{y}{x} = \frac{-3}{3} = -1$$

$$\csc\theta = \frac{r}{y} = \frac{3\sqrt{2}}{-3} = -\sqrt{2}$$

$$\sec\theta = \frac{r}{x} = \frac{3\sqrt{2}}{3} = \sqrt{2}$$

$$\cot\theta = \frac{x}{y} = \frac{3}{-3} = -1$$

7. We need values for x, y, and r. Because $P = (-2, -5)$ is a point on the terminal side of θ, $x = -2$ and $y = -5$. Furthermore,

$$r = \sqrt{x^2 + y^2} = \sqrt{(-2)^2 + (-5)^2} = \sqrt{4 + 25} = \sqrt{29}$$

Now that we know x, y, and r, we can find the

six trigonometric functions of θ.

$$\sin\theta = \frac{y}{r} = \frac{-5}{\sqrt{29}} = \frac{-5}{\sqrt{29}} \cdot \frac{\sqrt{29}}{\sqrt{29}} = -\frac{5\sqrt{29}}{29}$$

$$\cos\theta = \frac{x}{r} = \frac{-2}{\sqrt{29}} = \frac{-2}{\sqrt{29}} \cdot \frac{\sqrt{29}}{\sqrt{29}} = -\frac{2\sqrt{29}}{29}$$

$$\tan\theta = \frac{y}{x} = \frac{-5}{-2} = \frac{5}{2}$$

$$\csc\theta = \frac{r}{y} = \frac{\sqrt{29}}{-5} = -\frac{\sqrt{29}}{5}$$

$$\sec\theta = \frac{r}{x} = \frac{\sqrt{29}}{-2} = -\frac{\sqrt{29}}{2}$$

$$\cot\theta = \frac{x}{y} = \frac{-2}{-5} = \frac{2}{5}$$

9. $\theta = \pi$ radians
The terminal side of the angle is on the negative x-axis. Select the point $P = (-1, 0)$: $x = -1$, $y = 0$, $r = 1$ Apply the definition of the cosine function.

$$\cos\pi = \frac{x}{r} = \frac{-1}{1} = -1$$

11. $\theta = \pi$ radians
The terminal side of the angle is on the negative x-axis. Select the point $P = (-1, 0)$: $x = -1$, $y = 0$, $r = 1$ Apply the definition of the secant function.

$$\sec\pi = \frac{r}{x} = \frac{1}{-1} = -1$$

13. $\theta = \dfrac{3\pi}{2}$ radians

The terminal side of the angle is on the negative y-axis. Select the point $P = (0, -1)$: $x = 0$, $y = -1$, $r = 1$ Apply the definition of the tangent function. $\tan\dfrac{3\pi}{2} = \dfrac{y}{x} = \dfrac{-1}{0}$, undefined

15. $\theta = \dfrac{\pi}{2}$ radians

The terminal side of the angle is on the positive y-axis. Select the point $P = (0, 1)$:

$x = 0$, $y = 1$, $r = 1$ Apply the definition of the cotangent function. $\cot \dfrac{\pi}{2} = \dfrac{x}{y} = \dfrac{0}{1} = 0$

17. Because $\sin\theta > 0$, θ cannot lie in quadrant III or quadrant IV; the sine function is negative in those quadrants. Thus, with $\sin\theta > 0$, θ lies in quadrant I or quadrant II. We are also given that $\cos\theta > 0$. Because quadrant I is the only quadrant in which the cosine is positive and sine is positive, we conclude that θ lies in quadrant I.

19. Because $\sin\theta < 0$, θ cannot lie in quadrant I or quadrant II; the sine function is positive in those two quadrants. Thus, with $\sin\theta < 0$, θ lies in quadrant III or quadrant IV. We are also given that $\cos\theta < 0$. Because quadrant III is the only quadrant in which the cosine is positive and the sine is negative, we conclude that θ lies in quadrant III.

21. Because $\tan\theta < 0$, θ cannot lie in quadrant I or quadrant III; the tangent function is positive in those quadrants. Thus, with $\tan\theta < 0$, θ lies in quadrant II or quadrant IV. We are also given that $\cos\theta < 0$. Because quadrant II is the only quadrant in which the cosine is negative and the tangent is negative, we conclude that θ lies in quadrant II.

23. In quadrant III x is negative and y is negative. Thus, $\cos\theta = -\dfrac{3}{5} = \dfrac{x}{r} = \dfrac{-3}{5}$, $x = -3$, $r = 5$. Furthermore,
$$r^2 = x^2 + y^2$$
$$5^2 = (-3)^2 + y^2$$
$$y^2 = 25 - 9 = 16$$
$$y = -\sqrt{16} = -4$$
Now that we know x, y, and r, we can find the

remaining trigonometric functions of θ.
$$\sin\theta = \frac{y}{r} = \frac{-4}{5} = -\frac{4}{5}$$
$$\tan\theta = \frac{y}{x} = \frac{-4}{-3} = \frac{4}{3}$$
$$\csc\theta = \frac{r}{y} = \frac{5}{-4} = -\frac{5}{4}$$
$$\sec\theta = \frac{r}{x} = \frac{5}{-3} = -\frac{5}{3}$$
$$\cot\theta = \frac{x}{y} = \frac{-3}{-4} = \frac{3}{4}$$

25. In quadrant II x is negative and y is positive. Thus, $\sin\theta = \dfrac{5}{13} = \dfrac{y}{r}$, $y = 5$, $r = 13$. Furthermore,
$$x^2 + y^2 = r^2$$
$$x^2 + 5^2 = 13^2$$
$$x^2 = 169 - 25 = 144$$
$$x = -\sqrt{144} = -12$$
Now that we know x, y, and r, we can find the remaining trigonometric functions of θ.

$$\cos\theta = \frac{x}{r} = \frac{-12}{13} = -\frac{12}{13}$$
$$\tan\theta = \frac{y}{x} = \frac{5}{-12} = -\frac{5}{12}$$
$$\csc\theta = \frac{r}{y} = \frac{13}{5}$$
$$\sec\theta = \frac{r}{x} = \frac{13}{-12} = -\frac{13}{12}$$
$$\cot\theta = \frac{x}{y} = \frac{-12}{5} = -\frac{12}{5}$$

27. Because $270° < \theta < 360°$, θ is in quadrant IV. In quadrant IV x is positive and y is negative. Thus, $\cos\theta = \dfrac{8}{17} = \dfrac{x}{r}$, $x = 8$, $r = 17$. Furthermore

$$x^2 + y^2 = r^2$$
$$8^2 + y^2 = 17^2$$
$$y^2 = 289 - 64 = 225$$
$$y = -\sqrt{225} = -15$$

Now that we know *x, y,* and *r,* we can find the remaining trigonometric functions of θ.

$$\sin\theta = \frac{y}{r} = \frac{-15}{17} = -\frac{15}{17}$$

$$\tan\theta = \frac{y}{x} = \frac{-15}{8} = -\frac{15}{8}$$

$$\csc\theta = \frac{r}{y} = \frac{17}{-15} = -\frac{17}{15}$$

$$\sec\theta = \frac{r}{x} = \frac{17}{8}$$

$$\cot\theta = \frac{x}{y} = \frac{8}{-15} = -\frac{8}{15}$$

29. Because the tangent is negative and the sine is positive, θ lies in quadrant II. In quadrant II, *x* is negative and *y* is positive. Thus,

$$\tan\theta = -\frac{2}{3} = \frac{y}{x} = \frac{2}{-3}, \ x = -3, \ y = 2.$$

Furthermore,

$$r = \sqrt{x^2 + y^2} = \sqrt{(-3)^2 + 2^2} = \sqrt{9+4} = \sqrt{13} \text{ N}$$

ow that we know *x, y,* and *r,* we can find the remaining trigonometric functions of θ.

$$\sin\theta = \frac{y}{r} = \frac{2}{\sqrt{13}} = \frac{2}{\sqrt{13}} \cdot \frac{\sqrt{13}}{\sqrt{13}} = \frac{2\sqrt{13}}{13}$$

$$\cos\theta = \frac{x}{r} = \frac{-3}{\sqrt{13}} = \frac{-3}{\sqrt{13}} \cdot \frac{\sqrt{13}}{\sqrt{13}} = -\frac{3\sqrt{13}}{13}$$

$$\csc\theta = \frac{r}{y} = \frac{\sqrt{13}}{2}$$

$$\sec\theta = \frac{r}{x} = \frac{\sqrt{13}}{-3} = -\frac{\sqrt{13}}{3}$$

$$\cot\theta = \frac{x}{y} = \frac{-3}{2} = -\frac{3}{2}$$

31. Because the tangent is positive and the cosine is negative, θ lies in quadrant III. In quadrant III, *x* is negative and *y* is negative. Thus,

$$\tan\theta = \frac{4}{3} = \frac{y}{x} = \frac{-4}{-3}, \ x = -3, \ y = -4.$$

Furthermore,

$$r = \sqrt{x^2 + y^2} = \sqrt{(-3)^2 + (-4)^2} = \sqrt{9+16}$$
$$= \sqrt{25} = 5$$

Now that we know *x, y,* and *r,* we can find the remaining trigonometric functions of θ.

$$\sin\theta = \frac{y}{r} = \frac{-4}{5} = -\frac{4}{5}$$

$$\cos\theta = \frac{x}{r} = \frac{-3}{5} = -\frac{3}{5}$$

$$\csc\theta = \frac{r}{y} = \frac{5}{-4} = -\frac{5}{4}$$

$$\sec\theta = \frac{r}{x} = \frac{5}{-3} = -\frac{5}{3}$$

$$\cot\theta = \frac{x}{y} = \frac{-3}{-4} = \frac{3}{4}$$

33. Because the secant is negative and the tangent is positive, θ lies in quadrant III. In quadrant III, *x* is negative and *y* is negative. Thus,

$$\sec\theta = -3 = \frac{r}{x} = \frac{3}{-1}, \ x = -1, \ r = 3.$$

Furthermore,

$$x^2 + y^2 = r^2$$
$$(-1)^2 + y^2 = 3^2$$
$$y^2 = 9 - 1 = 8$$
$$y = -\sqrt{8} = -2\sqrt{2}$$

Now that we know *x, y,* and *r,* we can find the remaining trigonometric functions of θ.

$$\sin\theta = \frac{y}{r} = \frac{-2\sqrt{2}}{3} = -\frac{2\sqrt{2}}{3}$$

$$\cos\theta = \frac{x}{r} = \frac{-1}{3} = -\frac{1}{3}$$

$$\tan\theta = \frac{y}{x} = \frac{-2\sqrt{2}}{-1} = 2\sqrt{2}$$

$$\csc\theta = \frac{r}{y} = \frac{3}{-2\sqrt{2}} = \frac{3}{-2\sqrt{2}} \cdot \frac{\sqrt{2}}{\sqrt{2}} = -\frac{3\sqrt{2}}{4}$$

$$\cot\theta = \frac{x}{y} = \frac{-1}{-2\sqrt{2}} = \frac{1}{2\sqrt{2}} \cdot \frac{\sqrt{2}}{\sqrt{2}} = \frac{\sqrt{2}}{4}$$

35. Because 160° lies between 90° and 180°, it is in quadrant II. The reference angle is $\theta' = 180° - 160° = 20°$.

37. Because 205° lies between 180° and 270°, it is in quadrant III. The reference angle is $\theta' = 205° - 180° = 25°$.

39. Because 355° lies between 270° and 360°, it is in quadrant IV. The reference angle is $\theta' = 360° - 355° = 5°$.

41. Because $\dfrac{7\pi}{4}$ lies between $\dfrac{3\pi}{2} = \dfrac{6\pi}{4}$ and $2\pi = \dfrac{8\pi}{4}$, it is in quadrant IV. The reference angle is $\theta' = 2\pi - \dfrac{7\pi}{4} = \dfrac{8\pi}{4} - \dfrac{7\pi}{4} = \dfrac{\pi}{4}$.

43. Because $\dfrac{5\pi}{6}$ lies between $\dfrac{\pi}{2} = \dfrac{3\pi}{6}$ and $\pi = \dfrac{6\pi}{6}$, it is in quadrant II. The reference angle is $\theta' = \pi - \dfrac{5\pi}{6} = \dfrac{6\pi}{6} - \dfrac{5\pi}{6} = \dfrac{\pi}{6}$.

45. Because −150° lies between −90° and −180°, it is in quadrant III. The reference angle is $\theta' = 180° - 150° = 30°$.

47. Because −335° lies between −270° and −360°, it is in quadrant I. The reference angle is $\theta' = 360° - 335° = 25°$.

49. Because 4.7 lies between $\pi \approx 3.14$ and $\dfrac{3\pi}{2} \approx 4.71$, it is in quadrant III. The reference angle is $\theta' = 4.7 - \pi \approx 1.56$.

51. 225° lies in quadrant III. The reference angle is $\theta' = 225° - 180° = 45°$.
$$\cos 45° = \frac{\sqrt{2}}{2}$$
Because the cosine is negative in quadrant III, $\cos 225° = -\cos 45° = -\dfrac{\sqrt{2}}{2}$.

53. 210° lies in quadrant III. The reference angle is $\theta' = 210° - 180° = 30°$.
$$\tan 30° = \frac{\sqrt{3}}{3}$$
Because the tangent is positive in quadrant III, $\tan 210° = \tan 30° = \dfrac{\sqrt{3}}{3}$.

55. 420° lies in quadrant I. The reference angle is $\theta' = 420° - 360° = 60°$.
$$\tan 60° = \sqrt{3}$$
Because the tangent is positive in quadrant I, $\tan 420° = \tan 60° = \sqrt{3}$.

57. $\dfrac{2\pi}{3}$ lies in quadrant II. The reference angle is
$$\theta' = \pi - \frac{2\pi}{3} = \frac{3\pi}{3} - \frac{2\pi}{3} = \frac{\pi}{3}.$$
$$\sin \frac{\pi}{3} = \frac{\sqrt{3}}{2}$$
Because the sine is positive in quadrant II,
$$\sin \frac{2\pi}{3} = \sin \frac{\pi}{3} = \frac{\sqrt{3}}{2}.$$

59. $\dfrac{7\pi}{6}$ lies in quadrant III. The reference angle is
$$\theta' = \frac{7\pi}{6} - \pi = \frac{7\pi}{6} - \frac{6\pi}{6} = \frac{\pi}{6}.$$
$$\csc \frac{\pi}{6} = 2$$
Because the cosecant is negative in quadrant III, $\csc \dfrac{7\pi}{6} = -\csc \dfrac{\pi}{6} = -2$.

61. $\dfrac{9\pi}{4}$ lies in quadrant I. The reference angle is
$$\theta' = \frac{9\pi}{4} - 2\pi = \frac{9\pi}{4} - \frac{8\pi}{4} = \frac{\pi}{4}.$$
$$\tan \frac{\pi}{4} = 1$$
Because the tangent is positive in quadrant I,
$$\tan \frac{9\pi}{4} = \tan \frac{\pi}{4} = 1.$$

63. $-240°$ lies in quadrant II. The reference angle is $\theta' = 240° - 180° = 60°$.

$$\sin 60° = \frac{\sqrt{3}}{2}$$

Because the sine is positive in quadrant II,

$$\sin(-240°) = \sin 60° = \frac{\sqrt{3}}{2}.$$

65. $-\frac{\pi}{4}$ lies in quadrant IV. The reference angle is

$$\theta' = \frac{\pi}{4}.$$

$$\tan \frac{\pi}{4} = 1$$

Because the tangent is negative in quadrant IV,

$$\tan\left(-\frac{\pi}{4}\right) = -\tan \frac{\pi}{4} = -1$$

67.–71. Answers may vary.

Section 1.4

Checkpoint Exercises

1. The point P on the unit circle that corresponds to $t = \pi$ has coordinates $(-1, 0)$. We use $x = -1$ and $y = 0$ to find the values of the trigonometric functions.

$$\sin \pi = y = 0$$

$$\cos \pi = x = -1$$

$$\tan \pi = \frac{y}{x} = \frac{0}{-1} = 0$$

$$\sec \pi = \frac{1}{x} = \frac{1}{-1} = -1$$

$$\cot \pi = \frac{x}{y} = \frac{-1}{0} = \text{undefined}$$

$$\csc \pi = \frac{1}{y} = \frac{1}{0} = \text{undefined}$$

2. a. $\cos(-60°) = \cos 60° = \frac{1}{2}$

b. $\tan\left(-\frac{\pi}{6}\right) = -\tan\left(\frac{\pi}{6}\right) = -\frac{\sqrt{3}}{3}$

3. a. $\cos 405° = \cos(360° + 45°)$
$$= \cos 45° = \frac{\sqrt{2}}{2}$$

b. $\tan \frac{7\pi}{3} = \tan\left(2\pi + \frac{\pi}{3}\right) = \tan \frac{\pi}{3} = \sqrt{3}$

Exercise Set 1.4

1. The point P on the unit circle has coordinates $\left(-\dfrac{15}{17}, \dfrac{8}{17}\right)$. We use $x = -\dfrac{15}{17}$ and $y = \dfrac{8}{17}$ to find the values of the trigonometric functions.

$$\sin t = y = \frac{8}{17}$$

$$\cos t = x = -\frac{15}{17}$$

$$\tan t = \frac{y}{x} = \frac{\frac{8}{17}}{-\frac{15}{17}} = -\frac{8}{15}$$

$$\csc t = \frac{1}{y} = \frac{17}{8}$$

$$\sec t = \frac{1}{x} = -\frac{17}{15}$$

$$\cot t = \frac{x}{y} = -\frac{15}{8}$$

3. The point P on the unit circle that cooresponds to $t = -\dfrac{\pi}{4}$ has coordinates $\left(\dfrac{\sqrt{2}}{2}, -\dfrac{\sqrt{2}}{2}\right)$. We use $x = \dfrac{\sqrt{2}}{2}$ and $y = -\dfrac{\sqrt{2}}{2}$ to find the values of the trigonometric functions.

$$\sin t = y = -\frac{\sqrt{2}}{2}$$

$$\cos t = x = \frac{\sqrt{2}}{2}$$

$$\tan t = \frac{y}{x} = \frac{-\frac{\sqrt{2}}{2}}{\frac{\sqrt{2}}{2}} = -1$$

$$\csc t = \frac{1}{y} = -\sqrt{2}$$

$$\sec t = \frac{1}{x} = \sqrt{2}$$

$$\cot t = \frac{x}{y} = -1$$

5. $\sin(-45°) = -\sin 45° = -\dfrac{\sqrt{2}}{2}$

7. $\sec\left(-\dfrac{\pi}{3}\right) = \sec\left(\dfrac{\pi}{3}\right) = 2$

9. $\cos 585° = \cos(260° + 225°)$
$= \cos 225° = -\cos 45°$
$= -\dfrac{\sqrt{2}}{2}$

11. $\cot\dfrac{7\pi}{3} = \cot\left(2\pi + \dfrac{\pi}{3}\right) = \cot\dfrac{\pi}{3} = \dfrac{\sqrt{3}}{3}$

13. **a.** $H = 12 + 8.3\sin\left[\dfrac{2\pi}{365}(80 - 80)\right]$
$= 12 + 8.3\sin 0 = 12 + 8.3(0)$
$= 12$
There are 12 hours of daylight in Fairbanks on March 21.

    b. $H = 12 + 8.3\sin\left[\dfrac{2\pi}{365}(172 - 80)\right]$
$\approx 12 + 8.3\sin 1.5837$
≈ 20.3
There are about 20.3 hours of daylight in Fairbanks on June 21.

    c. $H = 12 + 8.3\sin\left[\dfrac{2\pi}{365}(355 - 80)\right]$
$\approx 12 + 8.3\sin 4.7339$
≈ 3.7
There are about 3.7 hours of daylight in Fairbanks on December 21.

15. **a.** For $t = 7$,
$$E = \sin\frac{\pi}{14}\cdot 7 = \sin\frac{\pi}{2} = 1$$

For $t = 14,$

$$E = \sin\frac{\pi}{14} \cdot 14 = \sin\pi = 0$$

For $t = 21,$

$$E = \sin\frac{\pi}{14} \cdot 21 = \sin\frac{3\pi}{2} = -1$$

For $t = 28,$

$$E = \sin\frac{\pi}{14} \cdot 28 = \sin 2\pi = \sin 0 = 0$$

For $t = 35,$

$$E = \sin\frac{\pi}{14} \cdot 35 = \sin\frac{5\pi}{2} = \sin\frac{\pi}{2} = 1$$

Observations may vary.

   b. Because $E(35) = E(7) = 1$, the period is 35 − 7 = 28 or 28 days.

17.–21. Answers may vary.

23. 91° lies in quadrant II. The reference angle is $\theta' = 180° - 91° = 89°$.
Becasue the cosine is negative in quadrant II, $\cos 91° = -\cos 89°$.
Likewise, 92°, 93°, . . . , 178°, and 179° all lie in quadrant II. Their reference angles are
$\theta' = 180° - 92° = 88°$

$\theta' = 180° - 93° = 87°$

. . .

$\theta' = 180° - 178° = 2°$

$\theta' = 180° - 179° = 1°$
Because the cosine is negative in quadrant II, $\cos 92° = -\cos 88°$

$\cos 93° = -\cos 87°$

. . .

$\cos 178° = -\cos 2°$

$\cos 179° = -\cos 1°$
Also, $\cos 180° = -1 = -\cos 0°$

Thus,
$$\cos 0° + \cos 1° + \cdots + \cos 88° + \cos 89°$$
$$+ \cos 90° + \cos 91° + \cos 92° + \cdots$$
$$+ \cos 179° \quad + \cos 180°$$
$$= \cos 0° + \cos 1° + \cdots + \cos 88° + \cos 89°$$
$$+ \cos 90° - \cos 89° - \cos 88° - \cdots$$
$$- \cos 1° - \cos 0°$$
$$= \cos 90° = 0$$

25. Because $f(x) = \sin x$, $f(x)$ is an odd function. Thus, $f(-a) = -f(a)$. Therefore,
$$f(a) + 2f(-a) = f(a) - 2f(a)$$
$$= \frac{1}{4} - 2 \cdot \frac{1}{4}$$
$$= -\frac{1}{4}$$

2. The equation $y = -\dfrac{1}{2}\sin x$ is of the form

$y = A\sin x$ with $A = -\dfrac{1}{2}$. Thus, the

amplitude is $\mid A \mid = \left|-\dfrac{1}{2}\right| = \dfrac{1}{2}$. The period for

both $y = -\dfrac{1}{2}\sin x$ and $y = \sin x$ is 2π.

Find the *x*–values for the five key points by dividing the period, 2π, by 4,

$\dfrac{\text{period}}{4} = \dfrac{2\pi}{4} = \dfrac{\pi}{2}$, then by adding quarter-periods. The five *x*-values are

$x = 0$

$x = 0 + \dfrac{\pi}{2} = \dfrac{\pi}{2}$

$x = \dfrac{\pi}{2} + \dfrac{\pi}{2} = \pi$

$x = \pi + \dfrac{\pi}{2} = \dfrac{3\pi}{2}$

$x = \dfrac{3\pi}{2} + \dfrac{\pi}{2} = 2\pi$

We evaluate the function at each value of *x*.

x	$y = -\dfrac{1}{2}\sin x$	coordinates
0	$y = -\dfrac{1}{2}\sin 0$ $= -\dfrac{1}{2}\cdot 0 = 0$	$(0,\,0)$
$\dfrac{\pi}{2}$	$y = -\dfrac{1}{2}\sin\dfrac{\pi}{2}$ $= -\dfrac{1}{2}\cdot 1 = -\dfrac{1}{2}$	$\left(\dfrac{\pi}{2},\,-\dfrac{1}{2}\right)$
π	$y = -\dfrac{1}{2}\sin \pi$ $= -\dfrac{1}{2}\cdot 0 = 0$	$(\pi,\,0)$
$\dfrac{3\pi}{2}$	$y = -\dfrac{1}{2}\sin\dfrac{3\pi}{2}$ $= -\dfrac{1}{2}\left(-1\right) = \dfrac{1}{2}$	$\left(\dfrac{3\pi}{2},\,\dfrac{1}{2}\right)$
2π	$y = -\dfrac{1}{2}\sin 2\pi$ $= -\dfrac{1}{2}\cdot 0 = 0$	$(2\pi,\,0)$

Connect the five key points with a smooth curve and graph one complete cycle of the given function with the graph of $y = \sin x$. Extend the pattern of each graph to the left and right as desired.

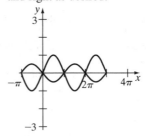

3. The equation $y = 2\sin\dfrac{1}{2}x$ is of the form

$y = A\sin Bx$ with $A = 2$ and $B = \dfrac{1}{2}$.

The amplitude is $\mid A \mid = \mid 2 \mid = 2$.

The period is $\dfrac{2\pi}{B} = \dfrac{2\pi}{\frac{1}{2}} = 4\pi$.

Find the *x*–values for the five key points by dividing the period, 4π, by 4,

$\dfrac{\text{period}}{4} = \dfrac{4\pi}{4} = \pi$, then by adding quarter-periods. The five *x*-values are

$x = 0$

$x = 0 + \pi = \pi$

$x = \pi + \pi = 2\pi$

$x = 2\pi + \pi = 3\pi$

$x = 3\pi + \pi = 4\pi$

We evaluate the function at each value of x.

x	$y = 2\sin\dfrac{1}{2}x$	coordinates
0	$y = 2\sin\left(\dfrac{1}{2}\cdot 0\right)$ $= 2\sin 0$ $= 2\cdot 0 = 0$	$(0, 0)$
π	$y = 2\sin\left(\dfrac{1}{2}\cdot \pi\right)$ $= 2\sin\dfrac{\pi}{2} = 2\cdot 1 = 2$	$(\pi, 2)$
2π	$y = 2\sin\left(\dfrac{1}{2}\cdot 2\pi\right)$ $= 2\sin\pi = 2\cdot 0 = 0$	$(2\pi, 0)$
3π	$y = 2\sin\left(\dfrac{1}{2}\cdot 3\pi\right)$ $= 2\sin\dfrac{3\pi}{2}$ $= 2\cdot(-1) = -2$	$(3\pi, -2)$
4π	$y = 2\sin\left(\dfrac{1}{2}\cdot 4\pi\right)$ $= 2\sin 2\pi = 2\cdot 0 = 0$	$(4\pi, 0)$

Connect the five key points with a smooth curve and graph one complete cycle of the given function. Extend the pattern of the

graph another full period to the right.

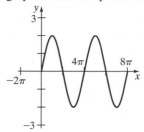

4. The equation $y = 3\sin\left(2x - \dfrac{\pi}{3}\right)$ is of the form $y = A\sin(Bx - C)$ with $A = 3$, $B = 2$, and $C = \dfrac{\pi}{3}$. The amplitude is

$|A| = |3| = 3$.

The period is $\dfrac{2\pi}{B} = \dfrac{2\pi}{2} = \pi$.

The phase shift is $\dfrac{C}{B} = \dfrac{\frac{\pi}{3}}{2} = \dfrac{\pi}{3}\cdot\dfrac{1}{2} = \dfrac{\pi}{6}$.

Find the x-values for the five key points by dividing the period, π, by 4, $\dfrac{\text{period}}{4} = \dfrac{\pi}{4}$, then by adding quarter-periods to the value of x where the cycle begins, $x = \dfrac{\pi}{6}$. The five x-values are

$x = \dfrac{\pi}{6}$

$x = \dfrac{\pi}{6} + \dfrac{\pi}{4} = \dfrac{2\pi}{12} + \dfrac{3\pi}{12} = \dfrac{5\pi}{12}$

$x = \dfrac{5\pi}{12} + \dfrac{\pi}{4} = \dfrac{5\pi}{12} + \dfrac{3\pi}{12} = \dfrac{8\pi}{12} = \dfrac{2\pi}{3}$

$x = \dfrac{2\pi}{3} + \dfrac{\pi}{4} = \dfrac{8\pi}{12} + \dfrac{3\pi}{12} = \dfrac{11\pi}{12}$

$x = \dfrac{11\pi}{12} + \dfrac{\pi}{4} = \dfrac{11\pi}{12} + \dfrac{3\pi}{12} = \dfrac{14\pi}{12} = \dfrac{7\pi}{6}$

We evaluate the function at each value of x.

x	$y = 3\sin\left(2x - \dfrac{\pi}{3}\right)$	coordinates
$\dfrac{\pi}{6}$	$\begin{aligned} y &= 3\sin\left(2 \cdot \dfrac{\pi}{6} - \dfrac{\pi}{3}\right) \\ &= 3\sin 0 = 3 \cdot 0 = 0 \end{aligned}$	$\left(\dfrac{\pi}{6}, 0\right)$
$\dfrac{5\pi}{12}$	$\begin{aligned} y &= 3\sin\left(2 \cdot \dfrac{5\pi}{12} - \dfrac{\pi}{3}\right) \\ &= 3\sin\left(\dfrac{5\pi}{6} - \dfrac{2\pi}{6}\right) \\ &= 3\sin\dfrac{3\pi}{6} = 3\sin\dfrac{\pi}{2} \\ &= 3 \cdot 1 = 3 \end{aligned}$	$\left(\dfrac{5\pi}{12}, 3\right)$
$\dfrac{2\pi}{3}$	$\begin{aligned} y &= 3\sin\left(2 \cdot \dfrac{2\pi}{3} - \dfrac{\pi}{3}\right) \\ &= 3\sin\left(\dfrac{4\pi}{3} - \dfrac{\pi}{3}\right) \\ &= 3\sin\dfrac{3\pi}{3} = 3\sin \pi \\ &= 3 \cdot 0 = 0 \end{aligned}$	$\left(\dfrac{2\pi}{3}, 0\right)$
$\dfrac{11\pi}{12}$	$\begin{aligned} y &= 3\sin\left(2 \cdot \dfrac{11\pi}{12} - \dfrac{\pi}{3}\right) \\ &= 3\sin\left(\dfrac{11\pi}{6} - \dfrac{2\pi}{6}\right) \\ &= 3\sin\dfrac{9\pi}{6} = 3\sin\dfrac{3\pi}{2} \\ &= 3(-1) = -3 \end{aligned}$	$\left(\dfrac{11\pi}{12}, -3\right)$
$\dfrac{7\pi}{6}$	$\begin{aligned} y &= 3\sin\left(2 \cdot \dfrac{7\pi}{6} - \dfrac{\pi}{3}\right) \\ &= 3\sin\dfrac{6\pi}{3} = 3\sin 2\pi \\ &= 3 \cdot 0 = 0 \end{aligned}$	$\left(\dfrac{7\pi}{6}, 0\right)$

Connect the five key points with a smooth curve and graph one complete cycle of the given graph.

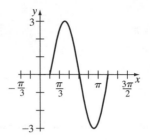

5. The equation $y = -4\cos \pi x$ is of the form $y = A\cos Bx$ with $A = -4$, and $B = \pi$. Thus, the amplitude is $|A| = |-4| = 4$.

The period is $\dfrac{2\pi}{B} = \dfrac{2\pi}{\pi} = 2$.

Find the x-values for the five key points by dividing the period, 2, by 4,

$\dfrac{\text{period}}{4} = \dfrac{2}{4} = \dfrac{1}{2}$, then by adding quarter-periods to the value of x where the cycle begins. The five x-values are

$x = 0$

$x = 0 + \dfrac{1}{2} = \dfrac{1}{2}$

$x = \dfrac{1}{2} + \dfrac{1}{2} = 1$

$x = 1 + \dfrac{1}{2} = \dfrac{3}{2}$

$x = \dfrac{3}{2} + \dfrac{1}{2} = 2$

We evaluate the function at each value of x.

x	$y = -4\cos \pi x$	coordinates
0	$y = -4\cos(\pi \cdot 0)$ $= -4\cos 0$ $= -4 \cdot 1 = -4$	$(0, -4)$
$\dfrac{1}{2}$	$y = -4\cos\left(\pi \cdot \dfrac{1}{2}\right)$ $= -4\cos\dfrac{\pi}{2}$ $= -4 \cdot 0 = 0$	$\left(\dfrac{1}{2}, 0\right)$
1	$y = -4\cos(\pi \cdot 1)$ $= -4\cos \pi$ $= -4 \cdot (-1) = 4$	$(1, 4)$
$\dfrac{3}{2}$	$y = -4\cos\left(\pi \cdot \dfrac{3}{2}\right)$ $= -4\cos\dfrac{3\pi}{2}$ $= -4 \cdot 0 = 0$	$\left(\dfrac{3}{2}, 0\right)$
2	$y = -4\cos(\pi \cdot 2)$ $= -4\cos 2\pi$ $= -4 \cdot 1 = -4$	$(2, -4)$

Connect the five key points with a smooth curve and graph one complete cycle of the given function. Extend the pattern of the graph another full period to the left.

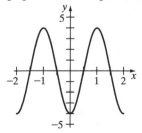

6. $y = \dfrac{3}{2}\cos(2x + \pi) = \dfrac{3}{2}\cos(2x - (-\pi))$

The equation is of the form

$y = A\cos(Bx - C)$ with $A = \dfrac{3}{2}$, $B = 2$, and $C = -\pi$.

Thus, the amplitude is $|A| = \left|\dfrac{3}{2}\right| = \dfrac{3}{2}$.

The period is $\dfrac{2\pi}{B} = \dfrac{2\pi}{2} = \pi$.

The phase shift is $\dfrac{C}{B} = \dfrac{-\pi}{2} = -\dfrac{\pi}{2}$.

Find the x-values for the five key points by dividing the period, π, by 4, $\dfrac{\text{period}}{4} = \dfrac{\pi}{4}$, then by adding quarter-periods to the value of x where the cycle begins, $x = -\dfrac{\pi}{2}$.

The five x-values are

$x = -\dfrac{\pi}{2}$

$x = -\dfrac{\pi}{2} + \dfrac{\pi}{4} = -\dfrac{\pi}{4}$

$x = -\dfrac{\pi}{4} + \dfrac{\pi}{4} = 0$

$x = 0 + \dfrac{\pi}{4} = \dfrac{\pi}{4}$

$x = \dfrac{\pi}{4} + \dfrac{\pi}{4} = \dfrac{\pi}{2}$

We evaluate the function at each value of x.

x	$y = \dfrac{3}{2}\cos(2x+\pi)$	coordinates
$-\dfrac{\pi}{2}$	$y = \dfrac{3}{2}\cos(-\pi+\pi)$ $= \dfrac{3}{2}\cdot 1 = \dfrac{3}{2}$	$\left(-\dfrac{\pi}{2}, \dfrac{3}{2}\right)$
$-\dfrac{\pi}{4}$	$y = \dfrac{3}{2}\cos\left(-\dfrac{\pi}{2}+\pi\right)$ $= \dfrac{3}{2}\cdot 0 = 0$	$\left(-\dfrac{\pi}{4}, 0\right)$
0	$y = \dfrac{3}{2}\cos(0+\pi)$ $= \dfrac{3}{2}\cdot -1 = -\dfrac{3}{2}$	$\left(0, -\dfrac{3}{2}\right)$
$\dfrac{\pi}{4}$	$y = \dfrac{3}{2}\cos\left(\dfrac{\pi}{2}+\pi\right)$ $= \dfrac{3}{2}\cdot 0 = 0$	$\left(\dfrac{\pi}{4}, 0\right)$
$\dfrac{\pi}{2}$	$y = \dfrac{3}{2}\cos(\pi+\pi)$ $= \dfrac{3}{2}\cdot 1 = \dfrac{3}{2}$	$\left(\dfrac{\pi}{2}, \dfrac{3}{2}\right)$

Connect the five key points with a smooth curve and graph one complete cycle of the given graph.

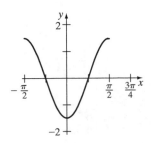

7. The graph of $y = 2\cos x + 1$ is the graph of $y = 2\cos x$ shifted one unit upwards. The period for both functions is 2π. The quarter-period is $\dfrac{2\pi}{4}$ or $\dfrac{\pi}{2}$. The cycle begins at $x = 0$. Add quarter-periods to generate x-values for the key points.

    $x = 0$

    $x = 0 + \dfrac{\pi}{2} = \dfrac{\pi}{2}$

    $x = \dfrac{\pi}{2} + \dfrac{\pi}{2} = \pi$

    $x = \pi + \dfrac{\pi}{2} = \dfrac{3\pi}{2}$

    $x = \dfrac{3\pi}{2} + \dfrac{\pi}{2} = 2\pi$

We evaluate the function at each value of x.

x	$y = 2\cos x + 1$	coordinates
0	$y = 2\cos 0 + 1$ $= 2\cdot 1 + 1 = 3$	$(0, 3)$
$\dfrac{\pi}{2}$	$y = 2\cos\dfrac{\pi}{2} + 1$ $= 2\cdot 0 + 1 = 1$	$\left(\dfrac{\pi}{2}, 1\right)$
π	$y = 2\cos\pi + 1$ $= 2\cdot(-1) + 1 = -1$	$(\pi, -1)$
$\dfrac{3\pi}{2}$	$y = 2\cos\dfrac{3\pi}{2} + 1$ $= 2\cdot 0 + 1 = 1$	$\left(\dfrac{3\pi}{2}, 1\right)$
2π	$y = 2\cos 2\pi + 1$ $= 2\cdot 1 + 1 = 3$	$(2\pi, 3)$
2π	$y = 2\cos 2\pi + 1$ $= 2\cdot 1 + 1 = 3$	$(2\pi, 3)$

By connecting the points with a smooth curve, we obtain one period of the graph.

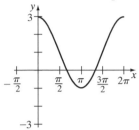

8. A, the amplitude, is the maximum value of y. The graph shows that this maximum value is 4, Thus, $A = 4$. The period is $\dfrac{\pi}{2}$, and period $= \dfrac{2\pi}{B}$.

 Thus, $\dfrac{\pi}{2} = \dfrac{2\pi}{B}$

 $\pi B = 4\pi$

 $B = 4$

 Substitute these values into $y = A \sin Bx$. The graph is modeled by $y = 4 \sin 4x$.

9. Because the hours of daylight ranges from a minimum of 10 hours to a maximum of 14 hours, the curve oscillates about the middle value, 12 hours. Thus, $D = 12$. The maximum number of hours is 2 hours above 12 hours. Thus, $A = 2$. The graph shows that one complete cycle occurs in 12–0, or 12 months. The period is 12. Thus,

 $12 = \dfrac{2\pi}{B}$

 $12B = 2\pi$

 $B = \dfrac{2\pi}{12} = \dfrac{\pi}{6}$

 The graph shows that the starting point of the cycle is shifted from 0 to 3. The phase shift, $\dfrac{C}{B}$, is 3.

$3 = \dfrac{C}{B}$

$3 = \dfrac{C}{\frac{\pi}{6}}$

$\dfrac{\pi}{2} = C$

Substitute these values into $y = A \sin(Bx - C) + D$. The number of hours of daylight is modeled by

$y = 2 \sin\left(\dfrac{\pi}{6} x - \dfrac{\pi}{2} \right) + 12$.

Exercise Set 1.5

1. The equation $y = 4 \sin x$ is of the form $y = A \sin x$ with $A = 4$. Thus, the amplitude is $|A| = |4| = 4$. The period is 2π. The quarter-period is $\dfrac{2\pi}{4}$ or $\dfrac{\pi}{2}$. The cycle begins at $x = 0$. Add quarter-periods to generate x-values for the key points.

 $x = 0$

 $x = 0 + \dfrac{\pi}{2} = \dfrac{\pi}{2}$

 $x = \dfrac{\pi}{2} + \dfrac{\pi}{2} = \pi$

 $x = \pi + \dfrac{\pi}{2} = \dfrac{3\pi}{2}$

 $x = \dfrac{3\pi}{2} + \dfrac{\pi}{2} = 2\pi$

 We evaluate the function at each value of x.

x	$y = 4 \sin x$	coordinates
0	$y = 4 \sin 0 = 4 \cdot 0 = 0$	$(0, 0)$
$\dfrac{\pi}{2}$	$y = 4 \sin \dfrac{\pi}{2} = 4 \cdot 1 = 4$	$\left(\dfrac{\pi}{2}, 4 \right)$
π	$y = 4 \sin \pi = 4 \cdot 0 = 0$	$(\pi, 0)$

$\dfrac{3\pi}{2}$	$y = 4\sin\dfrac{3\pi}{2}$ $= 4(-1) = -4$	$\left(\dfrac{3\pi}{2}, -4\right)$
2π	$y = 4\sin 2\pi = 4\cdot 0 = 0$	$(2\pi, 0)$

Connect the five key points with a smooth curve and graph one complete cycle of the given function with the graph of $y = \sin x$.

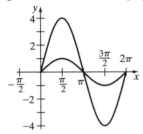

3. The equation $y = \dfrac{1}{3}\sin x$ is of the form

    $y = A\sin x$ with $A = \dfrac{1}{3}$. Thus, the amplitude

    is $|\, A\,| = \left|\, \dfrac{1}{3}\,\right| = \dfrac{1}{3}$. The period is 2π. The

    quarter-period is $\dfrac{2\pi}{4}$ or $\dfrac{\pi}{2}$. The cycle

    begins at $x = 0$. Add quarter-periods to generate x-values for the key points.
    $x = 0$

    $x = 0 + \dfrac{\pi}{2} = \dfrac{\pi}{2}$

    $x = \dfrac{\pi}{2} + \dfrac{\pi}{2} = \pi$

    $x = \pi + \dfrac{\pi}{2} = \dfrac{3\pi}{2}$

    $x = \dfrac{3\pi}{2} + \dfrac{\pi}{2} = 2\pi$

    We evaluate the function at each value of x.

x	$y = \dfrac{1}{3}\sin x$	coordinates
0	$y = \dfrac{1}{3}\sin 0 = \dfrac{1}{3}\cdot 0 = 0$	$(0, 0)$

$\dfrac{\pi}{2}$	$y = \dfrac{1}{3}\sin\dfrac{\pi}{2} = \dfrac{1}{3}\cdot 1 = \dfrac{1}{3}$	$\left(\dfrac{\pi}{2}, \dfrac{1}{3}\right)$
π	$y = \dfrac{1}{3}\sin\pi = \dfrac{1}{3}\cdot 0 = 0$	$(\pi, 0)$
$\dfrac{3\pi}{2}$	$y = \dfrac{1}{3}\sin\dfrac{3\pi}{2}$ $= \dfrac{1}{3}(-1) = -\dfrac{1}{3}$	$\left(\dfrac{3\pi}{2}, -\dfrac{1}{3}\right)$
2π	$y = \dfrac{1}{3}\sin 2\pi = \dfrac{1}{3}\cdot 0 = 0$	$(2\pi, 0)$

Connect the five key points with a smooth curve and graph one complete cycle of the given function with the graph of $y = \sin x$.

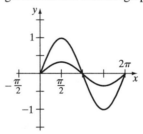

5. The equation $y = -3\sin x$ is of the form
    $y = A\sin x$ with $A = -3$. Thus, the amplitude
    is $|\, A\,| = |\, -3\,| = 3$. The period is 2π. The

    quarter-period is $\dfrac{2\pi}{4}$ or $\dfrac{\pi}{2}$. The cycle

    begins at $x = 0$. Add quarter-periods to generate x-values for the key points.
    $x = 0$

    $x = 0 + \dfrac{\pi}{2} = \dfrac{\pi}{2}$

    $x = \dfrac{\pi}{2} + \dfrac{\pi}{2} = \pi$

    $x = \pi + \dfrac{\pi}{2} = \dfrac{3\pi}{2}$

    $x = \dfrac{3\pi}{2} + \dfrac{\pi}{2} = 2\pi$

    We evaluate the function at each value of x.

x	$y = -3\sin x$	coordinates
0	$y = -3\sin x$ $= -3 \cdot 0 = 0$	$(0, 0)$
$\dfrac{\pi}{2}$	$y = -3\sin\dfrac{\pi}{2}$ $= -3 \cdot 1 = -3$	$\left(\dfrac{\pi}{2}, -3\right)$
π	$y = -3\sin \pi$ $= -3 \cdot 0 = 0$	$(\pi, 0)$
$\dfrac{3\pi}{2}$	$y = -3\sin\dfrac{3\pi}{2}$ $= -3(-1) = 3$	$\left(\dfrac{3\pi}{2}, 3\right)$
2π	$y = -3\sin 2\pi$ $= -3 \cdot 0 = 0$	$(2\pi, 0)$

Connect the five key points with a smooth curve and graph one complete cycle of the given function with the graph of $y = \sin x$.

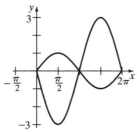

7. The equation $y = \sin 2x$ is of the form $y = A\sin Bx$ with $A = 1$ and $B = 2$. The amplitude is $|A| = |1| = 1$. The period is $\dfrac{2\pi}{B} = \dfrac{2\pi}{2} = \pi$. The quarter-period is $\dfrac{\pi}{4}$. The cycle begins at $x = 0$. Add quarter-periods to generate x-values for the key points.

$x = 0$

$x = 0 + \dfrac{\pi}{4}$

$x = \dfrac{\pi}{4} + \dfrac{\pi}{4} = \dfrac{\pi}{2}$

$x = \dfrac{\pi}{2} + \dfrac{\pi}{4} = \dfrac{3\pi}{4}$

$x = \dfrac{3\pi}{4} + \dfrac{\pi}{4} = \pi$

We evaluate the function at each value of x.

x	$y = \sin 2x$	coordinates
0	$y = \sin 2 \cdot 0 = \sin 0 = 0$	$(0, 0)$
$\dfrac{\pi}{4}$	$y = \sin\left(2 \cdot \dfrac{\pi}{4}\right)$ $= \sin\dfrac{\pi}{2} = 1$	$\left(\dfrac{\pi}{4}, 1\right)$
$\dfrac{\pi}{2}$	$y = \sin\left(2 \cdot \dfrac{\pi}{2}\right)$ $= \sin \pi = 0$	$\left(\dfrac{\pi}{2}, 0\right)$
$\dfrac{3\pi}{4}$	$y = \sin\left(2 \cdot \dfrac{3\pi}{4}\right)$ $= \sin\dfrac{3\pi}{2} = -1$	$\left(\dfrac{3\pi}{4}, -1\right)$
π	$y = \sin(2 \cdot \pi)$ $= \sin 2\pi = 0$	$(\pi, 0)$

Connect the five key points with a smooth curve and graph one complete cycle of the given function.

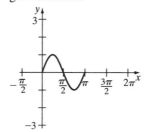

9. The equation $y = 3\sin\dfrac{1}{2}x$ is of the form

$y = A\sin Bx$ with $A = 3$ and $B = \dfrac{1}{2}$. The

amplitude is $\mid A \mid = \mid 3 \mid = 3$. The period is

$\dfrac{2\pi}{B} = \dfrac{2\pi}{\frac{1}{2}} = 2\pi \cdot 2 = 4\pi$. The quarter-period

is $\dfrac{4\pi}{4} = \pi$. The cycle begins at $x = 0$. Add

quarter-periods to generate x-values for the
key points.
$x = 0$

$x = 0 + \pi = \pi$

$x = \pi + \pi = 2\pi$

$x = 2\pi + \pi = 3\pi$

$x = 3\pi + \pi = 4\pi$

We evaluate the function at each value of x.

x	$y = 3\sin\dfrac{1}{2}x$	coordinates
0	$y = 3\sin\left(\dfrac{1}{2} \cdot 0\right)$ $= 3\sin 0 = 3 \cdot 0 = 0$	$(0, 0)$
π	$y = 3\sin\left(\dfrac{1}{2} \cdot \pi\right)$ $= 3\sin\dfrac{\pi}{2} = 3 \cdot 1 = 3$	$(\pi, 3)$
2π	$y = 3\sin\left(\dfrac{1}{2} \cdot 2\pi\right)$ $= 3\sin \pi = 3 \cdot 0 = 0$	$(2\pi, 0)$
3π	$y = 3\sin\left(\dfrac{1}{2} \cdot 3\pi\right)$ $= 3\sin\dfrac{3\pi}{2}$ $= 3(-1) = -3$	$(3\pi, -3)$
4π	$y = 3\sin\left(\dfrac{1}{2} \cdot 4\pi\right)$ $= 3\sin 2\pi = 3 \cdot 0 = 0$	$(4\pi, 0)$

Connect the five points with a smooth curve
and graph one complete cycle of the given
function.

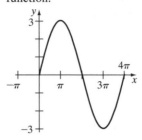

11. The equation $y = 4\sin \pi x$ is of the form
$y = A\sin Bx$ with $A = 4$ and $B = \pi$. The
amplitude is $\mid A \mid = \mid 4 \mid = 4$. The period is

$\dfrac{2\pi}{B} = \dfrac{2\pi}{\pi} = 2$. The quarter-period is $\dfrac{2}{4} = \dfrac{1}{2}$.

The cycle begins at $x = 0$. Add quarter-
periods to generate x-values for the key
points.
$x = 0$

$x = 0 + \dfrac{1}{2} = \dfrac{1}{2}$

$x = \dfrac{1}{2} + \dfrac{1}{2} = 1$

$x = 1 + \dfrac{1}{2} = \dfrac{3}{2}$

$x = \dfrac{3}{2} + \dfrac{1}{2} = 2$

We evaluate the function at each value of x.

x	$y = 4\sin \pi x$	coordinates
0	$y = 4\sin(\pi \cdot 0)$ $= 4\sin 0 = 4 \cdot 0 = 0$	$(0, 0)$
$\dfrac{1}{2}$	$y = 4\sin\left(\pi \cdot \dfrac{1}{2}\right)$ $= 4\sin\dfrac{\pi}{2} = 4(1) = 4$	$\left(\dfrac{1}{2}, 4\right)$
1	$y = 4\sin(\pi \cdot 1)$ $= 4\sin \pi = 4 \cdot 0 = 0$	$(1, 0)$

$\dfrac{3}{2}$	$y = 4\sin\left(\pi \cdot \dfrac{3}{2}\right)$ $= 4\sin\dfrac{3\pi}{2}$ $= 4(-1) = -4$	$\left(\dfrac{3}{2}, -4\right)$
2	$y = 4\sin(\pi \cdot 2)$ $= 4\sin 2\pi = 4 \cdot 0 = 0$	$(2, 0)$

Connect the five points with a smooth curve and graph one complete cycle of the given function.

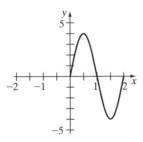

13. The equation $y = -3\sin 2\pi x$ is of the form $y = A\sin Bx$ with $A = -3$ and $B = 2\pi$. The amplitude is $|A| = |-3| = 3$. The period is $\dfrac{2\pi}{B} = \dfrac{2\pi}{2\pi} = 1$. The quarter-period is $\dfrac{1}{4}$. The cycle begins at $x = 0$. Add quarter-periods to generate x-values for the key points.
$x = 0$

$x = 0 + \dfrac{1}{4} = \dfrac{1}{4}$

$x = \dfrac{1}{4} + \dfrac{1}{4} = \dfrac{1}{2}$

$x = \dfrac{1}{2} + \dfrac{1}{4} = \dfrac{3}{4}$

$x = \dfrac{3}{4} + \dfrac{1}{4} = 1$

We evaluate the function at each value of x.

x	$y = -3\sin 2\pi x$	coordinates
0	$y = -3\sin(2\pi \cdot 0)$ $= -3\sin 0$ $= -3 \cdot 0 = 0$	$(0, 0)$
$\dfrac{1}{4}$	$y = -3\sin\left(2\pi \cdot \dfrac{1}{4}\right)$ $= -3\sin\dfrac{\pi}{2}$ $= -3 \cdot 1 = -3$	$\left(\dfrac{1}{4}, -3\right)$
$\dfrac{1}{2}$	$y = -3\sin\left(2\pi \cdot \dfrac{1}{2}\right)$ $= -3\sin \pi$ $= -3 \cdot 0 = 0$	$\left(\dfrac{1}{2}, 0\right)$
$\dfrac{3}{4}$	$y = -3\sin\left(2\pi \cdot \dfrac{3}{4}\right)$ $= -3\sin\dfrac{3\pi}{2}$ $= -3(-1) = 3$	$\left(\dfrac{3}{4}, 3\right)$
1	$y = -3\sin(2\pi \cdot 1)$ $= -3\sin 2\pi$ $= -3 \cdot 0 = 0$	$(1, 0)$

Connect the five points with a smooth curve and graph one complete cycle of the given function.

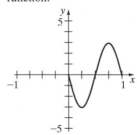

15. The equation $y = -\sin\dfrac{2}{3}x$ is of the form $y = A\sin Bx$ with $A = -1$ and $B = \dfrac{2}{3}$. The amplitude is $|A| = |-1| = 1$. The period is

$\dfrac{2\pi}{B} = \dfrac{2\pi}{\frac{2}{3}} = 2\pi \cdot \dfrac{3}{2} = 3\pi$. The quarter-period

is $\dfrac{3\pi}{4}$. The cycle begins at $x = 0$. Add

quarter-periods to generate x-values for the key points.

$x = 0$

$x = 0 + \dfrac{3\pi}{4} = \dfrac{3\pi}{4}$

$x = \dfrac{3\pi}{4} + \dfrac{3\pi}{4} = \dfrac{3\pi}{2}$

$x = \dfrac{3\pi}{2} + \dfrac{3\pi}{4} = \dfrac{9\pi}{4}$

$x = \dfrac{9\pi}{4} + \dfrac{3\pi}{4} = 3\pi$

We evaluate the function at each value of x.

x	$y = -\sin\dfrac{2}{3}x$	coordinates
0	$y = -\sin\left(\dfrac{2}{3}\cdot 0\right)$ $= -\sin 0 = 0$	$(0, 0)$
$\dfrac{3\pi}{4}$	$y = -\sin\left(\dfrac{2}{3}\cdot\dfrac{3\pi}{4}\right)$ $= -\sin\dfrac{\pi}{2} = -1$	$\left(\dfrac{3\pi}{4}, -1\right)$
$\dfrac{3\pi}{2}$	$y = -\sin\left(\dfrac{2}{3}\cdot\dfrac{3\pi}{2}\right)$ $= -\sin\pi = 0$	$\left(\dfrac{3\pi}{2}, 0\right)$
$\dfrac{9\pi}{4}$	$y = -\sin\left(\dfrac{2}{3}\cdot\dfrac{9\pi}{4}\right)$ $= -\sin\dfrac{3\pi}{2}$ $= -(-1) = 1$	$\left(\dfrac{9\pi}{4}, 1\right)$
3π	$y = -\sin\left(\dfrac{2}{3}\cdot 3\pi\right)$ $= -\sin 2\pi = 0$	$(3\pi, 0)$

Connect the five points with a smooth curve and graph one complete cycle of the given function.

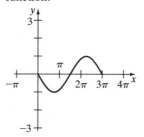

17. The equation $y = \sin(x - \pi)$ is of the form $y = A\sin(Bx - C)$ with $A = 1$, $B = 1$, and $C = \pi$. The amplitude is $|A| = |1| = 1$. The

period is $\dfrac{2\pi}{B} = \dfrac{2\pi}{1} = 2\pi$. The phase shift is

$\dfrac{C}{B} = \dfrac{\pi}{1} = \pi$. The quarter-period is $\dfrac{2\pi}{4} = \dfrac{\pi}{2}$.

The cycle begins at $x = \pi$. Add quarter-periods to generate x-values for the key points.

$x = \pi$

$x = \pi + \dfrac{\pi}{2} = \dfrac{3\pi}{2}$

$x = \dfrac{3\pi}{2} + \dfrac{\pi}{2} = 2\pi$

$x = 2\pi + \dfrac{\pi}{2} = \dfrac{5\pi}{2}$

$x = \dfrac{5\pi}{2} + \dfrac{\pi}{2} = 3\pi$

We evaluate the function at each value of x.

x	$y = \sin(x - \pi)$	coordinates
π	$y = \sin(\pi - \pi)$ $= \sin 0 = 0$	$(\pi, 0)$
$\dfrac{3\pi}{2}$	$y = \sin\left(\dfrac{3\pi}{2} - \pi\right)$ $= \sin\dfrac{\pi}{2} = 1$	$\left(\dfrac{3\pi}{2}, 1\right)$
2π	$y = \sin(2\pi - \pi)$ $= \sin \pi = 0$	$(2\pi, 0)$
$\dfrac{5\pi}{2}$	$y = \sin\left(\dfrac{5\pi}{2} - \pi\right)$ $= \sin\dfrac{3\pi}{2} = -1$	$\left(\dfrac{5\pi}{2}, -1\right)$
3π	$y = \sin(3\pi - \pi)$ $= \sin 2\pi = 0$	$(3\pi, 0)$

Connect the five points with a smooth curve and graph one complete cycle of the given function.

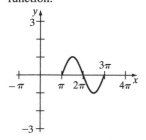

19. The equation $y = \sin(2x - \pi)$ is of the form $y = A\sin(Bx - C)$ with $A = 1$, $B = 2$, and $C = \pi$. The amplitude is $|A| = |1| = 1$. The period is $\dfrac{2\pi}{B} = \dfrac{2\pi}{2} = \pi$. The phase shift is $\dfrac{C}{B} = \dfrac{\pi}{2}$. The quarter-period is $\dfrac{\pi}{4}$. The cycle begins at $x = \dfrac{\pi}{2}$. Add quarter-periods to generate x-values for the key points.

$$x = \frac{\pi}{2}$$
$$x = \frac{\pi}{2} + \frac{\pi}{4} = \frac{3\pi}{4}$$
$$x = \frac{3\pi}{4} + \frac{\pi}{4} = \pi$$
$$x = \pi + \frac{\pi}{4} = \frac{5\pi}{4}$$
$$x = \frac{5\pi}{4} + \frac{\pi}{4} = \frac{3\pi}{2}$$

We evaluate the function at each value of x.

x	$y = \sin(2x - \pi)$	coordinates
$\dfrac{\pi}{2}$	$y = \sin\left(2 \cdot \dfrac{\pi}{2} - \pi\right)$ $= \sin(\pi - \pi)$ $= \sin 0 = 0$	$\left(\dfrac{\pi}{2}, 0\right)$
$\dfrac{3\pi}{4}$	$y = \sin\left(2 \cdot \dfrac{3\pi}{4} - \pi\right)$ $= \sin\left(\dfrac{3\pi}{2} - \pi\right)$ $= \sin\dfrac{\pi}{2} = 1$	$\left(\dfrac{3\pi}{4}, 1\right)$
π	$y = \sin(2 \cdot \pi - \pi)$ $= \sin(2\pi - \pi)$ $= \sin \pi = 0$	$(\pi, 0)$
$\dfrac{5\pi}{4}$	$y = \sin\left(2 \cdot \dfrac{5\pi}{4} - \pi\right)$ $= \sin\left(\dfrac{5\pi}{2} - \pi\right)$ $= \sin\dfrac{3\pi}{2} = -1$	$\left(\dfrac{5\pi}{4}, -1\right)$

| $\dfrac{3\pi}{2}$ | $\begin{aligned} y &= \sin\left(2\cdot\dfrac{3\pi}{2} - \pi\right) \\ &= \sin(3\pi - \pi) \\ &= \sin 2\pi = 0 \end{aligned}$ | $\left(\dfrac{3\pi}{2}, 0\right)$ |

Connect the five points with a smooth curve and graph one complete cycle of the given function.

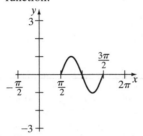

21. The equation $y = 3\sin(2x - \pi)$ is of the form $y = A\sin(Bx - C)$ with $A = 3$, $B = 2$, and $C = \pi$. The amplitude is $|A| = |3| = 3$.

The period is $\dfrac{2\pi}{B} = \dfrac{2\pi}{2} = \pi$. The phase shift is $\dfrac{C}{B} = \dfrac{\pi}{2}$. The quarter-period is $\dfrac{\pi}{4}$. The cycle begins at $x = \dfrac{\pi}{2}$. Add quarter-periods to generate x-values for the key points.

$x = \dfrac{\pi}{2}$

$x = \dfrac{\pi}{2} + \dfrac{\pi}{4} = \dfrac{3\pi}{4}$

$x = \dfrac{3\pi}{4} + \dfrac{\pi}{4} = \pi$

$x = \pi + \dfrac{\pi}{4} = \dfrac{5\pi}{4}$

$x = \dfrac{5\pi}{4} + \dfrac{\pi}{4} = \dfrac{3\pi}{2}$

We evaluate the function at each value of x.

x	$y = 3\sin(2x - \pi)$	coordinates

$\dfrac{\pi}{2}$	$\begin{aligned} y &= 3\sin\left(2\cdot\dfrac{\pi}{2} - \pi\right) \\ &= 3\sin(\pi - \pi) \\ &= 3\sin 0 = 3\cdot 0 = 0 \end{aligned}$	$\left(\dfrac{\pi}{2}, 0\right)$
$\dfrac{3\pi}{4}$	$\begin{aligned} y &= 3\sin\left(2\cdot\dfrac{3\pi}{4} - \pi\right) \\ &= 3\sin\left(\dfrac{3\pi}{2} - \pi\right) \\ &= 3\sin\dfrac{\pi}{2} = 3\cdot 1 = 3 \end{aligned}$	$\left(\dfrac{3\pi}{4}, 3\right)$
π	$\begin{aligned} y &= 3\sin(2\cdot\pi - \pi) \\ &= 3\sin(2\pi - \pi) \\ &= 3\sin\pi = 3\cdot 0 = 0 \end{aligned}$	$(\pi, 0)$
$\dfrac{5\pi}{4}$	$\begin{aligned} y &= 3\sin\left(2\cdot\dfrac{5\pi}{4} - \pi\right) \\ &= 3\sin\left(\dfrac{5\pi}{2} - \pi\right) \\ &= 3\sin\dfrac{3\pi}{2} \\ &= 3(-1) = -3 \end{aligned}$	$\left(\dfrac{5\pi}{4}, -3\right)$
$\dfrac{3\pi}{2}$	$\begin{aligned} y &= 3\sin\left(2\cdot\dfrac{3\pi}{2} - \pi\right) \\ &= 3\sin(3\pi - \pi) \\ &= 3\sin 2\pi = 3\cdot 0 = 0 \end{aligned}$	$\left(\dfrac{3\pi}{2}, 0\right)$

Connect the five points with a smooth curve and graph one complete cycle of the given function.

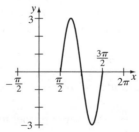

23. $y = \dfrac{1}{2}\sin\left(x + \dfrac{\pi}{2}\right) = \dfrac{1}{2}\sin\left(x - \left(-\dfrac{\pi}{2}\right)\right)$

The equation $y = \dfrac{1}{2}\sin\left(x - \left(-\dfrac{\pi}{2}\right)\right)$ is of the

form $y = A\sin(Bx - C)$ with $A = \dfrac{1}{2}$, $B = 1$,

and $C = -\dfrac{\pi}{2}$. The amplitude is

$|A| = \left|\dfrac{1}{2}\right| = \dfrac{1}{2}$. The period is

$\dfrac{2\pi}{B} = \dfrac{2\pi}{1} = 2\pi$. The phase shift is

$\dfrac{C}{B} = \dfrac{-\frac{\pi}{2}}{1} = -\dfrac{\pi}{2}$. The quarter-period is

$\dfrac{2\pi}{4} = \dfrac{\pi}{2}$. The cycle begins at $x = -\dfrac{\pi}{2}$. Add

quarter-periods to generate x-values for the key points.

$x = -\dfrac{\pi}{2}$

$x = -\dfrac{\pi}{2} + \dfrac{\pi}{2} = 0$

$x = 0 + \dfrac{\pi}{2} = \dfrac{\pi}{2}$

$x = \dfrac{\pi}{2} + \dfrac{\pi}{2} = \pi$

$x = \pi + \dfrac{\pi}{2} = \dfrac{3\pi}{2}$

We evaluate the function at each value of x.

x	$y = \dfrac{1}{2}\sin\left(x + \dfrac{\pi}{2}\right)$	coordinates
$-\dfrac{\pi}{2}$	$y = \dfrac{1}{2}\sin\left(-\dfrac{\pi}{2} + \dfrac{\pi}{2}\right)$ $= \dfrac{1}{2}\sin 0 = \dfrac{1}{2}\cdot 0 = 0$	$\left(-\dfrac{\pi}{2}, 0\right)$
0	$y = \dfrac{1}{2}\sin\left(0 + \dfrac{\pi}{2}\right)$ $= \dfrac{1}{2}\sin\dfrac{\pi}{2} = \dfrac{1}{2}\cdot 1 = \dfrac{1}{2}$	$\left(0, \dfrac{1}{2}\right)$
$\dfrac{\pi}{2}$	$y = \dfrac{1}{2}\sin\left(\dfrac{\pi}{2} + \dfrac{\pi}{2}\right)$ $= \dfrac{1}{2}\sin\pi = \dfrac{1}{2}\cdot 0 = 0$	$\left(\dfrac{\pi}{2}, 0\right)$
π	$y = \dfrac{1}{2}\sin\left(\pi + \dfrac{\pi}{2}\right)$ $= \dfrac{1}{2}\sin\dfrac{3\pi}{2}$ $= \dfrac{1}{2}\cdot(-1) = -\dfrac{1}{2}$	$\left(\pi, -\dfrac{1}{2}\right)$
$\dfrac{3\pi}{2}$	$y = \dfrac{1}{2}\sin\left(\dfrac{3\pi}{2} + \dfrac{\pi}{2}\right)$ $= \dfrac{1}{2}\sin 2\pi$ $= \dfrac{1}{2}\cdot 0 = 0$	$\left(\dfrac{3\pi}{2}, 0\right)$

Connect the five points with a smooth curve and graph one complete cycle of the given function.

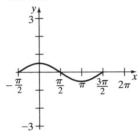

25. $y = -2\sin\left(2x + \dfrac{\pi}{2}\right) = -2\sin\left(2x - \left(-\dfrac{\pi}{2}\right)\right)$

The equation $y = -2\sin\left(2x - \left(-\dfrac{\pi}{2}\right)\right)$ is of

the form $y = A\sin(Bx - C)$ with $A = -2$,

$B = 2$, and $C = -\dfrac{\pi}{2}$. The amplitude is

$|A| = |-2| = 2$. The period is

$\dfrac{2\pi}{B} = \dfrac{2\pi}{2} = \pi$. The phase shift is

$\dfrac{C}{B} = \dfrac{-\frac{\pi}{2}}{2} = -\dfrac{\pi}{2}\cdot\dfrac{1}{2} = -\dfrac{\pi}{4}$. The quarter-

period is $\dfrac{\pi}{4}$. The cycle begins at $x = -\dfrac{\pi}{4}$.

Add quarter-periods to generate x-values for the key points.

$x = -\dfrac{\pi}{4}$

$x = -\dfrac{\pi}{4} + \dfrac{\pi}{4} = 0$

$x = 0 + \dfrac{\pi}{4} = \dfrac{\pi}{4}$

$x = \dfrac{\pi}{4} + \dfrac{\pi}{4} = \dfrac{\pi}{2}$

$x = \dfrac{\pi}{2} + \dfrac{\pi}{4} = \dfrac{3\pi}{4}$

We evaluate the function at each value of x.

x	$y = -2\sin\left(2x + \dfrac{\pi}{2}\right)$	coordinates
$-\dfrac{\pi}{4}$	$y = -2\sin\left(2\cdot\left(-\dfrac{\pi}{4}\right) + \dfrac{\pi}{2}\right)$ $= -2\sin\left(-\dfrac{\pi}{2} + \dfrac{\pi}{2}\right)$ $= -2\sin 0 = -2\cdot 0 = 0$	$\left(-\dfrac{\pi}{4},\, 0\right)$
0	$y = -2\sin\left(2\cdot 0 + \dfrac{\pi}{2}\right)$ $= -2\sin\left(0 + \dfrac{\pi}{2}\right)$ $= -2\sin\dfrac{\pi}{2}$ $= -2\cdot 1 = -2$	$(0, -2)$
$\dfrac{\pi}{4}$	$y = -2\sin\left(2\cdot\dfrac{\pi}{4} + \dfrac{\pi}{2}\right)$ $= -2\sin\left(\dfrac{\pi}{2} + \dfrac{\pi}{2}\right)$ $= -2\sin\pi$ $= -2\cdot 0 = 0$	$\left(\dfrac{\pi}{4},\, 0\right)$
$\dfrac{\pi}{2}$	$y = -2\sin\left(2\cdot\dfrac{\pi}{2} + \dfrac{\pi}{2}\right)$ $= -2\sin\left(\pi + \dfrac{\pi}{2}\right)$ $= -2\sin\dfrac{3\pi}{2}$ $= -2(-1) = 2$	$\left(\dfrac{\pi}{2},\, 2\right)$
$\dfrac{3\pi}{4}$	$y = -2\sin\left(2\cdot\dfrac{3\pi}{4} + \dfrac{\pi}{2}\right)$ $= -2\sin\left(\dfrac{3\pi}{2} + \dfrac{\pi}{2}\right)$ $= -2\sin 2\pi$ $= -2\cdot 0 = 0$	$\left(\dfrac{3\pi}{4},\, 0\right)$

Connect the five points with a smooth curve and graph one complete cycle of the given function.

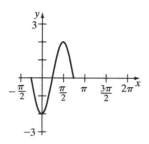

27. $y = 3\sin(\pi x + 2)$

The equation $y = 3\sin(\pi x - (-2))$ is of the form $y = A\sin(Bx - C)$ with $A = 3$, $B = \pi$, and $C = -2$. The amplitude is

$|A| = |3| = 3$. The period is $\dfrac{2\pi}{B} = \dfrac{2\pi}{\pi} = 2$.

The phase shift is $\dfrac{C}{B} = \dfrac{-2}{\pi} = -\dfrac{2}{\pi}$. The

quarter-period is $\dfrac{2}{4} = \dfrac{1}{2}$. The cycle begins at

$x = -\dfrac{2}{\pi}$. Add quarter-periods to generate x-values for the key points.

$x = -\dfrac{2}{\pi}$

$x = -\dfrac{2}{\pi} + \dfrac{1}{2} = \dfrac{\pi - 4}{2\pi}$

$x = \dfrac{\pi - 4}{2\pi} + \dfrac{1}{2} = \dfrac{\pi - 2}{\pi}$

$x = \dfrac{\pi - 2}{\pi} + \dfrac{1}{2} = \dfrac{3\pi - 4}{2\pi}$

$x = \dfrac{3\pi - 4}{2\pi} + \dfrac{1}{2} = \dfrac{2\pi - 2}{\pi}$

We evaluate the function at each value of x.

x	$y = 3\sin(\pi x + 2)$	coordinates
$-\dfrac{2}{\pi}$	$y = 3\sin\left(\pi\left(-\dfrac{2}{\pi}\right) + 2\right)$ $= 3\sin(-2 + 2)$ $= 3\sin 0 = 3 \cdot 0 = 0$	$\left(-\dfrac{2}{\pi},\, 0\right)$
$\dfrac{\pi - 4}{2\pi}$	$y = 3\sin\left(\pi\left(\dfrac{\pi - 4}{2\pi}\right) + 2\right)$ $= 3\sin\left(\dfrac{\pi - 4}{2} + 2\right)$ $= 3\sin\left(\dfrac{\pi}{2} - 2 + 2\right)$ $= 3\sin\dfrac{\pi}{2}$ $= 3 \cdot 1 = 3$	$\left(\dfrac{\pi - 4}{2\pi},\, 3\right)$
$\dfrac{\pi - 2}{\pi}$	$y = 3\sin\left(\pi\left(\dfrac{\pi - 2}{\pi}\right) + 2\right)$ $= 3\sin(\pi - 2 + 2)$ $= 3\sin\pi = 3 \cdot 0 = 0$	$\left(\dfrac{\pi - 2}{\pi},\, 0\right)$
$\dfrac{3\pi - 4}{2\pi}$	$y = 3\sin\left(\pi\left(\dfrac{3\pi - 4}{2\pi}\right) + 2\right)$ $= 3\sin\left(\dfrac{3\pi - 4}{2} + 2\right)$ $= 3\sin\left(\dfrac{3\pi}{2} - 2 + 2\right)$ $= 3\sin\dfrac{3\pi}{2}$ $= 3(-1) = -3$	$\left(\dfrac{5\pi}{4},\, -3\right)$
$\dfrac{2\pi - 2}{\pi}$	$y = 3\sin\left(\pi\left(\dfrac{2\pi - 2}{\pi}\right) + 2\right)$ $= 3\sin(2\pi - 2 + 2)$ $= 3\sin 2\pi = 3 \cdot 0 = 0$	$\left(\dfrac{2\pi - 2}{\pi},\, 0\right)$

Connect the five points with a smooth curve and graph one complete cycle of the given function.

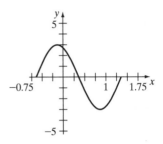

29. $y = -2\sin(2\pi x + 4\pi) = -2\sin(2\pi x - (-4\pi))$
The equation $y = -2\sin(2\pi x - (-4\pi))$ is of the form $y = A\sin(Bx - C)$ with $A = -2$, $B = 2\pi$, and $C = -4\pi$. The amplitude is $|A| = |-2| = 2$. The period is
$\dfrac{2\pi}{B} = \dfrac{2\pi}{2\pi} = 1$. The phase shift is
$\dfrac{C}{B} = \dfrac{-4\pi}{2\pi} = -2$. The quarter-period is $\dfrac{1}{4}$.
The cycle begins at $x = -2$. Add quarter-periods to generate x-values for the key points.
$x = -2$

$x = -2 + \dfrac{1}{4} = -\dfrac{7}{4}$

$x = -\dfrac{7}{4} + \dfrac{1}{4} = -\dfrac{3}{2}$

$x = -\dfrac{3}{2} + \dfrac{1}{4} = -\dfrac{5}{4}$

$x = -\dfrac{5}{4} + \dfrac{1}{4} = -1$

We evaluate the function at each value of x.

x	$y = -2\sin(2\pi x + 4\pi)$	coordinates
-2	$y = -2\sin(2\pi(-2) + 4\pi)$ $= -2\sin(-4\pi + 4\pi)$ $= -2\sin 0$ $= -2 \cdot 0 = 0$	$(-2, 0)$
$-\dfrac{7}{4}$	$y = -2\sin\left(2\pi\left(-\dfrac{7}{4}\right) + 4\pi\right)$ $= -2\sin\left(-\dfrac{7\pi}{2} + 4\pi\right)$ $= -2\sin\dfrac{\pi}{2} = -2 \cdot 1 = -2$	$\left(-\dfrac{7}{4}, -2\right)$
$-\dfrac{3}{2}$	$y = -2\sin\left(2\pi\left(-\dfrac{3}{2}\right) + 4\pi\right)$ $= -2\sin(-3\pi + 4\pi)$ $= -2\sin \pi = -2 \cdot 0 = 0$	$\left(-\dfrac{3}{2}, 0\right)$
$-\dfrac{5}{4}$	$y = -2\sin\left(2\pi\left(-\dfrac{5}{4}\right) + 4\pi\right)$ $= -2\sin\left(-\dfrac{5\pi}{2} + 4\pi\right)$ $= -2\sin\dfrac{3\pi}{2}$ $= -2(-1) = 2$	$\left(-\dfrac{5}{4}, 2\right)$
-1	$y = -2\sin(2\pi(-1) + 4\pi)$ $= -2\sin(-2\pi + 4\pi)$ $= -2\sin 2\pi$ $= -2 \cdot 0 = 0$	$(-1, 0)$

Connect the five points with a smooth curve and graph one complete cycle of the given function.

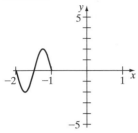

2π	$y = 2\cos 2\pi$	$(2\pi, 2)$
	$= 2 \cdot 1 = 2$	

Connect the five points with a smooth curve and graph one complete cycle of the given function with the graph of $y = 2\cos x$.

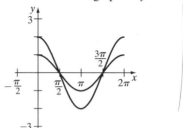

31. The equation $y = 2\cos x$ is of the form $y = A\cos x$ with $A = 2$. Thus, the amplitude is $|A| = |2| = 2$. The period is 2π. The quarter-period is $\dfrac{2\pi}{4}$ or $\dfrac{\pi}{2}$. The cycle begins at $x = 0$. Add quarter-periods to generate x-values for the key points.
$x = 0$

$x = 0 + \dfrac{\pi}{2} = \dfrac{\pi}{2}$

$x = \dfrac{\pi}{2} + \dfrac{\pi}{2} = \pi$

$x = \pi + \dfrac{\pi}{2} = \dfrac{3\pi}{2}$

$x = \dfrac{3\pi}{2} + \dfrac{\pi}{2} = 2\pi$

We evaluate the function at each value of x.

x	$y = 2\cos x$	coordinates
0	$y = 2\cos 0$ $= 2 \cdot 1 = 2$	$(0, 2)$
$\dfrac{\pi}{2}$	$y = 2\cos\dfrac{\pi}{2}$ $-2 \cdot 0 - 0$	$\left(\dfrac{\pi}{2}, 0\right)$
π	$y = 2\cos\pi$ $= 2 \cdot (-1) = -2$	$(\pi, -2)$
$\dfrac{3\pi}{2}$	$y = 2\cos\dfrac{3\pi}{2}$ $= 2 \cdot 0 = 0$	$\left(\dfrac{3\pi}{2}, 0\right)$

33. The equation $y = -2\cos x$ is of the form $y = A\cos x$ with $A = -2$. Thus, the amplitude is $|A| = |-2| = 2$. The period is 2π. The quarter-period is $\dfrac{2\pi}{4}$ or $\dfrac{\pi}{2}$. The cycle begins at $x = 0$. Add quarter-periods to generate x-values for the key points.
$x = 0$

$x = 0 + \dfrac{\pi}{2} = \dfrac{\pi}{2}$

$x = \dfrac{\pi}{2} + \dfrac{\pi}{2} = \pi$

$x = \pi + \dfrac{\pi}{2} = \dfrac{3\pi}{2}$

$x = \dfrac{3\pi}{2} + \dfrac{\pi}{2} = 2\pi$

We evaluate the function at each value of x.

x	$y = -2\cos x$	coordinates
0	$y = -2\cos 0$ $= -2 \cdot 1 = -2$	$(0, -2)$
$\dfrac{\pi}{2}$	$y = -2\cos\dfrac{\pi}{2}$ $= -2 \cdot 0 = 0$	$\left(\dfrac{\pi}{2}, 0\right)$
π	$y = -2\cos\pi$ $= -2 \cdot (-1) = 2$	$(\pi, 2)$

$\dfrac{3\pi}{2}$	$y = -2\cos\dfrac{3\pi}{2}$ $= -2\cdot 0 = 0$	$\left(\dfrac{3\pi}{2},\,0\right)$
2π	$y = -2\cos 2\pi$ $= -2\cdot 1 = -2$	$(2\pi,\,-2)$

Connect the five points with a smooth curve and graph one complete cycle of the given function with the graph of $y = \cos x$.

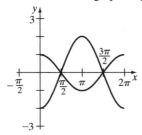

35. The equation $y = \cos 2x$ is of the form $y = A\cos Bx$ with $A = 1$ and $B = 2$. Thus, the amplitude is $|A| = |1| = 1$. The period is $\dfrac{2\pi}{B} = \dfrac{2\pi}{2} = \pi$. The quarter-period is $\dfrac{\pi}{4}$. The cycle begins at $x = 0$. Add quarter-periods to generate x-values for the key points.
$x = 0$

$x = 0 + \dfrac{\pi}{4} = \dfrac{\pi}{4}$

$x = \dfrac{\pi}{4} + \dfrac{\pi}{4} = \dfrac{\pi}{2}$

$x = \dfrac{\pi}{2} + \dfrac{\pi}{4} = \dfrac{3\pi}{4}$

$x = \dfrac{3\pi}{4} + \dfrac{\pi}{4} = \pi$

We evaluate the function at each value of x.

x	$y = \cos 2x$	coordinates
0	$y = \cos(2\cdot 0)$ $= \cos 0 = 1$	$(0,\,1)$

$\dfrac{\pi}{4}$	$y = \cos\left(2\cdot\dfrac{\pi}{4}\right)$ $= \cos\dfrac{\pi}{2} = 0$	$\left(\dfrac{\pi}{4},\,0\right)$
$\dfrac{\pi}{2}$	$y = \cos\left(2\cdot\dfrac{\pi}{2}\right)$ $= \cos\pi = -1$	$\left(\dfrac{\pi}{2},\,-1\right)$
$\dfrac{3\pi}{4}$	$y = \cos\left(2\cdot\dfrac{3\pi}{4}\right)$ $= \cos\dfrac{3\pi}{2} = 0$	$\left(\dfrac{3\pi}{4},\,0\right)$
π	$y = \cos(2\cdot\pi)$ $= \cos 2\pi = 1$	$(\pi,\,1)$

Connect the five points with a smooth curve and graph one complete cycle of the given function.

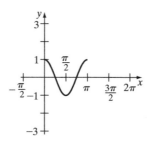

37. The equation $y = 4\cos 2\pi x$ is of the form $y = A\cos Bx$ with $A = 4$ and $B = 2\pi$. Thus, the amplitude is $|A| = |4| = 4$. The period is $\dfrac{2\pi}{B} = \dfrac{2\pi}{2\pi} = 1$. The quarter-period is $\dfrac{1}{4}$. The cycle begins at $x = 0$. Add quarter-periods to generate x-values for the key points.

$x = 0$

$x = 0 + \dfrac{1}{4} = \dfrac{1}{4}$

$x = \dfrac{1}{4} + \dfrac{1}{4} = \dfrac{1}{2}$

$x = \dfrac{1}{2} + \dfrac{1}{4} = \dfrac{3}{4}$

$x = \dfrac{3}{4} + \dfrac{1}{4} = 1$

We evaluate the function at each value of x.

x	$y = 4\cos 2\pi x$	coordinates
0	$\begin{aligned} y &= 4\cos(2\pi \cdot 0) \\ &= 4\cos 0 \\ &= 4 \cdot 1 = 4 \end{aligned}$	$(0, 4)$
$\dfrac{1}{4}$	$\begin{aligned} y &= 4\cos\left(2\pi \cdot \dfrac{1}{4}\right) \\ &= 4\cos\dfrac{\pi}{2} \\ &= 4 \cdot 0 = 0 \end{aligned}$	$\left(\dfrac{1}{4}, 0\right)$
$\dfrac{1}{2}$	$\begin{aligned} y &= 4\cos\left(2\pi \cdot \dfrac{1}{2}\right) \\ &= 4\cos\pi \\ &= 4 \cdot (-1) = -4 \end{aligned}$	$\left(\dfrac{1}{2}, -4\right)$
$\dfrac{3}{4}$	$\begin{aligned} y &= 4\cos\left(2\pi \cdot \dfrac{3}{4}\right) \\ &= 4\cos\dfrac{3\pi}{2} \\ &= 4 \cdot 0 = 0 \end{aligned}$	$\left(\dfrac{3}{4}, 0\right)$
1	$\begin{aligned} y &= 4\cos(2\pi \cdot 1) \\ &= 4\cos 2\pi \\ &= 4 \cdot 1 = 4 \end{aligned}$	$(1, 4)$

Connect the five points with a smooth curve and graph one complete cycle of the given function.

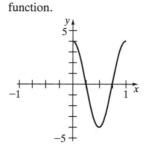

39. The equation $y = -4\cos\dfrac{1}{2}x$ is of the form $y = A\cos Bx$ with $A = -4$ and $B = \dfrac{1}{2}$. Thus, the amplitude is $|A| = |-4| = 4$. The period is $\dfrac{2\pi}{B} = \dfrac{2\pi}{\frac{1}{2}} = 2\pi \cdot 2 = 4\pi$. The quarter-period is $\dfrac{4\pi}{4} = \pi$. The cycle begins at $x = 0$. Add quarter-periods to generate x-values for the key points.

$x = 0$

$x = 0 + \pi = \pi$

$x = \pi + \pi = 2\pi$

$x = 2\pi + \pi = 3\pi$

$x = 3\pi + \pi = 4\pi$

We evaluate the function at each value of x.

x	$y = -4\cos\dfrac{1}{2}x$	coordinates
0	$\begin{aligned} y &= -4\cos\left(\dfrac{1}{2} \cdot 0\right) \\ &= -4\cos 0 \\ &= -4 \cdot 1 = -4 \end{aligned}$	$(0, -4)$
π	$\begin{aligned} y &= -4\cos\left(\dfrac{1}{2} \cdot \pi\right) \\ &= -4\cos\dfrac{\pi}{2} \\ &= -4 \cdot 0 = 0 \end{aligned}$	$(\pi, 0)$

2π	$y = -4\cos\left(\dfrac{1}{2}\cdot 2\pi\right)$ $= -4\cos\pi$ $= -4\cdot(-1) = 4$	$(2\pi,\ 4)$
3π	$y = -4\cos\left(\dfrac{1}{2}\cdot 3\pi\right)$ $= -4\cos\dfrac{3\pi}{2}$ $= -4\cdot 0 = 0$	$(3\pi,\ 0)$
4π	$y = -4\cos\left(\dfrac{1}{2}\cdot 4\pi\right)$ $= -4\cos 2\pi$ $= -4\cdot 1 = -4$	$(4\pi,\ -4)$

Connect the five points with a smooth curve and graph one complete cycle of the given function.

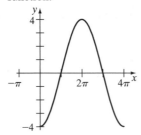

40. The equation $y = -\dfrac{1}{2}\cos\dfrac{\pi}{3}x$ is of the form

$y = A\cos Bx$ with $A = -\dfrac{1}{2}$ and $B = \dfrac{\pi}{3}$.

Thus, the amplitude is $|A| = \left|-\dfrac{1}{2}\right| = \dfrac{1}{2}$.

The period is $\dfrac{2\pi}{B} = \dfrac{2\pi}{\frac{\pi}{3}} = 2\pi\cdot\dfrac{3}{\pi} = 6$. The

quarter-period is $\dfrac{6}{4} = \dfrac{3}{2}$. The cycle begins at $x = 0$. Add quarter-periods to generate x-values for the key points.

$x = 0$

$x = 0 + \dfrac{3}{2} = \dfrac{3}{2}$

$x = \dfrac{3}{2} + \dfrac{3}{2} = 3$

$x = 3 + \dfrac{3}{2} = \dfrac{9}{2}$

$x = \dfrac{9}{2} + \dfrac{3}{2} = 6$

We evaluate the function at each value of x.

x	$y = -\dfrac{1}{2}\cos\dfrac{\pi}{3}x$	coordinates
0	$y = -\dfrac{1}{2}\cos\left(\dfrac{\pi}{3}\cdot 0\right)$ $= -\dfrac{1}{2}\cos 0$ $= -\dfrac{1}{2}\cdot 1 = -\dfrac{1}{2}$	$\left(0,\ -\dfrac{1}{2}\right)$
$\dfrac{3}{2}$	$y = -\dfrac{1}{2}\cos\left(\dfrac{\pi}{3}\cdot\dfrac{3}{2}\right)$ $= -\dfrac{1}{2}\cos\dfrac{\pi}{2}$ $= -\dfrac{1}{2}\cdot 0 = 0$	$\left(\dfrac{3}{2},\ 0\right)$
3	$y = -\dfrac{1}{2}\cos\left(\dfrac{\pi}{3}\cdot 3\right)$ $= -\dfrac{1}{2}\cos\pi$ $= -\dfrac{1}{2}\cdot(-1) = \dfrac{1}{2}$	$\left(3,\ \dfrac{1}{2}\right)$
$\dfrac{9}{2}$	$y = -\dfrac{1}{2}\cos\left(\dfrac{\pi}{3}\cdot\dfrac{9}{2}\right)$ $= -\dfrac{1}{2}\cos\dfrac{3\pi}{2}$ $= -\dfrac{1}{2}\cdot 0 = 0$	$\left(\dfrac{9}{2},\ 0\right)$

| 6 | $y = -\dfrac{1}{2}\cos\left(\dfrac{\pi}{3} \cdot 6\right)$ $= -\dfrac{1}{2}\cos 2\pi$ $= -\dfrac{1}{2} \cdot 1 = -\dfrac{1}{2}$ | $\left(6,\ -\dfrac{1}{2}\right)$ |

Connect the five points with a smooth curve and graph one complete cycle of the given function.

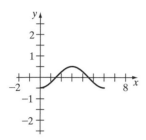

43. The equation $y = 3\cos(2x - \pi)$ is of the form $y = A\cos Bx$ with $A = 3$, and $B = 2$, and $C = \pi$. Thus, the amplitude is $|A| = |3| = 3$. The period is $\dfrac{2\pi}{B} = \dfrac{2\pi}{2} = \pi$.

The phase shift is $\dfrac{C}{B} = \dfrac{\pi}{2}$. The quarter-period is $\dfrac{\pi}{4}$. The cycle begins at $x = \dfrac{\pi}{2}$.

Add quarter-periods to generate x-values for the key points.

$$x = \frac{\pi}{2}$$
$$x = \frac{\pi}{2} + \frac{\pi}{4} = \frac{3\pi}{4}$$
$$x = \frac{3\pi}{4} + \frac{\pi}{4} = \pi$$
$$x = \pi + \frac{\pi}{4} = \frac{5\pi}{4}$$
$$x = \frac{5\pi}{4} + \frac{\pi}{4} = \frac{3\pi}{2}$$

We evaluate the function at each value of x.

x	$y = 3\cos(2x - \pi)$	coordinates
$\dfrac{\pi}{2}$	$y = 3\cos\left(2 \cdot \dfrac{\pi}{2} - \pi\right)$ $= 3\cos(\pi - \pi)$ $= 3\cos 0 = 3 \cdot 1 = 3$	$\left(\dfrac{\pi}{2},\ 3\right)$
$\dfrac{3\pi}{4}$	$y = 3\cos\left(2 \cdot \dfrac{3\pi}{4} - \pi\right)$ $= 3\cos\left(\dfrac{3\pi}{2} - \pi\right)$ $= 3\cos\dfrac{\pi}{2} = 3 \cdot 0 = 0$	$\left(\dfrac{3\pi}{4},\ 0\right)$
π	$y = 3\cos(2 \cdot \pi - \pi)$ $= 3\cos(2\pi - \pi)$ $= 3\cos\pi$ $= 3 \cdot (-1) = -3$	$(\pi,\ -3)$
$\dfrac{5\pi}{4}$	$y = 3\cos\left(2 \cdot \dfrac{5\pi}{4} - \pi\right)$ $= 3\cos\left(\dfrac{5\pi}{2} - \pi\right)$ $= 3\cos\dfrac{3\pi}{2} = 3 \cdot 0 = 0$	$\left(\dfrac{5\pi}{4},\ 0\right)$
$\dfrac{3\pi}{2}$	$y = 3\cos\left(2 \cdot \dfrac{3\pi}{2} - \pi\right)$ $= 3\cos(3\pi - \pi)$ $= 3\cos 2\pi = 3 \cdot 1 = 3$	$\left(\dfrac{3\pi}{2},\ 3\right)$

Connect the five points with a smooth curve and graph one complete cycle of the given

function

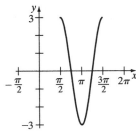

45. $y = \frac{1}{2}\cos\left(3x + \frac{\pi}{2}\right) = \frac{1}{2}\cos\left(3x - \left(-\frac{\pi}{2}\right)\right)$

The equation $y = \frac{1}{2}\cos\left(3x - \left(-\frac{\pi}{2}\right)\right)$ is of

the form $y = A\cos(Bx - C)$ with $A = \frac{1}{2}$, and

$B = 3$, and $C = -\frac{\pi}{2}$. Thus, the amplitude is

$|A| = \left|\frac{1}{2}\right| = \frac{1}{2}$. The period is $\frac{2\pi}{B} = \frac{2\pi}{3}$.

The phase shift is $\frac{C}{B} = \frac{-\frac{\pi}{2}}{3} = -\frac{\pi}{2} \cdot \frac{1}{3} = -\frac{\pi}{6}$.

The quarter-period is $\frac{\frac{2\pi}{3}}{4} = \frac{2\pi}{3} \cdot \frac{1}{4} = \frac{\pi}{6}$. The

cycle begins at $x = -\frac{\pi}{6}$. Add quarter-

periods to generate x-values for the key
points.

$x = -\frac{\pi}{6}$

$x = -\frac{\pi}{6} + \frac{\pi}{6} = 0$

$x = 0 + \frac{\pi}{6} = \frac{\pi}{6}$

$x = \frac{\pi}{6} + \frac{\pi}{6} = \frac{\pi}{3}$

$x = \frac{\pi}{3} + \frac{\pi}{6} = \frac{\pi}{2}$

We evaluate the function at each value of x.

x	$y = \frac{1}{2}\cos\left(3x + \frac{\pi}{2}\right)$	coordinates
$-\frac{\pi}{6}$	$y = \frac{1}{2}\cos\left(3 \cdot \left(-\frac{\pi}{6}\right) + \frac{\pi}{2}\right)$ $= \frac{1}{2}\cos\left(-\frac{\pi}{2} + \frac{\pi}{2}\right)$ $= \frac{1}{2}\cos 0 = \frac{1}{2} \cdot 1 = \frac{1}{2}$	$\left(-\frac{\pi}{6}, \frac{1}{2}\right)$
0	$y = \frac{1}{2}\cos\left(3 \cdot 0 + \frac{\pi}{2}\right)$ $= \frac{1}{2}\cos\left(0 + \frac{\pi}{2}\right)$ $= \frac{1}{2}\cos\frac{\pi}{2} = \frac{1}{2} \cdot 0 = 0$	$(0, 0)$
$\frac{\pi}{6}$	$y = \frac{1}{2}\cos\left(3 \cdot \frac{\pi}{6} + \frac{\pi}{2}\right)$ $= \frac{1}{2}\cos\left(\frac{\pi}{2} + \frac{\pi}{2}\right)$ $= \frac{1}{2}\cos\pi$ $= \frac{1}{2} \cdot (-1) = -\frac{1}{2}$	$\left(\frac{\pi}{6}, -\frac{1}{2}\right)$
$\frac{\pi}{3}$	$y = \frac{1}{2}\cos\left(3 \cdot \frac{\pi}{3} + \frac{\pi}{2}\right)$ $= \frac{1}{2}\cos\left(\pi + \frac{\pi}{2}\right)$ $= \frac{1}{2}\cos\frac{3\pi}{2} = \frac{1}{2} \cdot 0 = 0$	$\left(\frac{\pi}{3}, 0\right)$

| $\dfrac{\pi}{2}$ | $\begin{aligned} y &= \dfrac{1}{2}\cos\left(3\cdot\dfrac{\pi}{2}+\dfrac{\pi}{2}\right) \\ &= \dfrac{1}{2}\cos\left(\dfrac{3\pi}{2}+\dfrac{\pi}{2}\right) \\ &= \dfrac{1}{2}\cos 2\pi = \dfrac{1}{2}\cdot 1 = \dfrac{1}{2} \end{aligned}$ | $\left(\dfrac{\pi}{2},\dfrac{1}{2}\right)$ |

Connect the five points with a smooth curve and graph one complete cycle of the given function

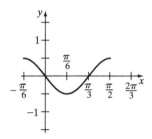

47. The equation $y = -3\cos\left(2x - \dfrac{\pi}{2}\right)$ is of the

form $y = A\cos(Bx - C)$ with $A = -3$, and

$B = 2$, and $C = \dfrac{\pi}{2}$. Thus, the amplitude is

$|A| = |-3| = 3$. The period is

$\dfrac{2\pi}{B} = \dfrac{2\pi}{2} = \pi$. The phase shift is

$\dfrac{C}{B} = \dfrac{\frac{\pi}{2}}{2} = \dfrac{\pi}{2}\cdot\dfrac{1}{2} = \dfrac{\pi}{4}$. The quarter-period is

$\dfrac{\pi}{4}$. The cycle begins at $x = \dfrac{\pi}{4}$. Add quarter-periods to generate x-values for the key points.

$$x = \dfrac{\pi}{4}$$

$$x = \dfrac{\pi}{4} + \dfrac{\pi}{4} = \dfrac{\pi}{2}$$

$$x = \dfrac{\pi}{2} + \dfrac{\pi}{4} = \dfrac{3\pi}{4}$$

$$x = \dfrac{3\pi}{4} + \dfrac{\pi}{4} = \pi$$

$$x = \pi + \dfrac{\pi}{4} = \dfrac{5\pi}{4}$$

We evaluate the function at each value of x.

x	$y = -3\cos\left(2x - \dfrac{\pi}{2}\right)$	coordinates
$\dfrac{\pi}{4}$	$\begin{aligned} y &= -3\cos\left(2\cdot\dfrac{\pi}{4}-\dfrac{\pi}{2}\right) \\ &= -3\cos\left(\dfrac{\pi}{2}-\dfrac{\pi}{2}\right) \\ &= -3\cos 0 \\ &= -3\cdot 1 = -3 \end{aligned}$	$\left(\dfrac{\pi}{4},-3\right)$
$\dfrac{\pi}{2}$	$\begin{aligned} y &= -3\cos\left(2\cdot\dfrac{\pi}{2}-\dfrac{\pi}{2}\right) \\ &= -3\cos\left(\pi-\dfrac{\pi}{2}\right) \\ &= -3\cos\dfrac{\pi}{2} \\ &= -3\cdot 0 = 0 \end{aligned}$	$\left(\dfrac{\pi}{2},0\right)$
$\dfrac{3\pi}{4}$	$\begin{aligned} y &= -3\cos\left(2\cdot\dfrac{3\pi}{4}-\dfrac{\pi}{2}\right) \\ &= -3\cos\left(\dfrac{3\pi}{2}-\dfrac{\pi}{2}\right) \\ &= -3\cos\pi \\ &= -3\cdot(-1) = 3 \end{aligned}$	$\left(\dfrac{3\pi}{4},3\right)$

π	$y = -3\cos\left(2\cdot\pi - \dfrac{\pi}{2}\right)$	$(\pi, 0)$
	$= -3\cos\left(2\pi - \dfrac{\pi}{2}\right)$	
	$= -3\cos\dfrac{3\pi}{2}$	
	$= -3\cdot 0 = 0$	
$\dfrac{5\pi}{4}$	$y = -3\cos\left(2\cdot\dfrac{5\pi}{4} - \dfrac{\pi}{2}\right)$	$\left(\dfrac{5\pi}{4}, -3\right)$
	$= -3\cos\left(\dfrac{5\pi}{2} - \dfrac{\pi}{2}\right)$	
	$= -3\cos 2\pi$	
	$= -3\cdot 1 = -3$	

Connect the five points with a smooth curve and graph one complete cycle of the given function

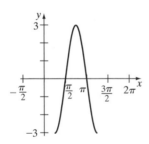

49. $y = 2\cos(2\pi x + 8\pi) = 2\cos(2\pi x - (-8\pi))$
The equation $y = 2\cos(2\pi x - (-8\pi))$ is of the form $y = A\cos(Bx - C)$ with $A = 2$, $B = 2\pi$, and $C = -8\pi$. Thus, the amplitude is $|A| = |2| = 2$. The period is
$\dfrac{2\pi}{B} = \dfrac{2\pi}{2\pi} = 1$. The phase shift is
$\dfrac{C}{B} = \dfrac{-8\pi}{2\pi} = -4$. The quarter-period is $\dfrac{1}{4}$.
The cycle begins at $x = -4$. Add quarter-periods to generate x-values for the key points.

$x = -4$

$x = -4 + \dfrac{1}{4} = -\dfrac{15}{4}$

$x = -\dfrac{15}{4} + \dfrac{1}{4} = -\dfrac{7}{2}$

$x = -\dfrac{7}{2} + \dfrac{1}{4} = -\dfrac{13}{4}$

$x = -\dfrac{13}{4} + \dfrac{1}{4} = -3$

We evaluate the function at each value of x.

x	$y = 2\cos(2\pi x + 8\pi)$	coordinates
-4	$y = 2\cos(2\pi(-4) + 8\pi)$ $= 2\cos(-8\pi + 8\pi)$ $= 2\cos 0 = 2\cdot 1 = 2$	$(-4, 2)$
$-\dfrac{15}{4}$	$y = 2\cos\left(2\pi\left(-\dfrac{15}{4}\right) + 8\pi\right)$ $= 2\cos\left(-\dfrac{15\pi}{2} + 8\pi\right)$ $= 2\cos\dfrac{\pi}{2} = 2\cdot 0 = 0$	$\left(-\dfrac{15}{4}, 0\right)$
$-\dfrac{7}{2}$	$y = 2\cos\left(2\pi\left(-\dfrac{7}{2}\right) + 8\pi\right)$ $= 2\cos(-7\pi + 8\pi)$ $= 2\cos\pi$ $= 2\cdot(-1) = -2$	$\left(-\dfrac{7}{2}, -2\right)$
$-\dfrac{13}{4}$	$y = 2\cos\left(2\pi\left(-\dfrac{13}{4}\right) + 8\pi\right)$ $= 2\cos\left(-\dfrac{13\pi}{2} + 8\pi\right)$ $= 2\cos\dfrac{3\pi}{2} = 2\cdot 0 = 0$	$\left(-\dfrac{13}{4}, 0\right)$

-3	$y = 2\cos(2\pi(-3) + 8\pi)$ $= 2\cos(-6\pi + 8\pi)$ $= 2\cos 2\pi = 2 \cdot 1 = 2$	$(-3, 2)$

Connect the five points with a smooth curve and graph one complete cycle of the given function

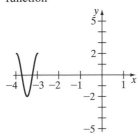

51. The graph of $y = \sin x + 2$ is the graph of $y = \sin x$ shifted up 2 units upward. The period for both functions is 2π. The quarter-period is $\dfrac{2\pi}{4}$ or $\dfrac{\pi}{2}$. The cycle begins at $x = 0$. Add quarter-periods to generate x-values for the key points.
$x = 0$

$x = 0 + \dfrac{\pi}{2} = \dfrac{\pi}{2}$

$x = \dfrac{\pi}{2} + \dfrac{\pi}{2} = \pi$

$x = \pi + \dfrac{\pi}{2} = \dfrac{3\pi}{2}$

$x = \dfrac{3\pi}{2} + \dfrac{\pi}{2} = 2\pi$

We evaluate the function at each value of x.

x	$y = \sin x + 2$	coordinates
0	$y = \sin 0 + 2$ $= 0 + 2 = 2$	$(0, 2)$
$\dfrac{\pi}{2}$	$y = \sin \dfrac{\pi}{2} + 2$ $= 1 + 2 = 3$	$\left(\dfrac{\pi}{2}, 3\right)$
π	$y = \sin \pi + 2$ $= 0 + 2 = 2$	$(\pi, 2)$

$\dfrac{3\pi}{2}$	$y = \sin \dfrac{3\pi}{2} + 2$ $= -1 + 2 = 1$	$\left(\dfrac{3\pi}{2}, 1\right)$
2π	$y = \sin 2\pi + 2$ $= 0 + 2 = 2$	$(2\pi, 2)$

By connecting the points with a smooth curve we obtain one period of the graph.

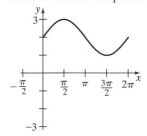

53. The graph of $y = \cos x - 3$ is the graph of $y = \cos x$ shifted 3 units downward. The period for both functions is 2π. The quarter-period is $\dfrac{2\pi}{4}$ or $\dfrac{\pi}{2}$. The cycle begins at $x = 0$. Add quarter-periods to generate x-values for the key points.
$x = 0$

$x = 0 + \dfrac{\pi}{2} = \dfrac{\pi}{2}$

$x = \dfrac{\pi}{2} + \dfrac{\pi}{2} = \pi$

$x = \pi + \dfrac{\pi}{2} = \dfrac{3\pi}{2}$

$x = \dfrac{3\pi}{2} + \dfrac{\pi}{2} = 2\pi$

We evaluate the function at each value of x.

x	$y = \cos x - 3$	coordinates
0	$y = \cos 0 - 3$ $= 1 - 3 = -2$	$(0, -2)$
$\dfrac{\pi}{2}$	$y = \cos \dfrac{\pi}{2} - 3$ $= 0 - 3 = -3$	$\left(\dfrac{\pi}{2}, -3\right)$

π	$\begin{aligned} y &= \cos\pi - 3 \\ &= -1 - 3 = -4 \end{aligned}$	$(\pi, -4)$
$\dfrac{3\pi}{2}$	$\begin{aligned} y &= \cos\dfrac{3\pi}{2} - 3 \\ &= 0 - 3 = -3 \end{aligned}$	$\left(\dfrac{3\pi}{2}, -3\right)$
2π	$\begin{aligned} y &= \cos 2\pi - 3 \\ &= 1 - 3 = -2 \end{aligned}$	$(2\pi, -2)$

By connecting the points with a smooth curve we obtain one period of the graph.

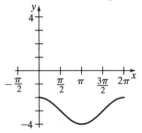

55. The graph of $y = 2\sin\frac{1}{2}x + 1$ is the graph of $y = 2\sin\frac{1}{2}x$ shifted one unit upward. The amplitude for both functions is $|\,2\,| = 2$. The period for both functions is $\dfrac{2\pi}{\frac{1}{2}} = 2\pi \cdot 2 = 4\pi$. The quarter-period is $\dfrac{4\pi}{4} = \pi$. The cycle begins at $x = 0$. Add quarter-periods to generate x-values for the key points.

$x = 0$

$x = 0 + \pi = \pi$

$x = \pi + \pi = 2\pi$

$x = 2\pi + \pi = 3\pi$

$x = 3\pi + \pi = 4\pi$

We evaluate the function at each value of x.

x	$y = 2\sin\dfrac{1}{2}x + 1$	coordinates

0	$\begin{aligned} y &= 2\sin\left(\dfrac{1}{2}\cdot 0\right) + 1 \\ &= 2\sin 0 + 1 \\ &= 2\cdot 0 + 1 = 0 + 1 = 1 \end{aligned}$	$(0, 1)$
π	$\begin{aligned} y &= 2\sin\left(\dfrac{1}{2}\cdot\pi\right) + 1 \\ &= 2\sin\dfrac{\pi}{2} + 1 \\ &= 2\cdot 1 + 1 = 2 + 1 = 3 \end{aligned}$	$(\pi, 3)$
2π	$\begin{aligned} y &= 2\sin\left(\dfrac{1}{2}\cdot 2\pi\right) + 1 \\ &= 2\sin\pi + 1 \\ &= 2\cdot 0 + 1 = 0 + 1 = 1 \end{aligned}$	$(2\pi, 1)$
3π	$\begin{aligned} y &= 2\sin\left(\dfrac{1}{2}\cdot 3\pi\right) + 1 \\ &= 2\sin\dfrac{3\pi}{2} + 1 \\ &= 2\cdot(-1) + 1 \\ &= -2 + 1 = -1 \end{aligned}$	$(3\pi, -1)$
4π	$\begin{aligned} y &= 2\sin\left(\dfrac{1}{2}\cdot 4\pi\right) + 1 \\ &= 2\sin 2\pi + 1 \\ &= 2\cdot 0 + 1 = 0 + 1 = 1 \end{aligned}$	$(4\pi, 1)$

By connecting the points with a smooth curve we obtain one period of the graph.

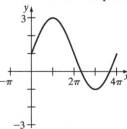

57. The graph of $y = -3\cos 2\pi x + 2$ is the graph of $y = -3\cos 2\pi x$ shifted 2 units upward. The amplitude for both functions is $|-3| = 3$. The period for both functions is

$\dfrac{2\pi}{2\pi} = 1.$ The quarter-period is $\dfrac{1}{4}.$ The cycle

begins at $x = 0.$ Add quarter-periods to
generate x-values for the key points.

$x = 0$

$x = 0 + \dfrac{1}{4} = \dfrac{1}{4}$

$x = \dfrac{1}{4} + \dfrac{1}{4} = \dfrac{1}{2}$

$x = \dfrac{1}{2} + \dfrac{1}{4} = \dfrac{3}{4}$

$x = \dfrac{3}{4} + \dfrac{1}{4} = 1$

We evaluate the function at each value of x.

x	$y = -3\cos 2\pi x + 2$	coordinates
0	$y = -3\cos(2\pi \cdot 0) + 2$ $= -3\cos 0 + 2$ $= -3 \cdot 1 + 2$ $= -3 + 2 = -1$	$(0, -1)$
$\dfrac{1}{4}$	$y = -3\cos\left(2\pi \cdot \dfrac{1}{4}\right) + 2$ $= -3\cos\dfrac{\pi}{2} + 2$ $= -3 \cdot 0 + 2$ $= 0 + 2 = 2$	$\left(\dfrac{1}{4}, 2\right)$
$\dfrac{1}{2}$	$y = -3\cos\left(2\pi \cdot \dfrac{1}{2}\right) + 2$ $= -3\cos\pi + 2$ $= -3 \cdot (-1) + 2$ $= 3 + 2 = 5$	$\left(\dfrac{1}{2}, 5\right)$
$\dfrac{3}{4}$	$y = -3\cos\left(2\pi \cdot \dfrac{3}{4}\right) + 2$ $= -3\cos\dfrac{3\pi}{2} + 2$ $= -3 \cdot 0 + 2$ $= 0 + 2 = 2$	$\left(\dfrac{3}{4}, 2\right)$

1	$y = -3\cos(2\pi \cdot 1) + 2$ $= -3\cos 2\pi + 2$ $= -3 \cdot 1 + 2$ $= -3 + 2 = -1$	$(1, -1)$

By connecting the points with a smooth
curve we obtain one period of the graph.

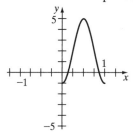

59. The period is the number of days from
1/24/00 to 2/26/00.
$7 + 26 = 33$
The period of the physical cycle is about
33 days.

61. The period is the number of days from
2/05/00 to 2/28/00.
$28 - 5 = 23$
The period of the intellectual cycle is
23 days.

63. In the month of March, 3/21/00 would be
the best day to meet an on-line friend for the
first time, because the emotional cycle is at a
maximum.

65. Answers may vary.

67. The information gives the five key point of
the graph.
(0, 14) corresponds to June,
(3, 12) corresponds to September,
(6, 10) corresponds to December,
(9, 12) corresponds to March,
(12, 14) corresponds to June
By connecting the five key points with a
smooth curve we graph the information from
June of one year to June of the following

year.

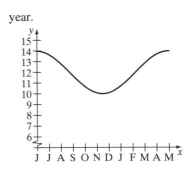

69. The function $y = 3\sin\dfrac{2\pi}{365}(x-79)+12$ is of

the form $y = A\sin B\left(x-\dfrac{C}{B}\right)+D$ with

$A = 3$ and $B = \dfrac{2\pi}{365}$.

a. The amplitude is $\mid A\mid=\mid 3\mid=3$.

b. The period is
$$\dfrac{2\pi}{B}=\dfrac{2\pi}{\frac{2\pi}{365}}=2\pi\cdot\dfrac{365}{2\pi}=365\,.$$

c. The longest day of the year will have the most hours of daylight. This occurs when the sine function equals 1.
$$y = 3\sin\dfrac{2\pi}{365}(x-79)+12$$
$$y = 3(1)+12$$
$$y = 15$$
There will be 15 hours of daylight.

d. The shortest day of the year will have the least hours of daylight. This occurs when the sine function equals -1.
$$y = 3\sin\dfrac{2\pi}{365}(x-79)+12$$
$$y = 3(-1)+12$$
$$y = 9$$
There will be 9 hours of daylight.

e. The amplitude is 3. The period is 365. The phase shift is $\dfrac{C}{B}=79$. The quarter-period is $\dfrac{365}{4}=91.25$. The cycle begins at $x = 79$. Add quarter-periods to find the x-values of the key points.
$x = 79$
$x = 79 + 91.25 = 170.25$
$x = 170.25 + 91.25 = 261.5$
$x = 261.5 + 91.25 = 352.75$
$x = 352.75 + 91.25 = 444$
Because we are graphing for $0 \le x \le 365$, we will evaluate the function for the first four x-values along with $x = 0$ and $x = 365$. Using a calculator we have the following points.
$(0, 9.07)$ $(79, 12)$ $(170.25, 15)$ $(261.5, 12)$ $(352.75, 9)$ $(365, 9.07)$
By connecting the points with a smooth curve we obtain one period of the graph, starting on January 1.

71. Because the depth of the water ranges from a minimum of 6 feet to a maximum of 12 feet, the curve oscillates about the middle value, 9 feet. Thus, $D = 9$. The maximum depth of the water is 3 feet above 9 feet. Thus, $A = 3$. The graph shows that one complete cycle occurs in 12-0, or 12 hours.

The period is 12. Thus, $\quad 12 = \dfrac{2\pi}{B}$

$$12B = 2\pi$$

$$B = \frac{2\pi}{12} = \frac{\pi}{6}$$

Substitute these values into $y = A \cos Bx + D$. The depth of the water is

modeled by $\ y = 3\cos\dfrac{\pi x}{6} + 9$.

73.–81. Answers may vary.

83. Exercise 35

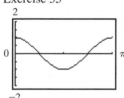

Exercise 37

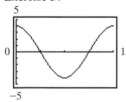

Exercise 39

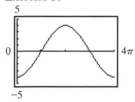

Exercise 41

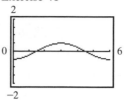

Exercise 43

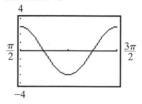

85. The function
$y = 3\sin(2x + \pi) = 3\sin(2x - (-\pi))$ is of the form $y = A\sin(Bx - C)$ with $A = 3$, $B = 2$, and $C = -\pi$. The amplitude is

$|\,A\,| = |\,3\,| = 3$. The period is $\dfrac{2\pi}{B} = \dfrac{2\pi}{2} = \pi$.

The cycle begins at $x = \dfrac{C}{B} = \dfrac{-\pi}{2} = -\dfrac{\pi}{2}$. We

choose $-\dfrac{\pi}{2} \le x \le \dfrac{3\pi}{2}$, and $-4 \le y \le 4$ for

our graph.

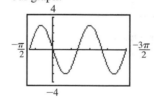

87. The function

$$y = 0.2\sin\left(\frac{\pi}{10}x + \pi\right) = 0.2\sin\left(\frac{\pi}{10}x - (-\pi)\right)$$

is of the form $y = A\sin(Bx - C)$ with

$A = 0.2$, $B = \dfrac{\pi}{10}$, and $C = -\pi$. The

amplitude is $|A| = |0.2| = 0.2$. The period

is $\dfrac{2\pi}{B} = \dfrac{2\pi}{\frac{\pi}{10}} = 2\pi \cdot \dfrac{10}{\pi} = 20$. The cycle

begins at $x = \dfrac{C}{B} = \dfrac{-\pi}{\frac{\pi}{10}} = -\pi \cdot \dfrac{10}{\pi} = -10$. We

choose $-10 \le x \le 30$, and $-1 \le y \le 1$ for our graph.

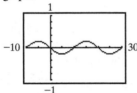

89.

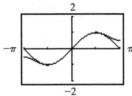

The graphs appear to be the same from

$-\dfrac{\pi}{2}$ to $\dfrac{\pi}{2}$.

91.

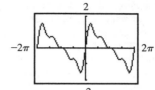

The graph is similar to $y = \sin x$, except the amplitude is greater and the curve is less smooth.

93. a.

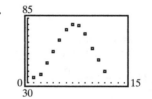

b. $y = 22.61\sin(0.50x - 2.04) + 57.17$

c.

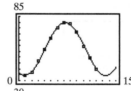

95. To graph $y = \sin x + \cos x$, we will make a table of values of (x, y) on the graph of $y = \sin x + \cos x$ for $0 \le x \le 2\pi$.

x	0	$\dfrac{\pi}{4}$	$\dfrac{\pi}{2}$	$\dfrac{3\pi}{4}$	π	$\dfrac{5\pi}{4}$	$\dfrac{3\pi}{2}$	$\dfrac{7\pi}{4}$	2π
y	1	1.4	1	0	-1	-1.4	-1	0	1

We connect these points with a smooth curve to obtain the graph shown.

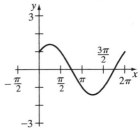

97. Because the y-values range from a maximum of 2 to a minimum of -2, the curve oscillates about 0. Thus, there is no vertical shift, $D = 0$. The maximum y-value is 2. Thus, $A = 2$. The graph shows that one complete cycle occurs in $\dfrac{\pi}{4} - \left(-\dfrac{\pi}{4} \right)$, or $\dfrac{\pi}{2}$ units.

Thus, $\dfrac{\pi}{2} = \dfrac{2\pi}{B}$

$\qquad B\pi = 4\pi$

$\qquad B = \dfrac{4\pi}{\pi} = 4$

The graph shows that the starting point of the cycle is shifted from 0 to $-\dfrac{\pi}{4}$.

The phase shift is $-\dfrac{\pi}{4}$.

$-\dfrac{\pi}{4} = \dfrac{C}{B}$

$-\dfrac{\pi}{4} = \dfrac{C}{4}$

$-\pi = C$

Substitute these values into $y = A\cos(Bx - C) + D$.

This graph is the equation $y = 2\cos(4x - (-\pi)) = 2\cos(4x + \pi)$.

Section 1.6

Check Point Exercises

1. We solve the equations

$$2x = -\frac{\pi}{2} \quad \text{and} \quad 2x = \frac{\pi}{2}$$
$$x = -\frac{\pi}{4} \qquad\qquad x = \frac{\pi}{4}$$

Thus, two consecutive asymptotes occur at $x = -\frac{\pi}{4}$ and $x = \frac{\pi}{4}$. Midway between these asymptotes is $x = 0$. An x-intercept is 0 and the graph passes through (0, 0). Because the coefficient of the tangent is 3, the points on the graph midway between an x-intercept and the asymptotes have y-coordinates of -3 and 3. We use the two asymptotes, the x-intercept, and the points midway between to graph one period of $y = 3\tan 2x$ from $-\frac{\pi}{4}$ to $\frac{\pi}{4}$. In order to graph for $-\frac{\pi}{4} < x < \frac{3\pi}{4}$, we continue the pattern and extend the graph another full period to the right.

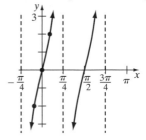

2. We solve the equations

$$x - \frac{\pi}{2} = -\frac{\pi}{2} \quad \text{and} \quad x - \frac{\pi}{2} = \frac{\pi}{2}$$
$$x = \frac{\pi}{2} - \frac{\pi}{2} \qquad\qquad x = \frac{\pi}{2} + \frac{\pi}{2}$$
$$x = 0 \qquad\qquad\qquad x = \pi$$

Thus, two consecutive asymptotes occur at $x = 0$ and $x = \pi$.

$$x\text{-intercept} = \frac{0 + \pi}{2} = \frac{\pi}{2}$$

An x-intercept is $\frac{\pi}{2}$ and the graph passes through $\left(\frac{\pi}{2}, 0\right)$. Because the coefficient of the tangent is 1, the points on the graph midway between an x-intercept and the asymptotes have y-coordinates of -1 and 1. We use the two consecutive asymptotes, $x = 0$ and $x = \pi$, to graph one full period of $y = \tan\left(x - \frac{\pi}{2}\right)$ from 0 to π. We continue the pattern and extend the graph another full period to the right.

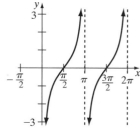

3. We solve the equations

$$\frac{\pi}{2}x = 0 \quad \text{and} \quad \frac{\pi}{2}x = \pi$$

$$x = 0 \qquad\qquad x = \frac{\pi}{\frac{\pi}{2}}$$

$$x = 2$$

Two consecutive asymptotes occur at $x = 0$ and $x = 2$. Midway between $x = 0$ and $x = 2$ is $x = 1$. An x-intercept is 1 and the graph passes through $(1, 0)$. Because the coefficient of the cotangent is $\frac{1}{2}$, the points on the graph midway between an x-intercept and the asymptotes have y-coordinates of $-\frac{1}{2}$ and $\frac{1}{2}$. We use the two consecutive asymptotes, $x = 0$ and $x = 2$, to graph one full period of $y = \frac{1}{2}\cot\frac{\pi}{2}x$. The curve is repeated along the x-axis one full period as shown.

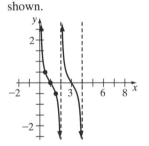

4. The x-intercepts of $y = \sin\left(x + \frac{\pi}{4}\right)$

correspond to vertical asymptotes of

$$y = \csc\left(x + \frac{\pi}{4}\right).$$

5. Graph the reciprocal cosine function, $y = 2\cos 2x$. The equation is of the form $y = A\cos Bx$ with $A = 2$ and $B = 2$.

amplitude: $|A| = |2| = 2$

$$\text{period: } \frac{2\pi}{B} = \frac{2\pi}{2} = \pi$$

Use quarter-periods, $\frac{\pi}{4}$, to find x-values for the five key points. Starting with $x = 0$, the x-values are $0, \frac{\pi}{4}, \frac{\pi}{2}, \frac{3\pi}{4}$, and π. Evaluating the function at each value of x, the key points are $(0, 2)$, $\left(\frac{\pi}{4}, 0\right)$, $\left(\frac{\pi}{2}, -2\right)$, $\left(\frac{3\pi}{4}, 0\right)$, $(\pi, 2)$. In order to graph for $-\frac{3\pi}{4} \le x \le \frac{3\pi}{4}$, we use the first four points and extend the graph $-\frac{3\pi}{4}$ units to the left. Use the graph to obtain the graph of the reciprocal function. Draw vertical asymptotes through the x-intercepts, and use them as guides to graph $y = 2\sec 2x$.

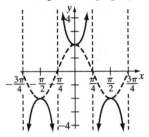

Exercise Set 1.6

For 1 and 3, in the given functions, $B = 1$.

1. The graph has an asymptote at $x = -\dfrac{\pi}{2}$.

   The phase shift, $\dfrac{C}{B}$, from $\dfrac{\pi}{2}$ to $-\dfrac{\pi}{2}$ is $-\pi$

   units. Thus, $\dfrac{C}{B} = -\pi$

   $$\dfrac{C}{1} = -\pi$$
   $$C = -\pi$$
   The function with $C = -\pi$ is $y = \tan(x + \pi)$.

3. The graph has an asymptote at $x = \pi$.

   $$\pi = \dfrac{\pi}{2} + C$$
   $$C = \dfrac{\pi}{2}$$
   The function is $y = -\tan\left(x - \dfrac{\pi}{2}\right)$.

5. We solve the equations

   $$\dfrac{x}{4} = -\dfrac{\pi}{2} \qquad \text{and} \qquad \dfrac{x}{4} = \dfrac{\pi}{2}$$
   $$x = \left(-\dfrac{\pi}{2}\right)4 \qquad\qquad x = \left(\dfrac{\pi}{2}\right)4$$
   $$x = -2\pi \qquad\qquad\qquad x = 2\pi$$
   Thus, two consecutive asymptotes occur at $x = -2\pi$ and $x = 2\pi$.

   $$x\text{-intercept} = \dfrac{-2\pi + 2\pi}{2} = \dfrac{0}{2} = 0$$

   An x-intercept is 0 and the graph passes through $(0, 0)$. Because the coefficient of the tangent is 3, the points on the graph midway between an x-intercept and the asymptotes have y-coordinates of -3 and 3. We use the two consecutive asymptotes, $x = -2\pi$ and $x = 2\pi$, to graph one full period of

   $y = 3\tan\dfrac{x}{4}$ from -2π to 2π. We continue

the pattern and extend the graph another full period to the right.

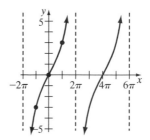

7. We solve the equations

   $$2x = -\dfrac{\pi}{2} \qquad \text{and} \qquad 2x = \dfrac{\pi}{2}$$
   $$x = \dfrac{-\dfrac{\pi}{2}}{2} \qquad\qquad x = \dfrac{\dfrac{\pi}{2}}{2}$$
   $$x = -\dfrac{\pi}{4} \qquad\qquad x = \dfrac{\pi}{4}$$
   Thus, two consecutive asymptotes occur at

   $x = -\dfrac{\pi}{4}$ and $x = \dfrac{\pi}{4}$.

   $$x\text{-intercept} = \dfrac{-\dfrac{\pi}{4} + \dfrac{\pi}{4}}{2} = \dfrac{0}{2} = 0$$

   An x-intercept is 0 and the graph passes through $(0, 0)$. Because the coefficient of the

   tangent is $\dfrac{1}{2}$, the points on the graph

   midway between an x-intercept and the

   asymptotes have y-coordinates of $-\dfrac{1}{2}$ and

   $\dfrac{1}{2}$. We use the two consecutive asymptotes,

   $x = -\dfrac{\pi}{4}$ and $x = \dfrac{\pi}{4}$, to graph one full period

   of $y = \dfrac{1}{2}\tan 2x$ from $-\dfrac{\pi}{4}$ to $\dfrac{\pi}{4}$. We

   continue the pattern and extend the graph

another full period to the right.

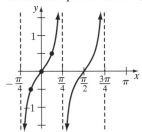

9. We solve the equations

$$\frac{1}{2}x = -\frac{\pi}{2} \quad \text{and} \quad \frac{1}{2}x = \frac{\pi}{2}$$

$$x = \left(-\frac{\pi}{2}\right)2 \qquad x = \left(\frac{\pi}{2}\right)2$$

$$x = -\pi \qquad\qquad x = \pi$$

Thus, two consecutive asymptotes occur at $x = -\pi$ and $x = \pi$.

$$x\text{-intercept} = \frac{-\pi + \pi}{2} = \frac{0}{2} = 0$$

An x-intercept is 0 and the graph passes through (0, 0). Because the coefficient of the tangent is –2, the points on the graph midway between an x-intercept and the asymptotes have y-coordinates of 2 and –2. We use the two consecutive asymptotes, $x = -\pi$ and $x = \pi$, to graph one full period of $y = -2\tan\frac{1}{2}x$ from $-\pi$ to π. We continue the pattern and extend the graph another full period to the right.

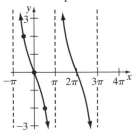

11. We solve the equations

$$x - \pi = -\frac{\pi}{2} \quad \text{and} \quad x - \pi = \frac{\pi}{2}$$

$$x = -\frac{\pi}{2} + \pi \qquad\qquad x = \frac{\pi}{2} + \pi$$

$$x = \frac{\pi}{2} \qquad\qquad\qquad x = \frac{3\pi}{2}$$

Thus, two consecutive asymptotes occur at $x = \frac{\pi}{2}$ and $x = \frac{3\pi}{2}$.

$$x\text{-intercept} = \frac{\frac{\pi}{2} + \frac{3\pi}{2}}{2} = \frac{\frac{4\pi}{2}}{2} = \frac{4\pi}{4} = \pi$$

An x-intercept is π and the graph passes through $(\pi, 0)$. Because the coefficient of the tangent is 1, the points on the graph midway between an x-intercept and the asymptotes have y-coordinates of –1 and 1. We use the two consecutive asymptotes,

$$x = \frac{\pi}{2} \text{ and } x = \frac{3\pi}{2}, \text{ to graph one full period}$$

of $y = \tan(x - \pi)$ from $\frac{\pi}{2}$ to $\frac{3\pi}{2}$. We continue the pattern and extend the graph another full period to the right.

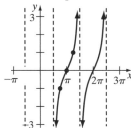

For 13 and 15, in the given functions, $B = 1$.

13. There is no phase shift. Thus,

$$\frac{C}{B} = 0$$

$$\frac{C}{1} = 0$$

$$C = 0$$

Because the points on the graph midway between an x-intercept and the asymptotes have y-coordinates of -1 and 1, $A = -1$. The function with $C = 0$ and $A = -1$ is $y = -\cot x$.

15. The graph has an asymptote at $-\dfrac{\pi}{2}$. The phase shift, $\dfrac{C}{B}$, from 0 to $-\dfrac{\pi}{2}$ is $-\dfrac{\pi}{2}$ units.

Thus, $\dfrac{C}{B} = -\dfrac{\pi}{2}$

$\dfrac{C}{1} = -\dfrac{\pi}{2}$

$C = -\dfrac{\pi}{2}$

The function with $C = -\dfrac{\pi}{2}$ is

$y = \cot\left(x + \dfrac{\pi}{2}\right)$.

17. We solve the equations $x = 0$ and $x = \pi$. Two consecutive asymptotes occur at $x = 0$ and $x = \pi$.

$x\text{-intercept} = \dfrac{0 + \pi}{2} = \dfrac{\pi}{2}$

An x-intercept is $\dfrac{\pi}{2}$ and the graph passes through $\left(\dfrac{\pi}{2},\, 0\right)$. Because the coefficient of the cotangent is 2, the points on the graph midway between an x-intercept and the asymptotes have y-coordinates of 2 and -2. We use the two consecutive asymptotes, $x = 0$ and $x = \pi$, to graph one full period of $y = 2\cot x$. The curve is repeated along the

x-axis one full period as shown.

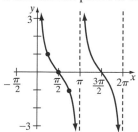

19. We solve the equations
$2x = 0$ and $2x = \pi$
$x = 0$ $x = \dfrac{\pi}{2}$

Two consecutive asymptotes occur at $x = 0$ and $x = \dfrac{\pi}{2}$.

$x\text{-intercept} = \dfrac{0 + \frac{\pi}{2}}{2} = \dfrac{\frac{\pi}{2}}{2} = \dfrac{\pi}{4}$

An x-intercept is $\dfrac{\pi}{4}$ and the graph passes through $\left(\dfrac{\pi}{4},\, 0\right)$. Because the coefficient of the cotangent is $\dfrac{1}{2}$, the points on the graph midway between an x-intercept and the asymptotes have y-coordinates of $\dfrac{1}{2}$ and $-\dfrac{1}{2}$. We use the two consecutive asymptotes, $x = 0$ and $x = \dfrac{\pi}{2}$, to graph one full period of $y = \dfrac{1}{2}\cot 2x$. The curve is repeated along the x-axis one full period as shown.

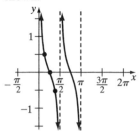

21. We solve the equations

$$\frac{\pi}{2}x = 0 \quad \text{and} \quad \frac{\pi}{2}x = \pi$$

$$x = 0 \qquad\qquad x = \frac{\pi}{\frac{\pi}{2}}$$

$$x = 2$$

Two consecutive asymptotes occur at $x = 0$ and $x = 2$.

$$x\text{-intercept} = \frac{0 + 2}{2} = \frac{2}{2} = 1$$

An x-intercept is 1 and the graph passes through (1, 0). Because the coefficient of the cotangent is -3, the points on the graph midway between an x-intercept and the asymptotes have y-coordinates of -3 and 3. We use the two consecutive asymptotes, $x = 0$ and $x = 2$, to graph one full period of $y = -3\cot\frac{\pi}{2}x$. The curve is repeated along the x-axis one full period as shown.

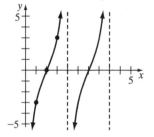

23. We solve the equations

$$x + \frac{\pi}{2} = 0 \qquad \text{and} \quad x + \frac{\pi}{2} = \pi$$

$$x = 0 - \frac{\pi}{2} \qquad\qquad x = \pi - \frac{\pi}{2}$$

$$x = -\frac{\pi}{2} \qquad\qquad x = \frac{\pi}{2}$$

Two consecutive asymptotes occur at

$$x = -\frac{\pi}{2} \text{ and } x = \frac{\pi}{2}.$$

$$x\text{-intercept} = \frac{-\frac{\pi}{2} + \frac{\pi}{2}}{2} = \frac{0}{2} = 0$$

An x-intercept is 0 and the graph passes through (0, 0). Because the coefficient of the cotangent is 3, the points on the graph midway between an x-intercept and the asymptotes have y-coordinates of 3 and -3. We use the two consecutive asymptotes,

$$x = -\frac{\pi}{2} \text{ and } x = \frac{\pi}{2}, \text{ to graph one full period}$$

of $y = 3\cot\left(x + \frac{\pi}{2}\right)$. The curve is repeated

along the x-axis one full period as shown.

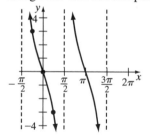

25. The *x*-intercepts of $y = -\dfrac{1}{2}\sin\dfrac{x}{2}$

corresponds to vertical asymptotes of

$y = -\dfrac{1}{2}\csc\dfrac{x}{2}$. Draw the vertical asymptotes,

and use them as a guide to sketch the graph

of $y = -\dfrac{1}{2}\csc\dfrac{x}{2}$.

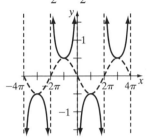

27. The *x*-intercepts of $y = \dfrac{1}{2}\cos 2\pi x$

corresponds to vertical asymptotes of

$y = \dfrac{1}{2}\sec 2\pi x$. Draw the vertical

asymptotes, and use them as a guide to

sketch the graph of $y = \dfrac{1}{2}\sec 2\pi x$.

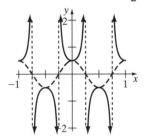

29. Graph the reciprocal sine function, $y = 3\sin x$. The equation is of the form $y = A\sin Bx$ with $A = 3$ and $B = 1$.

amplitude: $|A| = |3| = 3$

period: $\dfrac{2\pi}{B} = \dfrac{2\pi}{1} = 2\pi$

Use quarter-periods, $\dfrac{\pi}{2}$, to find x-values for the five key points. Starting with $x = 0$, the x-values are 0, $\dfrac{\pi}{2}$, π, $\dfrac{3\pi}{2}$, and 2π. Evaluating the function at each value of x, the key points are $(0, 0)$, $\left(\dfrac{\pi}{2}, 3\right)$, $(\pi, 0)$, $\left(\dfrac{3\pi}{2}, -3\right)$, and $(2\pi, 0)$. Use these key points to graph $y = 3\sin x$ from 0 to 2π. Extend the graph one cycle to the right. Use the graph to obtain the graph of the reciprocal function. Draw vertical asymptotes through the x-intercepts, and use them as guides to graph $y = 3\csc x$.

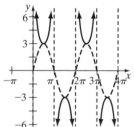

31. Graph the reciprocal sine function, $y = \dfrac{1}{2}\sin\dfrac{x}{2}$. The equation is of the form $y = A\sin Bx$ with $A = \dfrac{1}{2}$ and $B = \dfrac{1}{2}$.

amplitude: $|A| = \left|\dfrac{1}{2}\right| = \dfrac{1}{2}$

period: $\dfrac{2\pi}{B} = \dfrac{2\pi}{\frac{1}{2}} = 2\pi \cdot 2 = 4\pi$

Use quarter-periods, π, to find x-values for the five key points. Starting with $x = 0$, the x-values are 0, π, 2π, 3π, and 4π. Evaluating the function at each value of x, the key points are $(0, 0)$, $\left(\pi, \dfrac{1}{2}\right)$, $(2\pi, 0)$, $\left(3\pi, -\dfrac{1}{2}\right)$, and $(4\pi, 0)$. Use these key points to graph $y = \dfrac{1}{2}\sin\dfrac{x}{2}$ from 0 to 4π. Extend the graph one cycle to the right. Use the graph to obtain the graph of the reciprocal function. Draw vertical asymptotes through the x-intercepts, and use them as guides to graph $y = \dfrac{1}{2}\csc\dfrac{x}{2}$.

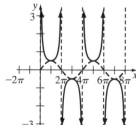

33. Graph the reciprocal cosine function, $y = 2\cos x$. The equation is of the form $y = A\cos Bx$ with $A = 2$ and $B = 1$.

amplitude: $|A| = |2| = 2$

period: $\dfrac{2\pi}{B} = \dfrac{2\pi}{1} = 2\pi$

Use quarter-periods, $\dfrac{\pi}{2}$, to find x-values for the five key points. Starting with $x = 0$, the x-values are 0, $\dfrac{\pi}{2}$, π, $\dfrac{3\pi}{2}$, 2π. Evaluating the function at each value of x, the key points are $(0, 2)$, $\left(\dfrac{\pi}{2}, 0\right)$, $(\pi, -2)$, $\left(\dfrac{3\pi}{2}, 0\right)$, and $(2\pi, 2)$. Use these key points to graph $y = 2\cos x$ from 0 to 2π. Extend the graph one cycle to the right. Use the graph to obtain the graph of the reciprocal function. Draw vertical asymptotes through the x-intercepts, and use them as guides to graph $y = 2\sec x$.

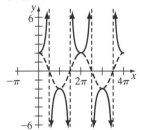

35. Graph the reciprocal cosine function, $y = \cos\dfrac{x}{3}$. The equation is of the form $y = A\cos Bx$ with $A = 1$ and $B = \dfrac{1}{3}$.

amplitude: $|A| = |1| = 1$

period: $\dfrac{2\pi}{B} = \dfrac{2\pi}{\frac{1}{3}} = 2\pi \cdot 3 = 6\pi$

Use quarter-periods, $\dfrac{6\pi}{4} = \dfrac{3\pi}{2}$, to find x-values for the five key points. Starting with $x = 0$, the x-values are 0, $\dfrac{3\pi}{2}$, 3π, $\dfrac{9\pi}{2}$, and 6π. Evaluating the function at each value of x, the key points are $(0, 1)$, $\left(\dfrac{3\pi}{2}, 0\right)$, $(3\pi, -1)$, $\left(\dfrac{9\pi}{2}, 0\right)$, and $(6\pi, 1)$. Use these key points to graph $y = \cos\dfrac{x}{3}$ from 0 to 6π. Extend the graph one cycle to the right. Use the graph to obtain the graph of the reciprocal function. Draw vertical asymptotes through the x-intercepts, and use them as guides to graph $y = \sec\dfrac{x}{3}$.

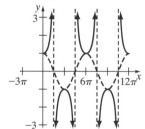

37. Graph the reciprocal sine function,
$y = -2 \sin \pi x$. The equation is of the form
$y = A \sin Bx$ with $A = -2$ and $B = \pi$.

amplitude: $|A| = |-2| = 2$

period: $\dfrac{2\pi}{B} = \dfrac{2\pi}{\pi} = 2$

Use quarter-periods, $\dfrac{2}{4} = \dfrac{1}{2}$, to find

x-values for the five key points. Starting

with $x = 0$, the x-values are $0, \dfrac{1}{2}, 1, \dfrac{3}{2}$, and

2. Evaluating the function at each value of x,

the key points are $(0, 0)$, $\left(\dfrac{1}{2}, -2\right)$, $(1, 0)$,

$\left(\dfrac{3}{2}, 2\right)$, and $(2, 0)$. Use these key points to

graph $y = -2 \sin \pi x$ from 0 to 2. Extend the
graph one cycle to the right. Use the graph
to obtain the graph of the reciprocal
function. Draw vertical asymptotes through
the
x-intercepts, and use them as guides to graph
$y = -2 \csc \pi x$.

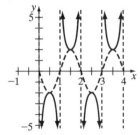

39. Graph the reciprocal cosine function,
$y = -\dfrac{1}{2} \cos \pi x$. The equation is of the form

$y = A \cos Bx$ with $A = -\dfrac{1}{2}$ and $B = \pi$.

amplitude: $|A| = \left|-\dfrac{1}{2}\right| = \dfrac{1}{2}$

period: $\dfrac{2\pi}{B} = \dfrac{2\pi}{\pi} = 2$

Use quarter-periods, $\dfrac{2}{4} = \dfrac{1}{2}$, to find x-values

for the five key points. Starting with $x = 0$,

the x-values are $0, \dfrac{1}{2}, 1, \dfrac{3}{2}$, and 2.

Evaluating the function at each value of x,

the key points are $\left(0, -\dfrac{1}{2}\right)$,

$\left(\dfrac{1}{2}, 0\right)$, $\left(1, \dfrac{1}{2}\right)$, $\left(\dfrac{3}{2}, 0\right)$, $\left(2, -\dfrac{1}{2}\right)$. Use

these key points to graph $y = -\dfrac{1}{2} \cos \pi x$

from 0 to 2. Extend the graph one cycle to
the right. Use the graph to obtain the graph
of the reciprocal function. Draw vertical
asymptotes through the
x-intercepts, and use them as guides to graph

$y = -\dfrac{1}{2} \sec \pi x$.

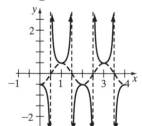

41. Graph the reciprocal sine function, $y = \sin(x - \pi)$. The equation is of the form $y = A\sin(Bx - C)$ with $A = 1$, and $B = 1$, and $C = \pi$.

amplitude: $|A| = |1| = 1$

period: $\dfrac{2\pi}{B} = \dfrac{2\pi}{1} = 2\pi$

phase shift: $\dfrac{C}{B} = \dfrac{\pi}{1} = \pi$

Use quarter-periods, $\dfrac{2\pi}{4} = \dfrac{\pi}{2}$, to find x-values for the five key points. Starting with $x = \pi$, the x-values are π, $\dfrac{3\pi}{2}$, 2π, $\dfrac{5\pi}{2}$, and 3π. Evaluating the function at each value of x, the key points are $(\pi, 0)$, $\left(\dfrac{3\pi}{2}, 1\right)$, $(2\pi, 0)$, $\left(\dfrac{5\pi}{2}, -1\right)$, $(3\pi, 0)$. Use these key points to graph $y = \sin(x - \pi)$ from π to 3π. Extend the graph one cycle to the right. Use the graph to obtain the graph of the reciprocal function. Draw vertical asymptotes through the x-intercepts, and use them as guides to graph $y = \csc(x - \pi)$.

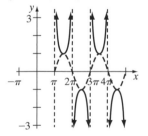

43. Graph the reciprocal cosine function, $y = 2\cos(x + \pi)$. The equation is of the form $y = A\cos(Bx + C)$ with $A = 2$, $B = 1$, and $C = -\pi$.

amplitude: $|A| = |2| = 2$

period: $\dfrac{2\pi}{B} = \dfrac{2\pi}{1} = 2\pi$

phase shift: $\dfrac{C}{B} = \dfrac{-\pi}{1} = -\pi$

Use quarter-periods, $\dfrac{2\pi}{4} = \dfrac{\pi}{2}$, to find x-values for the five key points. Starting with $x = -\pi$, the x-values are $-\pi$, $-\dfrac{\pi}{2}$, 0, $\dfrac{\pi}{2}$, and π. Evaluating the function at each value of x, the key points are $(-\pi, 2)$, $\left(-\dfrac{\pi}{2}, 0\right)$, $(0, -2)$, $\left(\dfrac{\pi}{2}, 0\right)$, and $(\pi, 2)$.

Use these key points to graph $y = 2\cos(x + \pi)$ from $-\pi$ to π. Extend the graph one cycle to the right. Use the graph to obtain the graph of the reciprocal function. Draw vertical asymptotes through the x-intercepts, and use them as guides to graph $y = 2\sec(x + \pi)$.

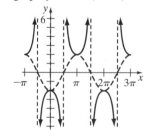

45. $d = 12 \tan 2\pi t$

a. We solve the equations

$$2\pi t = -\frac{\pi}{2} \quad \text{and} \quad 2\pi t = \frac{\pi}{2}$$

$$t = \frac{-\frac{\pi}{2}}{2\pi} \qquad\qquad t = \frac{\frac{\pi}{2}}{2\pi}$$

$$t = -\frac{1}{4} \qquad\qquad t = \frac{1}{4}$$

Thus, two consecutive asymptotes occur

at $x = -\frac{1}{4}$ and $x = \frac{1}{4}$.

$$x\text{-intercept} = \frac{-\frac{1}{4} + \frac{1}{4}}{2} = \frac{0}{2} = 0$$

An x-intercept is 0 and the graph passes through (0, 0). Because the coefficient of the tangent is 12, the points on the graph midway between an x-intercept and the asymptotes have y-coordinates of -12 and 12. Use the two consecutive

asymptotes, $x = -\frac{1}{4}$ and $x = \frac{1}{4}$, to

graph one full period of $d = 12 \tan 2\pi t$. To graph on [0, 2], continue the pattern and extend the graph to 2. (We do not use the left hand side of the first period of the graph on [0, 2].)

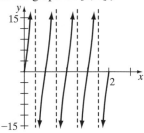

b. The function is undefined for $t = 0.25$, 0.75, 1.25, and 1.75.
The beacon is shining parallel to the wall at these times.

47. We want a function that relates the acute angle with the hypotenuse and the adjacent leg. Use the secant function.

$$\sec x = \frac{d}{10}$$

$$d = 10 \sec x$$

Graph the reciprocal cosine function, $y = 10 \cos x$. The equation is of the form $y = A \cos Bx$ with $A = 10$ and $B = 1$.

amplitude: $|A| = |10| = 10$

period: $\frac{2\pi}{B} = \frac{2\pi}{1} = 2\pi$

For $-\frac{\pi}{2} < x < \frac{\pi}{2}$, use the x-values $-\frac{\pi}{2}$, 0,

and $\frac{\pi}{2}$ to find the key points $\left(-\frac{\pi}{2}, 0\right)$,

(0, 10), and $\left(\frac{\pi}{2}, 0\right)$. Connect these points

with a smooth curve, then draw vertical asymptotes through the x-intercepts, and use them as guides to graph $d = 10 \sec x$ on

$$\left[-\frac{\pi}{2}, \frac{\pi}{2}\right].$$

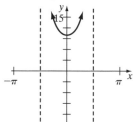

49.

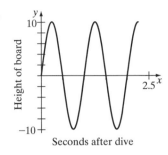

51.–57. Answers may vary.

For 59 and 61, the graphing utility graphs the asymptotes as a solid line when in the connected mode, but doesn't graph the asymptotes when in the dot mode.

59. Exercise 5

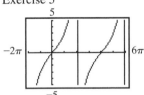

Exercise 7

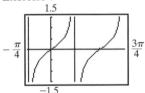

61. Exercise 29

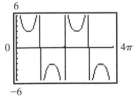

Exercise 31

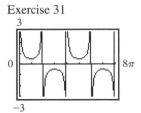

63. period: $\dfrac{\pi}{B} = \dfrac{\pi}{\frac{1}{4}} = \pi \cdot 4 = 4\pi$

Graph $y = \tan \dfrac{x}{4}$ for $0 \le x \le 8\pi$.

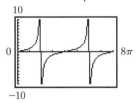

65. period: $\dfrac{\pi}{B} = \dfrac{\pi}{2}$

Graph $y = \cot 2x$ for $0 \le x \le \pi$.

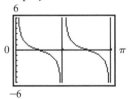

67. period: $\dfrac{\pi}{B} = \dfrac{\pi}{\pi} = 1$

Graph $y = \dfrac{1}{2}\tan \pi x$ for $0 \le x \le 2$.

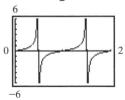

69. period: $\dfrac{2\pi}{B} = \dfrac{2\pi}{\frac{1}{2}} = 2\pi \cdot 2 = 4\pi$

Graph the functions for $0 \le x \le 8\pi$.

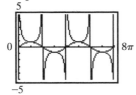

71. period: $\dfrac{2\pi}{B} = \dfrac{2\pi}{2} = \pi$

phase shift: $\dfrac{C}{B} = \dfrac{\frac{\pi}{6}}{2} = \dfrac{\pi}{12}$

Thus, we include $\dfrac{\pi}{12} \le x \le \dfrac{25\pi}{12}$ in our

graph, and graph for $0 \le x \le \dfrac{5\pi}{2}$.

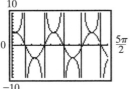

73.

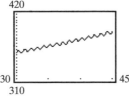

The graph shows that carbon dioxide concentration rises and falls each year, but over all the concentration increased from 1990 to 2005.

75. The graph has the shape of a cotangent function with consecutive asymptotes at

$x = 0$ and $x = \dfrac{2\pi}{3}$. The period is

$\dfrac{2\pi}{3} - 0 = \dfrac{2\pi}{3}$. Thus,

$\dfrac{\pi}{B} = \dfrac{2\pi}{3}$

$2\pi B = 3\pi$

$B = \dfrac{3\pi}{2\pi} = \dfrac{3}{2}$

The points on the graph midway between an x-intercept and the asymptotes have y-coordinates of 1 and -1. Thus, $A = 1$. There is no phase shift. Thus, $C = 0$. An equation

for this graph is $y = \cot \dfrac{3}{2}x$.

77. $y = 2^{-x} \sin x$

2^{-x} decreases the amplitude as x gets larger. Examples may vary.

Review Exercises

1. A 190° angle is a positive angle. It has a counterclockwise rotation of 180° followed by a counterclockwise rotation of 10°. The angle lies in quadrant III and is shown in the following graph.

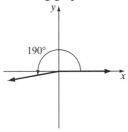

2. A −135° angle is a negative angle. It has a clockwise rotation of 90° followed by a clockwise rotation of 45°. The angle lies in quadrant III and is shown in the following graph.

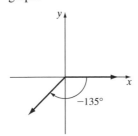

3. A $\dfrac{5\pi}{6}$ angle is a positive angle. It has a counterclockwise rotation of $\dfrac{\pi}{2}$ followed by a counterclockwise rotation of $\dfrac{\pi}{3}$. The angle lies in quadrant II and is shown in the

following graph.

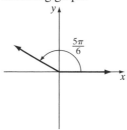

4. A $-\dfrac{2\pi}{3}$ angle is a negative angle. It has a clockwise rotation of $\dfrac{\pi}{2}$ followed by a clockwise rotation of $\dfrac{\pi}{6}$. The angle lies in quadrant III and is shown in the following graph.

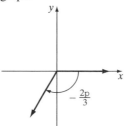

5. For a 400° angle, subtract 360°.
$400° - 360° = 40°$

6. For a −85° angle, add 360°.
$-85° + 360° = 275°$

7. complement = $90° - 73° = 17°$;
supplement = $180° - 73° = 107°$

8. no complement;
supplement = $\pi - \dfrac{2\pi}{3}$
$= \dfrac{3\pi}{3} - \dfrac{2\pi}{3} = \dfrac{\pi}{3}$ radians

9. The radian measure of a central angle is the length of the intercepted arc divided by the

circle's radius.

$$\theta = \frac{27}{6} = 4.5 \text{ radians}$$

10. $15° = 15° \cdot \dfrac{\pi \text{ radians}}{180°} = \dfrac{15\pi}{180}$ radian

$$= \frac{\pi}{12} \text{ radian}$$

11. $120° = 120° \cdot \dfrac{\pi \text{ radians}}{180°} = \dfrac{120\pi}{180}$ radian

$$= \frac{2\pi}{3} \text{ radian}$$

Chapter 1 Test

1. $135° = 135° \cdot \dfrac{\pi \text{ radians}}{180°}$

   $= \dfrac{135\pi}{180}$ radians

   $= \dfrac{3\pi}{4}$ radians

2. supplement: $\pi - \dfrac{9\pi}{13} = \dfrac{13\pi}{13} - \dfrac{9\pi}{13} = \dfrac{4\pi}{13}$

3. $75° = 75° \cdot \dfrac{\pi \text{ radians}}{180°} = \dfrac{75\pi}{180}$ radians

   $= \dfrac{5\pi}{12}$ radians

   $s = r\theta$

   $s = 20\left(\dfrac{5\pi}{12}\right) = \dfrac{25\pi}{3}$ ft ≈ 26.18 ft

4. We need values for x, y, and r. Because
   P = (–2, 5) is a point on the terminal side of
   θ, $x = -2$ and $y = 5$. Furthermore,

   $r = \sqrt{x^2 + y^2} = \sqrt{(-2)^2 + (5)^2}$

   $\quad = \sqrt{4 + 25} = \sqrt{29}$

   Now that we know x, y, and r, we can find
   the six trigonometric functions of θ.

   $\sin\theta = \dfrac{y}{r} = \dfrac{5}{\sqrt{29}} = \dfrac{5\sqrt{29}}{\sqrt{29}\sqrt{29}} = \dfrac{5\sqrt{29}}{29}$

   $\cos\theta = \dfrac{x}{r} = \dfrac{-2}{\sqrt{29}} = -\dfrac{2\sqrt{29}}{\sqrt{29}\sqrt{29}} = -\dfrac{2\sqrt{29}}{29}$

   $\tan\theta = \dfrac{y}{x} = \dfrac{5}{-2} = -\dfrac{5}{2}$

   $\csc\theta = \dfrac{r}{y} = \dfrac{\sqrt{29}}{5}$

   $\sec\theta = \dfrac{r}{x} = \dfrac{\sqrt{29}}{-2} = -\dfrac{\sqrt{29}}{2}$

   $\cot\theta = \dfrac{x}{y} = \dfrac{-2}{5} = -\dfrac{2}{5}$

5. Because $\cos\theta < 0$, θ cannot lie in quadrant
   I and quadrant IV; the cosine function is
   positive in those two quadrants. Thus, with
   $\cos\theta < 0$, θ lies in quadrant II or quadrant
   III. We are also given that $\cot\theta > 0$.
   Because quadrant III is the only quadrant in
   which the cosine is negative and the
   cotangent is positive, we conclude that θ
   lies in quadrant III.

6. Because the cosine is positive and the
   tangent is negative, θ lies in quadrant IV. In
   quadrant IV x is positive and y is negative.
   Thus, $\cos\theta = \dfrac{1}{3} = \dfrac{x}{r}$, $x = 1$, $r = 3$.
   Furthermore,

   $x^2 + y^2 = r^3$

   $1^2 + y^2 = 3^2$

   $\quad y^2 = 9 - 1 = 8$

   $\quad\quad y = -\sqrt{8} = -2\sqrt{2}$

   Now that we know x, y, and r, we can find
   the six trigonometric functions of θ.

   $\sin\theta = \dfrac{y}{r} = \dfrac{-2\sqrt{2}}{3} = -\dfrac{2\sqrt{2}}{3}$

   $\tan\theta = \dfrac{y}{x} = \dfrac{-2\sqrt{2}}{1} = -2\sqrt{2}$

   $\csc\theta = \dfrac{r}{y} = \dfrac{3}{-2\sqrt{2}} = -\dfrac{3\sqrt{2}}{2\sqrt{2}\cdot\sqrt{2}} = -\dfrac{3\sqrt{2}}{4}$

   $\sec\theta = \dfrac{r}{x} = \dfrac{3}{1} = 3$

   $\cot\theta = \dfrac{x}{y} = \dfrac{1}{-2\sqrt{2}} = -\dfrac{1\cdot\sqrt{2}}{2\sqrt{2}\sqrt{2}} = -\dfrac{\sqrt{2}}{4}$

7. $\tan\dfrac{\pi}{6}\cos\dfrac{\pi}{3} - \cos\dfrac{\pi}{2} = \dfrac{\sqrt{3}}{3}\cdot\dfrac{1}{2} - 0 = \dfrac{\sqrt{3}}{6}$

8. 300° lies in quadrant IV.
   The reference angle is

$\theta' = 360° - 300° = 60°$

$\tan 60° = \sqrt{3}$

In quadrant IV, $\tan\theta < 0$, so

$\tan 300° = -\tan 60 = -\sqrt{3}$.

9. $\dfrac{7\pi}{4}$ lies in quadrant IV.

The reference angle is

$\theta' = 2\pi - \dfrac{7\pi}{4} = \dfrac{8\pi}{4} - \dfrac{7\pi}{4} = \dfrac{\pi}{4}$

$\sin\dfrac{\pi}{4} = \dfrac{\sqrt{2}}{2}$

In quadrant IV, $\sin\theta < 0$, so

$\sin\dfrac{7\pi}{4} = -\sin\dfrac{\pi}{4} = -\dfrac{\sqrt{2}}{2}$.

10. The equation $y = 3\sin 2x$ is of the form $y = A\sin Bx$ with $A = 3$ and $B = 2$. The amplitude is $|A| = |3| = 3$. The period is

$\dfrac{2\pi}{B} = \dfrac{2\pi}{2} = \pi$. The quarter-period is $\dfrac{\pi}{4}$.

The cycle begins at $x = 0$. Add quarter-periods to generate x-values for the key points.

$x = 0$

$x = 0 + \dfrac{\pi}{4} = \dfrac{\pi}{4}$

$x = \dfrac{\pi}{4} + \dfrac{\pi}{4} = \dfrac{\pi}{2}$

$x = \dfrac{\pi}{2} + \dfrac{\pi}{4} = \dfrac{3\pi}{4}$

$x = \dfrac{3\pi}{4} + \dfrac{\pi}{4} = \pi$

We evaluate the function at each value of x.

x	$y = 3\sin 2x$	coordinates
0	$y = 3\sin(2 \cdot 0) = 3\sin 0$ $= 3 \cdot 0 = 0$	$(0, 0)$

$\dfrac{\pi}{4}$	$y = 3\sin\left(2 \cdot \dfrac{\pi}{4}\right)$ $= 3\sin\dfrac{\pi}{2} = 3 \cdot 1 = 3$	$\left(\dfrac{\pi}{4}, 3\right)$
$\dfrac{\pi}{2}$	$y = 3\sin\left(2 \cdot \dfrac{\pi}{2}\right)$ $= 3\sin\pi = 3 \cdot 0 = 0$	$\left(\dfrac{\pi}{2}, 0\right)$
$\dfrac{3\pi}{4}$	$y = 3\sin\left(2 \cdot \dfrac{3\pi}{4}\right)$ $= 3\sin\dfrac{3\pi}{2} = 3 \cdot (-1)$ $= -3$	$\left(\dfrac{3\pi}{4}, -3\right)$
π	$y = 3\sin(2 \cdot \pi)$ $= 3\sin 2\pi = 3 \cdot 0$ $= 0$	$(\pi, 0)$

Connect the five key points with a smooth curve and graph one complete cycle of the given function.

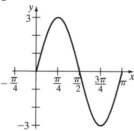

11. The equation $y = -2\cos\left(x - \dfrac{\pi}{2}\right)$ is of the form $y = A\cos(Bx - C)$ with $A = -2$, $B = 1$, and

$C = \dfrac{\pi}{2}$. The amplitude is $|A| = |-2| = 2$.

The period is $\dfrac{2\pi}{B} = \dfrac{2\pi}{1} = 2\pi$. The phase

shift is $\dfrac{C}{B} = \dfrac{\frac{\pi}{2}}{1} = \dfrac{\pi}{2}$. The quarter-period is

$$\frac{2\pi}{4} = \frac{\pi}{2}.$$

The cycle begins at $x = \dfrac{\pi}{2}$. Add quarter-periods to generate x-values for the key points.

$$x = \frac{\pi}{2}$$

$$x = \frac{\pi}{2} + \frac{\pi}{2} = \pi$$

$$x = \pi + \frac{\pi}{2} = \frac{3\pi}{2}$$

$$x = \frac{3\pi}{2} + \frac{\pi}{2} = 2\pi$$

$$x = 2\pi + \frac{\pi}{2} = \frac{5\pi}{2}$$

We evaluate the function at each value of x.

x	$y = -2\cos\left(x - \dfrac{\pi}{2}\right)$	coordinates
$\dfrac{\pi}{2}$	$y = -2\cos\left(\dfrac{\pi}{2} - \dfrac{\pi}{2}\right)$ $= -2\cos 0$ $= -2 \cdot 1 = -2$	$\left(\dfrac{\pi}{2}, -2\right)$
π	$y = -2\cos\left(\pi - \dfrac{\pi}{2}\right)$ $= -2\cos\dfrac{\pi}{2}$ $= -2 \cdot 0 = 0$	$(\pi, 0)$
$\dfrac{3\pi}{2}$	$y = -2\cos\left(\dfrac{3\pi}{2} - \dfrac{\pi}{2}\right)$ $= -2\cos\pi$ $= -2 \cdot (-1) = 2$	$\left(\dfrac{3\pi}{2}, 2\right)$

2π	$y = -2\cos\left(2\pi - \dfrac{\pi}{2}\right)$ $= -2\cos\dfrac{3\pi}{2}$ $= -2 \cdot 0 = 0$	$(2\pi, 0)$
$\dfrac{5\pi}{2}$	$y = -2\cos\left(\dfrac{5\pi}{2} - \dfrac{\pi}{2}\right)$ $= -2\cos 2\pi$ $= -2 \cdot 1 = -2$	$\left(\dfrac{5\pi}{2}, -2\right)$

Connect the five key points with a smooth curve and graph one complete cycle of the given function.

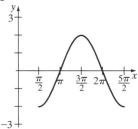

12. We solve the equations

$$\frac{x}{2} = -\frac{\pi}{2} \qquad \text{and} \qquad \frac{x}{2} = \frac{\pi}{2}$$

$$x = -\frac{\pi}{2} \cdot 2 \qquad\qquad x = \frac{\pi}{2} \cdot 2$$

$$x = -\pi \qquad\qquad\qquad x = \pi$$

Thus, two consecutive asymptotes occur at $x = -\pi$ and $x = \pi$.

$$x\text{-intercept} = \frac{-\pi + \pi}{2} = \frac{0}{2} = 0$$

An x-intercept is 0 and the graph passes through (0, 0). Because the coefficient of the tangent is 2, the points on the graph midway between an x-intercept and the asymptotes have y-coordinates of –2 and 2. We use the two consecutive asymptotes, $x = -\pi$ and $x = \pi$, to graph one full period of $y = 2\tan\dfrac{x}{2}$ from $-\pi$ to π.

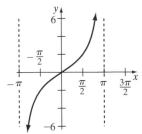

$y = -\dfrac{1}{2}\csc\pi x.$

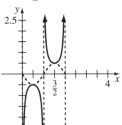

13. Graph the reciprocal sine function,

$y = -\dfrac{1}{2}\sin\pi x.$ The equation is of the form

$y = A\sin Bx$ with $A = -\dfrac{1}{2}$ and $B = \pi.$

amplitude: $|A| = \left|-\dfrac{1}{2}\right| = \dfrac{1}{2}$

period: $\dfrac{2\pi}{B} = \dfrac{2\pi}{\pi} = 2$

Use quarter-periods, $\dfrac{2}{4} = \dfrac{1}{2}$, to find x-values

for the five key points. Starting with $x = 0$, the

x-values are $0, \dfrac{1}{2}, 1, \dfrac{3}{2}, 2.$ Evaluating the

function at each value of x, the key points are

$(0, 3), \left(\dfrac{1}{2}, -\dfrac{1}{2}\right), (1, 0), \left(\dfrac{3}{2}, \dfrac{1}{2}\right), (2, 0).$

Use these key points to graph

$y = -\dfrac{1}{2}\sin\pi x$ from 0 to 2. Use the graph to

obtain the graph of the reciprocal function. Draw vertical asymptotes through the x-intercepts, and use them as guides to graph

14. Let $\theta = \cos^{-1}\left(-\dfrac{1}{2}\right)$, then $\cos\theta = -\dfrac{1}{2}.$

Because $\cos\theta$ is negative, θ is in quadrant II.

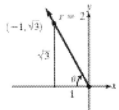

We use the Pythagorean Theorem to find y.

$(-1)^2 + y^2 = 2^2$

$y^2 = 4 - 1 = 3$

$y = \sqrt{3}$

We use the right triangle to find the exact value.

$\tan\left[\cos^{-1}\left(-\dfrac{1}{2}\right)\right] = \tan\theta = \dfrac{\sqrt{3}}{-1} = -\sqrt{3}$

15. Find the measure of angle B. Because
$C = 90°, A + B = 90°.$
Thus, $B = 90° - A = 90° - 21° = 69°.$
We have a known angle, a known hypotenuse, and an unknown opposite side.
We use the sine function.

$\sin 21° = \dfrac{a}{13}$

$a = 13\sin 21° \approx 4.7$

We have a known angle, a known

hypotenuse, and an unknown adjacent side. We use the cosine function.

$$\cos 21° = \frac{b}{13}$$
$$b = 13\cos 21° \approx 12.1$$

In summary, $B = 69°$, $a \approx 4.7$, and $b \approx 12.1$.

16. Using a right triangle, we have a known angle, an unknown opposite side, h, and a known adjacent side. Therefore, we use the tangent function.

$$\tan 37° = \frac{h}{30}$$
$$h = 30\tan 37° \approx 23$$

The building is about 23 yards high.

17. Using a right triangle, we have a known hypotenuse, a known opposite side, and an unknown angle. Therefore, we use the sine function.

$$\sin\theta = \frac{43}{73}$$
$$\theta = \sin^{-1}\left(\frac{43}{73}\right) \approx 36.1°$$

The rope makes an angle of about 36.1° with the pole.

Chapter 2

Check Point Exercises

1. Begin by finding B, the third angle of the triangle.

$$A + B + C = 180°$$

$$64° + B + 82° = 180°$$

$$146° + B = 180°$$

$$B = 34°$$

In this problem, we are given c and C: $c = 14$ and $C = 82°$. Thus, we use the ratio $\dfrac{c}{\sin C}$, or $\dfrac{14}{\sin 82°}$, to find the other two sides. Use the Law of Sines to find a.

$$\frac{a}{\sin A} = \frac{c}{\sin C}$$

$$\frac{a}{\sin 64°} = \frac{14}{\sin 82°}$$

$$a = \frac{14 \sin 64°}{\sin 82°}$$

$$a \approx 13 \text{ centimeters}$$

Use the Law of Sines again, this time to find b.

$$\frac{b}{\sin B} = \frac{c}{\sin C}$$

$$\frac{b}{\sin 34°} = \frac{14}{\sin 82°}$$

$$b = \frac{14 \sin 34°}{\sin 82°}$$

$$b \approx 8 \text{ centimeters}$$

The solution is $B = 34°$, $a \approx 13$ centimeters, and $b \approx 8$ centimeters.

2. Begin by finding B.

$$A + B + C = 180°$$

$$40° + B + 22.5° = 180°$$

$$62.5° + B = 180°$$

$$B = 117.5°$$

In this problem, we are given that $b = 12$ and we find that $B = 117.5°$. Thus, we use the ratio $\dfrac{b}{\sin B}$, or $\dfrac{12}{\sin 117.5°}$, to find the other two sides. Use the Law of Sines to find a.

$$\frac{a}{\sin A} = \frac{b}{\sin B}$$

$$\frac{a}{\sin 40°} = \frac{12}{\sin 117.5°}$$

$$a = \frac{12 \sin 40°}{\sin 117.5°} \approx 9$$

Use the Law of Sines again, this time to find c.

$$\frac{c}{\sin C} = \frac{b}{\sin B}$$

$$\frac{c}{\sin 22.5°} = \frac{12}{\sin 117.5°}$$

$$c = \frac{12 \sin 22.5°}{\sin 117.5°} \approx 5$$

The solution is $B = 117.5°$, $a \approx 9$, and $c \approx 5$.

3. The known ratio is $\dfrac{a}{\sin A}$, or $\dfrac{47}{\sin 123°}$. Because side c is given, we use the Law of Sines to find angle C,

$$\frac{a}{\sin A} = \frac{c}{\sin C}$$

$$\frac{47}{\sin 123°} = \frac{23}{\sin C}$$

$$47 \sin C = 23 \sin 123°$$

$$\sin C = \frac{23 \sin 123°}{47}$$

$$\sin C \approx 0.4104$$

There are two angles possible:

$C_1 \approx 24°$, $C_2 \approx 180° - 24° = 156°$

C_2 is impossible, since $123° + 156° = 279°$.

We find B using C, and the given information $A = 123°$.

$$B = 180° - C_1 - A \approx 180° - 24° - 123° = 33°$$

Use the Law of Sines to find side b.

$$\frac{b}{\sin B}=\frac{a}{\sin A}$$

$$\frac{b}{\sin 33°}=\frac{47}{\sin 123°}$$

$$b=\frac{47\sin 33°}{\sin 123°}\approx 31$$

There is one triangle and the solution is
C_1 (or C) $\approx 24°$, $B \approx 33°$, and $b \approx 31$.

4. The known ratio is $\dfrac{a}{\sin A}$, or $\dfrac{10}{\sin 50°}$.
   Because side b is given, we use the Law of
   Sines to find angle B.

$$\frac{a}{\sin A}=\frac{b}{\sin B}$$

$$\frac{10}{\sin 50}=\frac{20}{\sin B}$$

$$10\sin B=20\sin 50$$

$$\sin B=\frac{20\sin 50}{10}\approx 1.53$$

Because the sine can never exceed 1, there is
no angle B for which $\sin B \approx 1.53$. There is
no triangle with the given measurements.

5. The known ratio is $\dfrac{a}{\sin A}$, or $\dfrac{12}{\sin 35°}$.
   Because side b is given, we use the Law of
   Sines to find angle B.

$$\frac{a}{\sin A}=\frac{b}{\sin B}$$

$$\frac{12}{\sin 35°}=\frac{16}{\sin B}$$

$$12\sin B=16\sin 35°$$

$$\sin B=\frac{16\sin 35°}{12}\approx 0.7648$$

There are two angles possible:
$B_1 \approx 50°$, $B_2 \approx 180° - 50° = 130°$
There are two triangles:
$C_1 = 180° - A - B_1 \approx 180° - 35° - 50° = 95°$
$C_2 = 180° - A - B_2 \approx 180° - 35° - 130° = 15°$
We use the Law of Sines to find c_1 and c_2.

$$\frac{c_1}{\sin C_1}=\frac{a}{\sin A}$$

$$\frac{c_1}{\sin 95°}=\frac{12}{\sin 35°}$$

$$c_1=\frac{12\sin 95°}{\sin 35°}\approx 21$$

$$\frac{c_2}{\sin C_2}=\frac{a}{\sin A}$$

$$\frac{c_2}{\sin 15°}=\frac{12}{\sin 35°}$$

$$c_2=\frac{12\sin 15°}{\sin 35°}\approx 5$$

In one triangle, the solution is $B_1 \approx 50°$,
$C_1 \approx 95°$, and $c_1 \approx 21$. In the other triangle,
$B_2 \approx 130°$, $C_2 \approx 15°$, and $c_2 \approx 5$.

6. The area of the triangle is half the product of
   the lengths of the two sides times the sine of
   the included angle.

$$\text{Area}=\frac{1}{2}(8)(12)(\sin 135°)\approx 34$$

The area of the triangle is approximately 34
square meters.

7.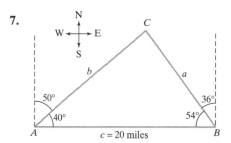

Using a north-south line, the interior angles
are found as follows:
$A=90° - 35° = 55°$

$B=90° - 49° = 41°$
Find angle C using a $180°$ angle sum in the
triangle.
$C=180° - A - B = 180° - 55° - 41° = 84°$

The ratio $\dfrac{c}{\sin C}$, or $\dfrac{13}{\sin 84°}$ is now known. We use this ratio and the Law of Sines to find a.

$$\frac{a}{\sin A} = \frac{c}{\sin C}$$

$$\frac{a}{\sin 55°} = \frac{13}{\sin 84°}$$

$$a = \frac{13 \sin 55°}{\sin 84°} \approx 11$$

The fire is approximately 11 miles from station B.

Exercise Set 2.1

1. Begin by finding B.
$$A + B + C = 180°$$
$$42° + B + 96° = 180°$$
$$138° + B = 180°$$
$$B = 42°$$

Use the ratio $\dfrac{c}{\sin C}$, or $\dfrac{12}{\sin 96°}$, to find the other two sides. Use the Law of Sines to find a.

$$\frac{a}{\sin A} = \frac{c}{\sin C}$$

$$\frac{a}{\sin 42°} = \frac{12}{\sin 96°}$$

$$a = \frac{12 \sin 42°}{\sin 96°}$$

$$a \approx 8.1$$

Use the Law of Sines again, this time to find b.

$$\frac{b}{\sin B} = \frac{c}{\sin C}$$

$$\frac{b}{\sin 42°} = \frac{12}{\sin 96°}$$

$$b = \frac{12 \sin 42°}{\sin 96°}$$

$$b \approx 8.1$$

The solution is $B = 42°$, $a \approx 8.1$, and $b \approx 8.1$.

3. Begin by finding A.
$$A + B + C = 180°$$
$$A + 54° + 82° = 180°$$
$$A + 136° = 180°$$
$$A = 44°$$

Use the ratio $\dfrac{a}{\sin A}$, or $\dfrac{16}{\sin 44°}$, to find the other two sides. Use the Law of Sines to find b.

$$\frac{b}{\sin B} = \frac{a}{\sin A}$$

$$\frac{b}{\sin 54°} = \frac{16}{\sin 44°}$$

$$b = \frac{16 \sin 54°}{\sin 44°}$$

$$b \approx 18.6$$

Use the Law of Sines again, this time to find c.

$$\frac{c}{\sin C} = \frac{a}{\sin A}$$

$$\frac{c}{\sin 82°} = \frac{16}{\sin 44°}$$

$$c = \frac{16 \sin 82°}{\sin 44°}$$

$$c \approx 22.8$$

The solution is $A = 44°$, $b \approx 18.6$, and $c \approx 22.8$.

5. Begin by finding C.
$$A + B + C = 180°$$
$$48° + 37° + C = 180°$$
$$85° + C = 180°$$
$$C = 95°$$

Use the ratio $\dfrac{a}{\sin A}$, or $\dfrac{100}{\sin 48°}$, to find the other two sides. Use the Law of Sines to find b.

$$\frac{b}{\sin B} = \frac{a}{\sin A}$$

$$\frac{b}{\sin 37°} = \frac{100}{\sin 48°}$$

$$b = \frac{100\sin 37°}{\sin 48°}$$

$$b \approx 81.0$$

Use the Law of Sines again, this time to find c.

$$\frac{c}{\sin C} = \frac{a}{\sin A}$$

$$\frac{c}{\sin 95°} = \frac{100}{\sin 48°}$$

$$c = \frac{100\sin 95°}{\sin 48°}$$

$$c \approx 134.1$$

The solution is $C = 95°$, $b \approx 81.0$, and $c \approx 134.1$.

7. Begin by finding B.

$$A + B + C = 180°$$
$$38° + B + 102° = 180°$$
$$B + 140° = 180°$$
$$B = 40°$$

Use the ratio $\frac{a}{\sin A}$, or $\frac{20}{\sin 38°}$, to find the other two sides. Use the Law of Sines to find b.

$$\frac{b}{\sin B} = \frac{a}{\sin A}$$
$$\frac{b}{\sin 40°} = \frac{20}{\sin 38°}$$
$$b = \frac{20\sin 40°}{\sin 38°}$$
$$b \approx 20.9$$

Use the Law of Sines again, this time to find c.

$$\frac{c}{\sin C} = \frac{a}{\sin A}$$
$$\frac{c}{\sin 102°} = \frac{20}{\sin 38°}$$
$$c = \frac{20\sin 102°}{\sin 38°}$$
$$c \approx 31.8$$

The solution is $B = 40°$, $b \approx 20.9$, and $c \approx 31.8$.

9. Begin by finding C.

$$A + B + C = 180°$$
$$44° + 25° + C = 180°$$
$$69° + C = 180°$$
$$C = 111°$$

Use the ratio $\frac{a}{\sin A}$, or $\frac{12}{\sin 44°}$, to find the other two sides. Use the Law of Sines to find b.

$$\frac{b}{\sin B} = \frac{a}{\sin A}$$
$$\frac{b}{\sin 25°} = \frac{12}{\sin 44°}$$
$$b = \frac{12\sin 25°}{\sin 44°}$$
$$b \approx 7.3$$

Use the Law of Sines again, this time to find c.

$$\frac{c}{\sin C} = \frac{a}{\sin A}$$
$$\frac{c}{\sin 111°} = \frac{12}{\sin 44°}$$
$$c = \frac{12\sin 111°}{\sin 44°}$$
$$c \approx 16.1$$

The solution is $C = 111°$, $b \approx 7.3$, and $c \approx 16.1$.

11. Begin by finding A.

$$A + B + C = 180°$$
$$A + 85° + 15° = 180°$$
$$A + 100° = 180°$$
$$A = 80°$$

Use the ratio $\frac{b}{\sin B}$, or $\frac{40}{\sin 85°}$, to find the other two sides. Use the Law of Sines to find a.

$$\frac{a}{\sin A} = \frac{b}{\sin B}$$

$$\frac{a}{\sin 80°} = \frac{40}{\sin 85°}$$

$$a = \frac{40 \sin 80°}{\sin 85°}$$

$$a \approx 39.5$$

Use the Law of Sines again, this time to find c.

$$\frac{c}{\sin C} = \frac{b}{\sin B}$$

$$\frac{c}{\sin 15°} = \frac{40}{\sin 85°}$$

$$c = \frac{40 \sin 15°}{\sin 85°}$$

$$c \approx 10.4$$

The solution is $A = 80°$, $a \approx 39.5$, and $c \approx 10.4$.

13. Begin by finding B.
$$A + B + C = 180°$$
$$115° + B + 35° = 180°$$
$$B + 150° = 180°$$
$$B = 30°$$

Use the ratio $\frac{c}{\sin C}$, or $\frac{200}{\sin 35°}$, to find the other two sides. Use the Law of Sines to find a.

$$\frac{a}{\sin A} = \frac{c}{\sin C}$$

$$\frac{a}{\sin 115°} = \frac{200}{\sin 35°}$$

$$a = \frac{200 \sin 115°}{\sin 35°}$$

$$a \approx 316.0$$

Use the Law of Sines again, this time to find b.

$$\frac{b}{\sin B} = \frac{c}{\sin C}$$

$$\frac{b}{\sin 30°} = \frac{200}{\sin 35°}$$

$$b = \frac{200 \sin 30°}{\sin 35°}$$

$$b \approx 174.3$$

The solution is $B = 30°$, $a \approx 316.0$, and $b \approx 174.3$.

15. Begin by finding C.
$$A + B + C = 180°$$
$$65° + 65° + C = 180°$$
$$130° + C = 180°$$
$$C = 50°$$

Use the ratio $\frac{c}{\sin C}$, or $\frac{6}{\sin 50°}$, to find the other two sides. Use the Law of Sines to find a.

$$\frac{a}{\sin A} = \frac{c}{\sin C}$$

$$\frac{a}{\sin 65°} = \frac{6}{\sin 50°}$$

$$a = \frac{6 \sin 65°}{\sin 50°}$$

$$a \approx 7.1$$

Use the Law of Sines to find angle B.

$$\frac{b}{\sin B} = \frac{c}{\sin C}$$

$$\frac{b}{\sin 65°} = \frac{6}{\sin 50°}$$

$$b = \frac{6\sin 65°}{\sin 50°}$$

$$b \approx 7.1$$

The solution is $C = 50°$, $a \approx 7.1$, and $b \approx 7.1$.

17. The known ratio is $\dfrac{a}{\sin A}$, or $\dfrac{20}{\sin 40°}$.

We use the Law of Sines to find angle B.

$$\frac{a}{\sin A} = \frac{b}{\sin B}$$

$$\frac{20}{\sin 40°} = \frac{15}{\sin B}$$

$$20\sin B = 15\sin 40°$$

$$\sin B = \frac{15\sin 40°}{20}$$

$$\sin B \approx 0.4821$$

There are two angles possible:

$B_1 \approx 29°$, $B_2 \approx 180° - 29° = 151°$

B_2 is impossible, since $40° + 151° = 191°$.

We find C using B_1 and the given information $A = 40°$.

$$C = 180° - B_1 - A \approx 180° - 29° - 40° = 111°$$

Use the Law of Sines to find side c.

$$\frac{c}{\sin C} = \frac{a}{\sin A}$$

$$\frac{c}{\sin 111°} = \frac{20}{\sin 40°}$$

$$c = \frac{20\sin 111°}{\sin 40°} \approx 29.0$$

There is one triangle and the solution is B_1 (or B) $\approx 29°$, $C \approx 111°$, and $c \approx 29.0$.

19. The known ratio is $\dfrac{a}{\sin A}$, or $\dfrac{10}{\sin 63°}$.

We use the Law of Sines to find angle C.

$$\frac{a}{\sin A} = \frac{c}{\sin C}$$

$$\frac{10}{\sin 63°} = \frac{8.9}{\sin C}$$

$$10\sin C = 8.9\sin 63°$$

$$\sin C = \frac{8.9\sin 63°}{10}$$

$$\sin C \approx 0.7930$$

There are two angles possible:

$C_1 \approx 52°$, $C_2 \approx 180° - 52° = 128°$

C_2 is impossible, since $63° + 128° = 191°$.

We find B using C_1 and the given information $A = 63°$.

$$B = 180° - C_1 - A \approx 180° - 52° - 63° = 65°$$

Use the Law of Sines to find side b.

$$\frac{b}{\sin B} = \frac{a}{\sin A}$$

$$\frac{b}{\sin 65°} = \frac{10}{\sin 63°}$$

$$b = \frac{10\sin 65°}{\sin 63°} \approx 10.2$$

There is one triangle and the solution is C_1 (or C) $\approx 52°$, $B \approx 65°$, and $b \approx 10.2$.

21. The known ratio is $\dfrac{a}{\sin A}$, or $\dfrac{42.1}{\sin 112°}$.

We use the Law of Sines to find angle C.

$$\frac{a}{\sin A} = \frac{c}{\sin C}$$

$$\frac{42.1}{\sin 112°} = \frac{37}{\sin C}$$

$$42.1\sin C = 37\sin 112°$$

$$\sin C = \frac{37\sin 112°}{42.1}$$

$$\sin C \approx 0.8149$$

There are two angles possible:

$C_1 \approx 55°$, $C_2 \approx 180° - 55° = 125°$

C_2 is impossible, since $112° + 125° = 237°$.
We find B using C_1 and the given
information $A = 112°$.
$B = 180° - C_1 - A \approx 180° - 55° - 112° = 13°$
Use the Law of Sines to find b.

$$\frac{b}{\sin B} = \frac{a}{\sin A}$$

$$\frac{b}{\sin 13°} = \frac{42.1}{\sin 112°}$$

$$b = \frac{42.1 \sin 13°}{\sin 112°} \approx 10.2$$

There is one triangle and the solution is
C_1 (or C) $\approx 55°$, $B \approx 13°$, and $b \approx 10.2$.

23. The known ratio is $\dfrac{a}{\sin A}$, or $\dfrac{10}{\sin 30°}$.
We use the Law of Sines to find angle B.

$$\frac{a}{\sin A} = \frac{b}{\sin B}$$

$$\frac{10}{\sin 30°} = \frac{40}{\sin B}$$

$$10 \sin B = 40 \sin 30°$$

$$\sin B = \frac{40 \sin 30°}{10} = 2$$

Because the sine can never exceed 1, there is
no angle B for which $\sin B = 2$. There is no
triangle with the given measurements.

25. The known ratio is $\dfrac{a}{\sin A}$, or $\dfrac{16}{\sin 60°}$.
We use the Law of Sines to find angle B.

$$\frac{a}{\sin A} = \frac{b}{\sin B}$$

$$\frac{16}{\sin 60°} = \frac{18}{\sin B}$$

$$16 \sin B = 18 \sin 60°$$

$$\sin B = \frac{18 \sin 60°}{16}$$

$$\sin B \approx 0.9743$$

There are two angles possible:
$B_1 \approx 77°$, $B_2 \approx 180° - 77° = 103°$

There are two triangles:
$C_1 = 180° - B_1 - A \approx 180° - 77° - 60° = 43°$
$C_2 = 180° - B_2 - A \approx 180° - 103° - 60° = 17°$
Use the Law of Sines to find c_1 and c_2.

$$\frac{c_1}{\sin C_1} = \frac{a}{\sin A}$$

$$\frac{c_1}{\sin 43°} = \frac{16}{\sin 60°}$$

$$c_1 = \frac{16 \sin 43°}{\sin 60°} \approx 12.6$$

$$\frac{c_2}{\sin C_2} = \frac{a}{\sin A}$$

$$\frac{c_2}{\sin 17°} = \frac{16}{\sin 60°}$$

$$c_2 = \frac{16 \sin 17°}{\sin 60°} \approx 5.4$$

In one triangle, the solution is
$B_1 \approx 77°$, $C_1 \approx 43°$, and $c_1 \approx 12.6$. In the
other triangle, $B_2 \approx 103°$, $C_2 \approx 17°$, and
$c_2 \approx 5.4$.

27. The known ratio is $\dfrac{a}{\sin A}$, or $\dfrac{12}{\sin 37°}$.
We use the Law of Sines to find angle B.

$$\frac{a}{\sin A} = \frac{b}{\sin B}$$

$$\frac{12}{\sin 37°} = \frac{16.1}{\sin B}$$

$$12 \sin B = 16.1 \sin 37°$$

$$\sin B = \frac{16.1 \sin 37°}{12}$$

$$\sin B \approx 0.8074$$

There are two angles possible:
$B_1 \approx 54°$, $B_2 \approx 180° - 54° = 126°$
There are two triangles:
$C_1 = 180° - B_1 - A \approx 180° - 54° - 37° = 89°$
$C_2 = 180° - B_2 - A \approx 180° - 126° - 37° = 17°$
Use the Law of Sines to find c_1 and c_2.

$$\frac{c_1}{\sin C_1} = \frac{a}{\sin A}$$

$$\frac{c_1}{\sin 89°} = \frac{12}{\sin 37°}$$

$$c_1 = \frac{12 \sin 89°}{\sin 37°} \approx 19.9$$

$$\frac{c_2}{\sin C_2} = \frac{a}{\sin A}$$

$$\frac{c_2}{\sin 17°} = \frac{12}{\sin 37°}$$

$$c_2 = \frac{12 \sin 17°}{\sin 37°} \approx 5.8$$

In one triangle, the solution is $B_1 \approx 54°$, $C_1 \approx 89°$, and $c_1 \approx 19.9$. In the other triangle, $B_2 \approx 126°$, $C_2 \approx 17°$, and $c_2 \approx 5.8$.

29. The known ratio is $\frac{a}{\sin A}$, or $\frac{22}{\sin 58°}$.
We use the Law of Sines to find angle C.

$$\frac{a}{\sin A} = \frac{c}{\sin C}$$

$$\frac{22}{\sin 58°} = \frac{24.1}{\sin C}$$

$$22 \sin C = 24.1 \sin 58°$$

$$\sin C = \frac{24.1 \sin 58°}{22}$$

$$\sin C \approx 0.9290$$

There are two angles possible:
$C_1 \approx 68°$, $C_2 \approx 180° - 68° = 112°$
There are two triangles:
$B_1 = 180° - C_1 - A \approx 180° - 68° - 58° = 54°$
$B_2 = 180° - C_2 - A \approx 180° - 112° - 58° = 10°$
We use the Law of Sines to find b_1 and b_2.

$$\frac{b_1}{\sin B_1} = \frac{a}{\sin A}$$

$$\frac{b_1}{\sin 54°} = \frac{22}{\sin 58°}$$

$$b_1 = \frac{22 \sin 54°}{\sin 58°} \approx 21.0$$

$$\frac{b_2}{\sin B_2} = \frac{a}{\sin A}$$

$$\frac{b_2}{\sin 10°} = \frac{22}{\sin 58°}$$

$$b_2 = \frac{22 \sin 10°}{\sin 58°} \approx 4.5$$

In one triangle, the solution is $C_1 \approx 68°$, $B_1 \approx 54°$, and $b_1 \approx 21.0$. In the other triangle, $C_2 \approx 112°$, $B_2 \approx 10°$, and $b_2 \approx 4.5$.

31. The known ratio is $\frac{a}{\sin A}$, or $\frac{9.3}{\sin 18°}$.
We use the Law of Sines to find angle B.

$$\frac{a}{\sin A} = \frac{b}{\sin B}$$

$$\frac{9.3}{\sin 18°} = \frac{41}{\sin B}$$

$$9.3 \sin B = 41 \sin 18°$$

$$\sin B = \frac{41 \sin 18°}{9.3} \approx 1.36$$

Because the sine can never exceed 1, there is no angle B for which $\sin B = 1.36$. There is no triangle with the given measurements.

33. Area
$$= \frac{1}{2} bc \sin A = \frac{1}{2}(20)(40)(\sin 48°) \approx 297$$
The area of the triangle is approximately 297 square feet.

35. Area $= \frac{1}{2} ac \sin B = \frac{1}{2}(3)(6)(\sin 36°) \approx 5$
The area of the triangle is approximately 5 square yards.

37. Area $= \frac{1}{2}ab\sin C = \frac{1}{2}(4)(6)(\sin 124°) \approx 10$

The area of the triangle is approximately 10 square meters.

39.

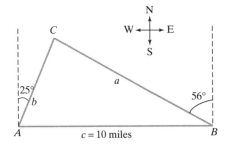

Using a north-south line, the interior angles are found as follows:
$A = 90° - 25° = 65°$

$B = 90° - 56° = 34°$

Find angle C using a 180° angle sum in the triangle.
$C = 180° - A - B = 180° - 65° - 34° = 81°$

The ratio $\dfrac{c}{\sin C}$, or $\dfrac{10}{\sin 81°}$, is now known.
We use this ratio and the Law of Sines to find b and a.

$$\frac{b}{\sin B} = \frac{c}{\sin C}$$

$$\frac{b}{\sin 34°} = \frac{10}{\sin 81°}$$

$$b = \frac{10\sin 34°}{\sin 81°} \approx 6$$

Station A is about 6 miles from the fire.

$$\frac{a}{\sin A} = \frac{c}{\sin C}$$

$$\frac{a}{\sin 65°} = \frac{10}{\sin 81°}$$

$$a = \frac{10\sin 65°}{\sin 81°} \approx 9$$

Station B is about 9 miles from the fire.

41.

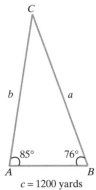

$c = 1200$ yards

Using the figure,
$C = 180° - A - B = 180° - 85° - 76° = 19°$

The ratio $\dfrac{c}{\sin C}$, or $\dfrac{1200}{\sin 19°}$, is now known.
We use this ratio and the Law of Sines to find a and b.

$$\frac{a}{\sin A} = \frac{c}{\sin C}$$

$$\frac{a}{\sin 85°} = \frac{1200}{\sin 19°}$$

$$a = \frac{1200\sin 85°}{\sin 19°} \approx 3672$$

$$\frac{b}{\sin B} = \frac{c}{\sin C}$$

$$\frac{b}{\sin 76°} = \frac{1200}{\sin 19°}$$

$$b = \frac{1200\sin 76°}{\sin 19°} \approx 3576$$

The platform is about 3672 yards from one end of the beach and 3576 yards from the other.

43. According to the figure,
$C = 180° - A - B = 180° - 84.7° - 50° = 45.3°$

The ratio $\dfrac{c}{\sin C}$, or $\dfrac{171}{\sin 45.3°}$, is now known. We use this ratio and the Law of Sines to find b.

$$\frac{b}{\sin B} = \frac{c}{\sin C}$$

$$\frac{b}{\sin 50°} = \frac{171}{\sin 45.3°}$$

$$b = \frac{171\sin 50°}{\sin 45.3°} \approx 184$$

The distance is about 184 feet.

45. The ratio $\dfrac{b}{\sin B}$, or $\dfrac{562}{\sin 85.3°}$, is known.

We use this ratio, the figure, and the Law of Sines to find c.

$$\frac{c}{\sin C} = \frac{b}{\sin B}$$

$$\frac{c}{\sin 5.7°} = \frac{562}{\sin 85.3°}$$

$$c = \frac{562\sin 5.7°}{\sin 85.3°} \approx 56$$

The toss was about 56 feet.

47.

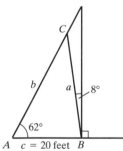

$$A \quad c = 20 \text{ feet} \quad B$$

Using the figure,
$B = 90° - 8° = 82°$

$C = 180° - A - B = 180° - 62° - 82° = 36°$

The ratio $\dfrac{c}{\sin C}$, or $\dfrac{20}{\sin 36°}$, is now known.

We use this ratio and the Law of Sines to find a.

$$\frac{a}{\sin A} = \frac{c}{\sin C}$$

$$\frac{a}{\sin 62°} = \frac{20}{\sin 36°}$$

$$a = \frac{20\sin 62°}{\sin 36°} \approx 30$$

The length of the pole is about 30 feet.

49. a. Using the figure and the measurements shown,
$B = 180° - 44° = 136°$

$C = 180° - B - A = 180° - 136° - 37° = 7°$

The ratio $\dfrac{c}{\sin C}$, or $\dfrac{100}{\sin 7°}$, is now known. We use this ratio and the Law of Sines to find a.

$$\frac{a}{\sin A} = \frac{c}{\sin C}$$

$$\frac{a}{\sin 37°} = \frac{100}{\sin 7°}$$

$$a = \frac{100\sin 37°}{\sin 7°} \approx 494$$

To the nearest foot, $a = 494$ feet.

b. Let $a = 494$ be the hypotenuse of the right triangle. Then if h represents the height of the tree,

$$\frac{h}{\sin 44°} = \frac{494}{\sin 90°}$$

$$h = \frac{494 \sin 44°}{\sin 90°} \approx 343$$

A typical redwood tree is about 343 feet.

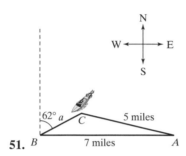

51.

Using the figure,
$B = 90° - 62° = 28°$

The known ratio is $\dfrac{b}{\sin B}$, or $\dfrac{5}{\sin 28°}$.

We use the Law of Sines to find angle C.

$$\frac{b}{\sin B} = \frac{c}{\sin C}$$

$$\frac{5}{\sin 28°} = \frac{7}{\sin C}$$

$$5 \sin C = 7 \sin 28°$$

$$\sin C = \frac{7 \sin 28°}{5} \approx 0.6573$$

There are two angles possible:
$C_1 \approx 41°,\; C_2 \approx 180° - 41° = 139°$
There are two triangles:
$A_1 = 180° - C_1 - B \approx 180° - 41° - 28° = 111°$
$A_2 = 180° - C_2 - B \approx 180° - 139° - 28° = 13°$
We use the Law of Sines to find a_1 and a_2.

$$\frac{a_1}{\sin A_1} = \frac{b}{\sin B}$$

$$\frac{a_1}{\sin 111°} = \frac{5}{\sin 28°}$$

$$a_1 = \frac{5 \sin 111°}{\sin 28°} \approx 9.9$$

$$\frac{a_2}{\sin A_2} = \frac{b}{\sin B}$$

$$\frac{a_2}{\sin 13°} = \frac{5}{\sin 28°}$$

$$a_2 = \frac{5 \sin 13°}{\sin 28°} \approx 2.4$$

The boat is either 9.9 miles or 2.4 miles from lighthouse B, to the nearest tenth of a mile.

53.–61. Answers may vary.

63. Yes. Explanations may vary.

65.

Using the figure,
$A = 180° - 150° = 30°$
Using the Law of Sines we have,

$$\frac{d}{\sin A} = \frac{36}{\sin 90°}$$

$$\frac{d}{\sin 30°} = \frac{36}{\sin 90°}$$

$$d = \frac{36 \sin 30°}{\sin 90°} = 18$$

$CC' = 18 + 5 + 18 = 41$
The wingspan CC' is 41 feet.

Section 2.2

Check Point Exercises

1. Apply the three-step procedure for solving a SAS triangle. Use the Law of Cosines to find the side opposite the given angle. Thus, we will find a.

$$a^2 = b^2 + c^2 - 2bc \cos A$$

$$a^2 = 7^2 + 8^2 - 2(7)(8) \cos 120°$$

$$= 49 + 64 - 112(-0.5)$$

$$= 169$$

$$a = \sqrt{169} = 13$$

Use the Law of Sines to find the angle opposite the shorter of the two sides. Thus, we will find acute angle B.

$$\frac{b}{\sin B} = \frac{a}{\sin A}$$

$$\frac{7}{\sin B} = \frac{13}{\sin 120°}$$

$$13 \sin B = 7 \sin 120°$$

$$\sin B = \frac{7 \sin 120°}{13} \approx 0.4663$$

$$B \approx 28°$$

Find the third angle.

$$C = 180° - A - B \approx 180° - 120° - 28° = 32°$$

The solution is
$a = 13, B \approx 28°,$ and $C \approx 32°$.

2. Apply the three-step procedure for solving a SSS triangle. Use the Law of Cosines to find the angle opposite the longest side. Thus, we will find angle B.

$$b^2 = a^2 + c^2 - 2ac \cos B$$

$$2ac \cos B = a^2 + c^2 - b^2$$

$$\cos B = \frac{a^2 + c^2 - b^2}{2ac}$$

$$\cos B = \frac{8^2 + 5^2 - 10^2}{2 \cdot 8 \cdot 5} = -\frac{11}{80}$$

$$\cos^{-1}\left(\frac{11}{80}\right) \approx 82.1°$$

B is obtuse, since $\cos B$ is negative.
$B \approx 180° - 82.1° = 97.9°$
Use the Law of Sines to find either of the

two remaining acute angles. We will find angle A.

$$\frac{a}{\sin A} = \frac{b}{\sin B}$$

$$\frac{8}{\sin A} = \frac{10}{\sin 97.9°}$$

$$10 \sin A = 8 \sin 97.9°$$

$$\sin A = \frac{8 \sin 97.9°}{10} \approx 0.7924$$

$$A \approx 52.4°$$

Find the third angle.
$$C = 180° - A - B \approx 180° - 52.4° - 97.9°$$

$$= 29.7°$$

The solution is $B \approx 97.9°, A \approx 52.4°,$ and $C \approx 29.7°$

3. The plane flying 400 miles per hour travels $400 \cdot 2 = 800$ miles in 2 hours. Similarly, the other plane travels 700 miles.

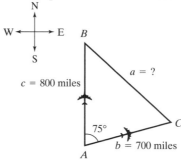

Use the figure and the Law of Cosines to find a in this SAS situation.

$$a^2 = b^2 + c^2 - 2bc \cos A$$

$$a^2 = 700^2 + 800^2 - 2(700)(800) \cos 75°$$

$$\approx 840,123$$

$$a \approx \sqrt{840,123} \approx 917$$

After 2 hours, the planes are approximately 917 miles apart.

4. Begin by calculating one-half the perimeter:
$$s = \frac{1}{2}(a + b + c) = \frac{1}{2}(6 + 16 + 18) = 20$$
Use Heron's formula to find the area.

$$\text{Area} = \sqrt{s(s-a)(s-b)(s-c)}$$
$$= \sqrt{20(20-6)(20-16)(20-18)}$$
$$= \sqrt{2240} \approx 47$$

The area of the triangle is approximately 47 square meters.

Exercise Set 2.2

1. Apply the three-step procedure for solving a SAS triangle. Use the Law of Cosines to find the side opposite the given angle. Thus, we will find a.

$$a^2 = b^2 + c^2 - 2bc \cos A$$
$$a^2 = 4^2 + 8^2 - 2(4)(8) \cos 46°$$
$$a^2 = 16 + 64 - 64(\cos 46°)$$
$$a^2 \approx 35.54$$
$$a \approx \sqrt{35.54} \approx 6.0$$

Use the Law of Sines to find the angle opposite the shorter of the two given sides. Thus, we will find acute angle B.

$$\frac{b}{\sin B} = \frac{a}{\sin A}$$
$$\frac{4}{\sin B} = \frac{\sqrt{35.54}}{\sin 46°}$$
$$\sqrt{35.54} \sin B = 4 \sin 46°$$
$$\sin B = \frac{4 \sin 46°}{\sqrt{35.54}} \approx 0.4827$$
$$B \approx 29°$$

Find the third angle.
$$C = 180° - A - B \approx 180° - 46° - 29° = 105°$$
The solution is $a \approx 6.0, B \approx 29°,$ and $C \approx 105°$.

3. Apply the three-step procedure for solving a SAS triangle. Use the Law of Cosines to find the side opposite the given angle. Thus, we will find c.

$$c^2 = a^2 + b^2 - 2ab \cos C$$
$$c^2 = 6^2 + 4^2 - 2(6)(4) \cos 96°$$
$$c^2 = 36 + 16 - 48(\cos 96°)$$
$$c^2 \approx 57.02$$
$$c \approx \sqrt{57.02} \approx 7.6$$

Use the Law of Sines to find the angle opposite the shorter of the two given sides. Thus, we will find acute angle B.

$$\frac{b}{\sin B} = \frac{c}{\sin C}$$
$$\frac{4}{\sin B} = \frac{\sqrt{57.02}}{\sin 96°}$$
$$\sqrt{57.02} \sin B = 4 \sin 96°$$
$$\sin B = \frac{4 \sin 96°}{\sqrt{57.02}} \approx 0.5268$$
$$B \approx 32°$$

Find the third angle.
$$A = 180° - B - C \approx 180° - 32° - 96° = 52°$$
The solution is $c \approx 7.6, A \approx 52°,$ and $B \approx 32°$.

5. Apply the three-step procedure for solving a SSS triangle. Use the Law of Cosines to find the angle opposite the longest side. Since two sides have length 8, we can begin by finding angle B or C.

$$b^2 = a^2 + c^2 - 2ac \cos B$$
$$\cos B = \frac{a^2 + c^2 - b^2}{2ac}$$
$$\cos B = \frac{6^2 + 8^2 - 8^2}{2 \cdot 6 \cdot 8} = \frac{36}{96} = \frac{3}{8}$$
$$B \approx 68°$$

Use the Law of Sines to find either of the two remaining acute angles. We will find angle A.

$$\frac{a}{\sin A} = \frac{b}{\sin B}$$

$$\frac{6}{\sin A} = \frac{8}{\sin 68°}$$

$$8\sin A = 6\sin 68°$$

$$\sin A = \frac{6\sin 68°}{8} \approx 0.6954$$

$$A \approx 44°$$

Find the third angle.

$$C = 180° - B - A \approx 180° - 68° - 44° = 68°$$

The solution is $A \approx 44°, B \approx 68°,$ and $C \approx 68°$.

7. Apply the three-step procedure for solving a SSS triangle. Use the Law of Cosines to find the angle opposite the longest side. Thus, we will find angle A

$$a^2 = b^2 + c^2 - 2bc\cos A$$

$$\cos A = \frac{b^2 + c^2 - a^2}{2bc}$$

$$\cos A = \frac{4^2 + 3^2 - 6^2}{2 \cdot 4 \cdot 3} = -\frac{11}{24}$$

A is obtuse, since $\cos A$ is negative.

$$\cos^{-1}\left(\frac{11}{24}\right) \approx 63°$$

$$A \approx 180° - 63° = 117°$$

Use the Law of Sines to find either of the two remaining acute angles. We will find angle B.

$$\frac{b}{\sin B} = \frac{a}{\sin A}$$

$$\frac{4}{\sin B} = \frac{6}{\sin 117°}$$

$$6\sin B = 4\sin 117°$$

$$\sin B = \frac{4\sin 117°}{6} \approx 0.5940$$

$$B \approx 36°$$

Find the third angle.

$$C = 180° - B - A \approx 180° - 36° - 117° = 27°$$

The solution is $A \approx 117°, B \approx 36°,$ and $C \approx 27°$.

9. Apply the three-step procedure for solving a SAS triangle. Use the Law of Cosines to find the side opposite the given angle. Thus, we will find c.

$$c^2 = a^2 + b^2 - 2ab\cos C$$

$$c^2 = 5^2 + 7^2 - 2(5)(7)\cos 42°$$

$$c^2 = 25 + 49 - 70(\cos 42°)$$

$$c^2 \approx 21.98$$

$$c \approx \sqrt{21.98} \approx 4.7$$

Use the Law of Sines to find the angle opposite the shorter of the two given sides. Thus, we will find acute angle A.

$$\frac{a}{\sin A} = \frac{c}{\sin C}$$

$$\frac{5}{\sin A} = \frac{\sqrt{21.98}}{\sin 42°}$$

$$\sqrt{21.98}\sin A = 5\sin 42°$$

$$\sin A = \frac{5\sin 42°}{\sqrt{21.98}} \approx 0.7136$$

$$A \approx 46°$$

Find the third angle.

$$B = 180° - C - A \approx 180° - 42° - 46° = 92°$$

The solution is $c \approx 4.7, A \approx 46°,$ and $B \approx 92°$.

11. Apply the three-step procedure for solving a SAS triangle. Use the Law of Cosines to find the side opposite the given angle. Thus, we will find a.

$$a^2 = b^2 + c^2 - 2bc\cos A$$

$$a^2 = 5^2 + 3^2 - 2(5)(3)\cos 102°$$

$$a^2 = 25 + 9 - 30(\cos 102°)$$

$$a^2 \approx 40.24$$

$$a \approx \sqrt{40.24} \approx 6.3$$

Use the Law of Sines to find the angle opposite the shorter of the two given sides. Thus, we will find acute angle C.

$$\frac{c}{\sin C} = \frac{a}{\sin A}$$

$$\frac{3}{\sin C} = \frac{\sqrt{40.24}}{\sin 102°}$$

$$\sqrt{40.24}\,\sin C = 3\sin 102°$$

$$\sin C = \frac{3\sin 102°}{\sqrt{40.24}} \approx 0.4626$$

$$C \approx 28°$$

Find the third angle.
$$B = 180° - C - A \approx 180° - 28° - 102° = 50°$$
The solution is $a \approx 6.3, C \approx 28°,$ and
$B \approx 50°.$

13. Apply the three-step procedure for solving a SAS triangle. Use the Law of Cosines to find the side opposite the given angle. Thus, we will find b.

$$b^2 = a^2 + c^2 - 2ac\cos B$$

$$b^2 = 6^2 + 5^2 - 2(6)(5)\cos 50°$$

$$b^2 = 36 + 25 - 60(\cos 50°)$$

$$b^2 \approx 22.43$$

$$b \approx \sqrt{22.43} \approx 4.7$$

Use the Law of Sines to find the angle opposite the shorter of the two given sides. Thus, we will find acute angle C.

$$\frac{c}{\sin C} = \frac{b}{\sin B}$$

$$\frac{5}{\sin C} = \frac{\sqrt{22.43}}{\sin 50°}$$

$$\sqrt{22.43}\,\sin C = 5\sin 50°$$

$$\sin C = \frac{5\sin 50°}{\sqrt{22.43}} \approx 0.8087$$

$$C \approx 54°$$

Find the third angle.
$$A = 180° - C - B \approx 180° - 54° - 50° = 76°$$
The solution is $b \approx 4.7, C \approx 54°,$ and
$A \approx 76°.$

15. Apply the three-step procedure for solving a SAS triangle. Use the Law of Cosines to find

the side opposite the given angle. Thus, we will find b.

$$b^2 = a^2 + c^2 - 2ac\cos 90°$$

$$b^2 = 5^2 + 2^2 - 2(5)(2)\cos 90°$$

$$b^2 = 25 + 4 - 20\cos 90°$$

$$b^2 = 29$$

$$b = \sqrt{29} \approx 5.4$$

(use exact value of b from previous step) Use the Law of Sines to find the angle opposite the shorter of the two given sides. Thus, we will find acute angle C.

$$\frac{c}{\sin C} = \frac{b}{\sin B}$$

$$\frac{2}{\sin C} = \frac{\sqrt{29}}{\sin 90°}$$

$$\sqrt{29}\,\sin C = 2\sin 90°$$

$$\sin C = \frac{2\sin 90°}{\sqrt{29}} \approx 0.3714$$

$$C \approx 22°$$

Find the third angle.
$$A = 180° - C - B \approx 180° - 22° - 90° = 68°$$
The solution is $b \approx 5.4, C \approx 22°,$ and $A \approx 68°.$

17. Apply the three-step procedure for solving a SSS triangle. Use the Law of Cosines to find the angle opposite the longest side. Thus, we will find C.

$$c^2 = a^2 + b^2 - 2ab\cos C$$

$$\cos C = \frac{a^2 + b^2 - c^2}{2ab}$$

$$\cos C = \frac{5^2 + 7^2 - 10^2}{2\cdot 5\cdot 7} = -\frac{13}{35}$$

C is obtuse, since $\cos C$ is negative.

$$\cos^{-1}\left(\frac{13}{35}\right) \approx 68°$$

$$C \approx 180° - 68° = 112°$$

Use the Law of Sines to find either of the two remaining angles. We will find angle A.

$$\frac{a}{\sin A} = \frac{c}{\sin C}$$

$$\frac{5}{\sin A} = \frac{10}{\sin 112°}$$

$$10\sin A = 5\sin 112°$$

$$\sin A = \frac{5\sin 112°}{10} \approx 0.4636$$

$$A \approx 28°$$

Find the third angle.

$$B = 180° - C - A \approx 180° - 112° - 28° = 40°$$

The solution is $C \approx 112°, A \approx 28°,$ and $B \approx 40°$.

19. Apply the three-step procedure for solving a SSS triangle. Use the Law of Cosines to find the angle opposite the longest side. Thus, we will find B.

$$b^2 = a^2 + c^2 - 2ac\cos B$$

$$\cos B = \frac{a^2 + c^2 - b^2}{2ac}$$

$$\cos B = \frac{3^2 + 8^2 - 9^2}{2\cdot 3\cdot 8} = -\frac{1}{6}$$

B is obtuse, since $\cos B$ is negative.

$$\cos^{-1}\left(\frac{1}{6}\right) \approx 80°$$

$$B \approx 180° - 80° = 100°$$

Use the Law of Sines to find either of the two remaining angles. We will find angle A.

$$\frac{a}{\sin A} = \frac{b}{\sin B}$$

$$\frac{3}{\sin A} = \frac{9}{\sin 100°}$$

$$9\sin A = 3\sin 100°$$

$$\sin A = \frac{3\sin 100°}{9} \approx 0.3283$$

$$A \approx 19°$$

Find the third angle.

$$C = 180° - B - A \approx 180° - 100° - 19° = 61°$$

The solution is $B \approx 100°, A \approx 19°,$ and $C \approx 61°$.

21. Apply the three-step procedure for solving a SSS triangle. Use the Law of Cosines to find any of the three angles, since each side has the same measure.

$$a^2 = b^2 + c^2 - 2bc\cos A$$

$$\cos A = \frac{b^2 + c^2 - a^2}{2bc}$$

$$\cos A = \frac{3^2 + 3^2 - 3^2}{2\cdot 3\cdot 3} = \frac{1}{2}$$

$$A = 60°$$

Use the Law of Sines to find either of the two remaining angles. We will find angle B.

$$\frac{b}{\sin B} = \frac{a}{\sin A}$$

$$\frac{3}{\sin B} = \frac{3}{\sin 60°}$$

$$3\sin B = 3\sin 60°$$

$$\sin B = \sin 60°$$

$$B = 60°$$

Find the third angle.

$$C = 180° - A - B = 180° - 60° - 60° = 60°$$

The solution is $A = 60°, B = 60°,$ and $C = 60°$.

23. Apply the three-step procedure for solving a SSS triangle. Use the Law of Cosines to find the angle opposite the longest side. Thus, we will find A.

$$a^2 = b^2 + c^2 - 2bc\cos A$$

$$\cos A = \frac{b^2 + c^2 - a^2}{2bc}$$

$$\cos A = \frac{22^2 + 50^2 - 73^2}{2\cdot 22\cdot 50} = -\frac{469}{440}$$

Since $\cos A$ must be between -1 and 1, no such triangle exists.

25. $s = \dfrac{1}{2}(a + b + c) = \dfrac{1}{2}(4 + 4 + 2) = 5$

$$\text{Area} = \sqrt{s(s-a)(s-b)(s-c)}$$

$$= \sqrt{5(5-4)(5-4)(5-2)}$$

$$= \sqrt{15} \approx 4$$

The area of the triangle is approximately 4 square feet.

27. $s = \dfrac{1}{2}(a+b+c) = \dfrac{1}{2}(14+12+4) = 15$

Area $= \sqrt{s(s-a)(s-b)(s-c)}$

$\quad = \sqrt{15(15-14)(15-12)(15-4)}$

$\quad = \sqrt{495} \approx 22$

The area of the triangle is approximately 22 square meters.

29. $s = \dfrac{1}{2}(a+b+c) = \dfrac{1}{2}(11+9+7) = 13.5$

Area $= \sqrt{s(s-a)(s-b)(s-c)}$

$\quad = \sqrt{13.5(13.5-11)(13.5-9)(13.5-7)}$

$\quad = \sqrt{987.1875} \approx 31$

The area of the triangle is approximately 31 square yards.

31. Let b = the distance between the ships after three hours.
After three hours, the ship traveling 14 miles per hour has gone $3 \cdot 14$ or 42 miles. Similarly, the ship traveling 10 miles per hour has gone 30 miles.

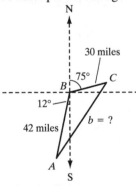

Using the figure,
$B = 180° - 75° + 12° = 117°$

$b^2 = a^2 + c^2 - 2ac \cos B$

$b^2 = 30^2 + 42^2 - 2(30)(42) \cos 117° \approx 3808$

$b \approx 61.7$

After three hours, the ships will be about 61.7 miles apart.

33. Let b = the distance across the lake.

$b^2 = a^2 + c^2 - 2ac \cos B$

$b^2 = 160^2 + 140^2 - 2(160)(140) \cos 80°$

$\quad \approx 37,421$

$b \approx \sqrt{37,421} \approx 193$

The distance across the lake is about 193 yards.

35. Assume that Island B is due east of Island A. Let A = angle at Island A.

$a^2 = b^2 + c^2 - 2bc \cos A$

$\cos A = \dfrac{b^2 + c^2 - a^2}{2bc}$

$\cos A = \dfrac{5^2 + 6^2 - 7^2}{2 \cdot 5 \cdot 6} = \dfrac{1}{5}$

$A \approx 78°$

Since $90° - 78° = 12°$, you should navigate on a bearing of N12°E.

37. a. Using the figure,
$B = 90° - 40° = 50°$

$b^2 = a^2 + c^2 - 2ac \cos B$

$b^2 = 13.5^2 + 25^2 - 2(13.5)(25) \cos 50°$

$\quad \approx 373$

$b \approx \sqrt{373} \approx 19.3$

You are about 19.3 miles from the pier.

b. $\dfrac{a}{\sin A} = \dfrac{b}{\sin B}$

$\dfrac{13.5}{\sin A} = \dfrac{\sqrt{373}}{\sin 50°}$

$\sqrt{373} \sin A = 13.5 \sin 50°$

$\sin A = \dfrac{13.5 \sin 50°}{\sqrt{373}} \approx 0.5355$

$A \approx 32°$

Since $90° - 32° = 58°$, the original bearing could have been S58°E.

39.

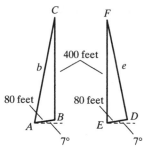

In the figure, b = the guy wire anchored downhill, e = the guy wire anchored uphill.
$$B = 90° + 7° = 97°$$
$$E = 90° - 7° = 83°$$
$$b^2 = a^2 + c^2 - 2ac \cos B$$
$$b^2 = 400^2 + 80^2 - 2(400)(80) \cos 97°$$
$$\approx 174,200$$
$$b \approx \sqrt{174,200} \approx 417.4$$
$$e^2 = d^2 + f^2 - 2df \cos E$$
$$e^2 = 400^2 + 80^2 - 2(400)(80) \cos 83°$$
$$\approx 158,600$$
$$e \approx \sqrt{158.600} \approx 398.2$$
The guy wire anchored downhill is about 417.4 feet long. The one anchored uphill is about 398.2 feet long.

41.

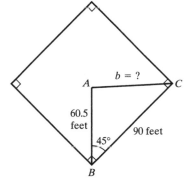

Using the figure,
$$B = 90° \div 2 = 45° \ \ \text{(using symmetry)}$$
$$b^2 = a^2 + c^2 - 2ac \cos B$$
$$b^2 = 90^2 + 60.5^2 - 2(90)(60.5) \cos 45°$$
$$\approx 4060$$
$$b \approx \sqrt{4060} \approx 63.7$$
It is about 63.7 feet from the pitcher's mound to first base.

43. First, find the area using Heron's formula.
$$s = \frac{1}{2}(a + b + c) = \frac{1}{2}(240 + 300 + 420) = 480$$
Area
$$= \sqrt{s(s-a)(s-b)(s-c)}$$
$$= \sqrt{480(480 - 240)(480 - 300)(480 - 420)}$$
$$= \sqrt{1,244,160,000} \approx 35,272.65$$
Now multiply by the price per square foot.
$$(35,272.65)(3.50) \approx 123,454$$
The cost is $123,454, to the nearest dollar.

45.–51. Answers may vary.

53. Let c = distance from A to B,
      a = distance from B to C,
      b = distance from C to A.
Using the distance formula,
$$c = \sqrt{(4-2)^2 + (-3-1)^2} = \sqrt{20} \approx 4.5$$
$$a = \sqrt{(2-(-2))^2 + (1-4)^2} = \sqrt{25} = 5$$
$$b = \sqrt{(-2-4)^2 + (4-(-3))^2} = \sqrt{85} \approx 9.2$$
Since b is the longest side, B is the largest angle.
$$b^2 = a^2 + c^2 - 2ac \cos B$$
$$\cos B = \frac{a^2 + c^2 - b^2}{2ac}$$
$$\cos B = \frac{5^2 + \left(\sqrt{20}\right)^2 - \left(\sqrt{85}\right)^2}{2 \cdot 5 \cdot \sqrt{20}} = -\frac{4}{\sqrt{20}}$$
B is obtuse, since $\cos B$ is negative.

$$\cos^{-1}\left(\frac{4}{\sqrt{20}}\right) \approx 26.6°$$

$B \approx 180° - 26.6° = 153.4°$
The largest angle is about 153.4°.

Section 2.3

Check Point Exercises

1. **a.** $(r,\ \theta) = (3, 315°)$

   Because 315° is a positive angle, draw
   $\theta = 315°$ counterclockwise from the
   polar axis. Because $r > 0$, plot the point
   by going out 3 units on the terminal side
   of θ.

   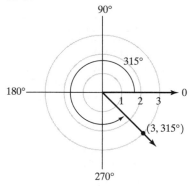

   b. $(r,\ \theta) = (-2, \pi)$

   Because π is a positive angle, draw
   $\theta = \pi$ counterclockwise from the polar
   axis. Because $r < 0$, plot the point by
   going out 2 units along the ray opposite

   the terminal side of θ.

   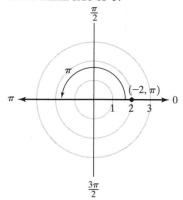

   c. $(r,\ \theta) = \left(-1, -\dfrac{\pi}{2}\right)$

   Because $-\dfrac{\pi}{2}$ is a negative angle, draw

   $\theta = -\dfrac{\pi}{2}$ clockwise from the polar axis.

   Because $r < 0$, plot the point by going
   out one unit along the ray opposite the
   terminal side of θ.

   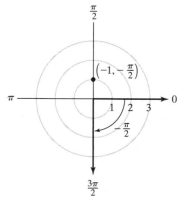

2. a. Add 2π to the angle and do not change r.

$$\left(5, \frac{\pi}{4}\right) = \left(5, \frac{\pi}{4} + 2\pi\right) = \left(5, \frac{\pi}{4} + \frac{8\pi}{4}\right)$$

$$= \left(5, \frac{9\pi}{4}\right)$$

b. Add π to the angle and replace r by $-r$.

$$\left(5, \frac{\pi}{4}\right) = \left(-5, \frac{\pi}{4} + \pi\right) = \left(-5, \frac{\pi}{4} + \frac{4\pi}{4}\right)$$

$$= \left(-5, \frac{5\pi}{4}\right)$$

c. Subtract 2π from the angle and do not change r.

$$\left(5, \frac{\pi}{4}\right) = \left(5, \frac{\pi}{4} - 2\pi\right) = \left(5, \frac{\pi}{4} - \frac{8\pi}{4}\right)$$

$$= \left(5, -\frac{7\pi}{4}\right)$$

3. a. $(r, \theta) = (3, \pi)$
$x = r \cos\theta = 3\cos\pi = 3(-1) = -3$
$y = r \sin\theta = 3\sin\pi = 3(0) = 0$
The rectangular coordinates of $(3, \pi)$ are $(-3, 0)$.

b. $(r, \theta) = \left(-10, \dfrac{\pi}{6}\right)$

$$x = r \cos\theta = -10\cos\frac{\pi}{6} = -10\left(\frac{\sqrt{3}}{2}\right)$$

$$= -5\sqrt{3}$$

$$y = r \sin\theta = -10\sin\frac{\pi}{6} = -10\left(\frac{1}{2}\right) = -5$$

The rectangular coordinates of

$\left(-10, \dfrac{\pi}{6}\right)$ are $\left(-5\sqrt{3}, -5\right)$.

4.

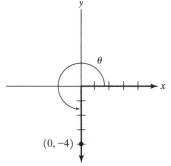

$$r = \sqrt{x^2 + y^2} = \sqrt{1^2 + \left(-\sqrt{3}\right)^2}$$

$$= \sqrt{1+3} = \sqrt{4} = 2$$

$$\tan\theta = \frac{y}{x} = \frac{-\sqrt{3}}{1} = -\sqrt{3}$$

Because $\tan\dfrac{\pi}{3} = \sqrt{3}$ and θ lies in quadrant

IV, $\theta = 2\pi - \dfrac{\pi}{3} = \dfrac{6\pi}{3} - \dfrac{\pi}{3} = \dfrac{5\pi}{3}$

The polar coordinates of $\left(1, -\sqrt{3}\right)$ are

$$(r, \theta) = \left(2, \frac{5\pi}{3}\right)$$

5.

$$r = \sqrt{x^2 + y^2} = \sqrt{(0)^2 + (-4)^2} = \sqrt{16} = 4$$

The point $(0, -4)$ is on the negative y-axis.

Thus, $\theta = \dfrac{3\pi}{2}$. Polar coordinates of $(0, -4)$

are $\left(4, \dfrac{3\pi}{2}\right)$.

6.
$$3x - y = 6$$
$$3r\cos\theta - r\sin\theta = 6$$
$$r(3\cos\theta - \sin\theta) = 6$$
$$r = \frac{6}{3\cos\theta - \sin\theta}$$

7. a. Use $r^2 = x^2 + y^2$ to convert to a rectangular equation.
$$r = 4$$
$$r^2 = 16$$
$$x^2 + y^2 = 16$$
The rectangular equation for $r = 4$ is
$$x^2 + y^2 = 16.$$

b. Use $\tan\theta = \dfrac{y}{x}$ to convert to a rectangular equation in x and y.
$$\theta = \frac{3\pi}{4}$$
$$\tan\theta = \tan\frac{3\pi}{4}$$
$$\tan\theta = -1$$
$$\frac{y}{x} = -1$$
$$y = -x$$
The rectangular equation for $\theta = \dfrac{3\pi}{4}$ is
$$y = -x.$$

c. Use $r\cos\theta = x$ to convert to a rectangular equation. Express the secant in terms of cosine.
$$r = \sec\theta$$
$$r = \frac{1}{\cos\theta}$$
$$r\cos\theta = 1$$
$$x = 1$$
The rectangular equation for $r = \sec\theta$ is $x = 1$.

Exercise Set 2.3

1. 225° is in the third quadrant.
C

3. $\dfrac{5\pi}{4} = 225°$ is in the third quadrant. Since r is negative, the point lies along the ray opposite the terminal side of θ, in the first quadrant.
A

5. $\pi = 180°$ lies on the negative x-axis.
B

7. $-135°$ is measured clockwise 135° from the positive x-axis. The point lies in the third quadrant.
C

9. $-\dfrac{3\pi}{4} = -135°$ is measured clockwise 135° from the positive x-axis. Since r is negative, the point lies along the ray opposite the terminal side of θ, in the first quadrant.
A

11. Draw $\theta = 45°$ counterclockwise, since θ is positive, from the polar axis. Go out 2 units on the terminal side of θ, since $r > 0$.

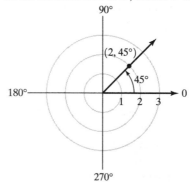

13. Draw $\theta = 90°$ counterclockwise, since θ is positive, from the polar axis. Go out 3 units on the terminal side of θ, since $r > 0$.

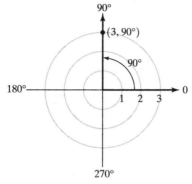

of θ, since $r < 0$.

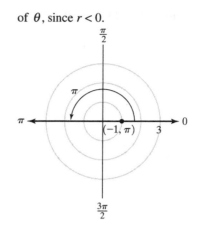

15. Draw $\theta = \dfrac{4\pi}{3} = 240°$ counterclockwise,

since θ is positive, from polar axis. Go out 3 units on the terminal side of θ, since $r > 0$.

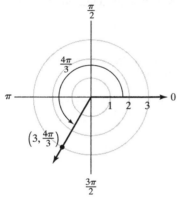

17. Draw $\theta = \pi = 180°$ counterclockwise, since θ is positive, from the polar axis. Go one unit out on the ray opposite the terminal side

19. Draw $\theta = -\dfrac{\pi}{2} = -90°$ clockwise, since θ is positive, from the polar axis. Go 2 units out on the ray opposite the terminal side of θ, since $r < 0$.

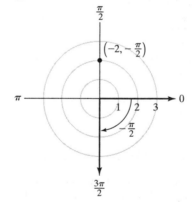

21. Draw $\theta = \dfrac{\pi}{6} = 30°$ counterclockwise, since θ is positive, from the polar axis. Go 5 units

out on the terminal side of θ, since $r > 0$.

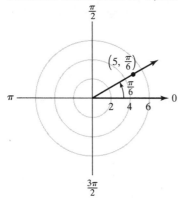

$r > 0$.

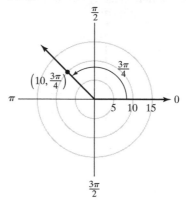

a. Add 2π to the angle and do not change r.

$$\left(5, \frac{\pi}{6}\right) = \left(5, \frac{\pi}{6} + 2\pi\right) = \left(5, \frac{13\pi}{6}\right)$$

b. Add π to the angle and replace r by $-r$.

$$\left(5, \frac{\pi}{6}\right) = \left(-5, \frac{\pi}{6} + \pi\right) = \left(-5, \frac{7\pi}{6}\right)$$

c. Subtract 2π from the angle and do not change r.

$$\left(5, \frac{\pi}{6}\right) = \left(5, \frac{\pi}{6} - 2\pi\right) = \left(5, -\frac{11\pi}{6}\right)$$

a. Add 2π to the angle and do not change r.

$$\left(10, \frac{3\pi}{4}\right) = \left(10, \frac{3\pi}{4} + 2\pi\right) = \left(10, \frac{11\pi}{4}\right)$$

b. Add π to the angle and replace r by $-r$.

$$\left(10, \frac{3\pi}{4}\right) = \left(-10, \frac{3\pi}{4} + \pi\right) = \left(-10, \frac{7\pi}{4}\right)$$

c. Subtract 2π from the angle and do not change r.

$$\left(10, \frac{3\pi}{4}\right) = \left(10, \frac{3\pi}{4} - 2\pi\right) = \left(10, \frac{-5\pi}{4}\right)$$

23. Draw $\theta = \dfrac{3\pi}{4} = 135°$ counterclockwise, since θ is positive, from the polar axis. Go out 10 units on the terminal side of θ, since

25. Draw $\theta = \dfrac{\pi}{2} = 90°$ counterclockwise, since

θ is positive, from the polar axis. Go 4 units out on the terminal side of θ, since $r > 0$.

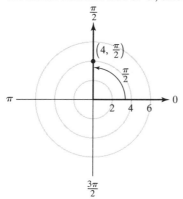

a. Add 2π to the angle and do not change r.

$$\left(4, \frac{\pi}{2}\right) = \left(4, \frac{\pi}{2} + 2\pi\right) = \left(4, \frac{5\pi}{2}\right)$$

b. Add π to the angle and replace r by $-r$.

$$\left(4, \frac{\pi}{2}\right) = \left(-4, \frac{\pi}{2} + \pi\right) = \left(-4, \frac{3\pi}{2}\right)$$

c. Subtract 2π from the angle and do not change r.

$$\left(4, \frac{\pi}{2}\right) = \left(4, \frac{\pi}{2} - 2\pi\right) = \left(4, -\frac{3\pi}{2}\right)$$

27. a, b, d

29. b, d

31. a, b

33. The rectangular coordinates of (4, 90°) are (0, 4).

35. $x = r\cos\theta = 2\cos\dfrac{\pi}{3} = 2\left(\dfrac{1}{2}\right) = 1$

$y = r\sin\theta = 2\sin\dfrac{\pi}{3} = 2\left(\dfrac{\sqrt{3}}{2}\right) = \sqrt{3}$

The rectangular coordinates of $\left(2, \dfrac{\pi}{3}\right)$ are $\left(1, \sqrt{3}\right)$.

37. $x = r\cos\theta = -4\cos\dfrac{\pi}{2} = -4 \cdot 0 = 0$

$y = r\sin\theta = -4\sin\dfrac{\pi}{2} = -4(1) = -4$

The rectangular coordinates of $\left(-4, \dfrac{\pi}{2}\right)$ are (0, –4).

39. $x = r\cos\theta = 7.4\cos 2.5 \approx 7.4(-0.80) \approx -5.9$
$y = r\sin\theta = 7.4\sin 2.5 \approx 7.4(0.60) \approx 4.4$
The rectangular coordinates of (7.4, 2.5) are approximately (–5.9, 4.4).

43. $\left(\sqrt{8}, \dfrac{3\pi}{4}\right)$

$r = \sqrt{x^2 + y^2} = \sqrt{(2)^2 + \left(-2\sqrt{3}\right)^2}$

$= \sqrt{4 + 12} = \sqrt{16} = 4$

$\tan\theta = \dfrac{y}{x} = \dfrac{-2\sqrt{3}}{2} = -\sqrt{3}$

Because $\tan\dfrac{\pi}{3} = \sqrt{3}$ and θ lies in quadrant

IV, $\theta = 2\pi - \dfrac{\pi}{3} = \dfrac{5\pi}{3}$.

The polar coordinates of $\left(2, -2\sqrt{3}\right)$ are

$(r, \theta) = \left(4, \dfrac{5\pi}{3}\right)$.

45. $\left(2, \dfrac{7\pi}{6}\right)$

$$r = \sqrt{x^2 + y^2} = \sqrt{\left(-\sqrt{3}\right)^2 + (-1)^2}$$

$$= \sqrt{3+1} = \sqrt{4} = 2$$

$$\tan\theta = \frac{y}{x} = \frac{-1}{-\sqrt{3}} = \frac{1}{\sqrt{3}}$$

Because $\tan\dfrac{\pi}{6} = \dfrac{1}{\sqrt{3}}$ and θ lies in quadrant

III, $\theta = \pi + \dfrac{\pi}{6} = \dfrac{7\pi}{6}$.

The polar coordinates of $\left(-\sqrt{3}, -1\right)$ are

$$(r, \theta) = \left(2, \frac{7\pi}{6}\right).$$

47. $(5, 0)$

$$r = \sqrt{x^2 + y^2} = \sqrt{(5)^2 + (0)^2} = \sqrt{25} = 5$$

$$\tan\theta = \frac{y}{x} = \frac{0}{5} = 0$$

Because $\tan 0 = 0$ and θ lies on the polar
axis, $\theta = 0$.
The polar coordinates of $(5, 0)$ are
$(r, \theta) = (5, 0)$.

49.
$$3x + y = 7$$
$$3r\cos\theta + r\sin\theta = 7$$
$$r(3\cos\theta + \sin\theta) = 7$$
$$r = \frac{7}{3\cos\theta + \sin\theta}$$

51.
$$x = 7$$
$$r\cos\theta = 7$$
$$r = \frac{7}{\cos\theta}$$

53. $x^2 + y^2 = 9$
$$r^2 = 9$$
$$r = 3$$

55. $x^2 + y^2 = 4x$
$$r^2 = 4r\cos\theta$$
$$r = 4\cos\theta$$

57.
$$y^2 = 6x$$
$$(r\sin\theta)^2 = 6r\cos\theta$$
$$r^2\sin^2\theta = 6r\cos\theta$$
$$r\sin^2\theta = 6\cos\theta$$
$$r = \frac{6\cos\theta}{\sin^2\theta}$$

59.
$$r = 8$$
$$r^2 = 64$$
$$x^2 + y^2 = 64$$

61.
$$\theta = \frac{\pi}{2}$$
$$\tan\theta = \tan\frac{\pi}{2}$$
$$\tan\theta \text{ is undefined}$$
$$\frac{y}{x} \text{ is undefined}$$
$$x = 0$$

63. $r\sin\theta = 3$
$$y = 3$$

65.
$$r = 4\csc\theta$$
$$r = \frac{4}{\sin\theta}$$
$$r\sin\theta = 4$$
$$y = 4$$

67.
$$r = \sin\theta$$
$$r \cdot r = r \cdot \sin\theta$$
$$r^2 = r\sin\theta$$
$$x^2 + y^2 = y$$

69.
$$r = 6\cos\theta + 4\sin\theta$$
$$r \cdot r = r(6\cos\theta + 4\sin\theta)$$
$$r^2 = 6r\cos\theta + 4r\sin\theta$$
$$x^2 + y^2 = 6x + 4y$$

71.
$$r^2 \sin 2\theta = 2$$
$$r^2(2\sin\theta\cos\theta) = 2$$
$$2r\sin\theta\, r\cos\theta = 2$$
$$2yx = 2$$
$$xy = 1$$
$$y = \frac{1}{x}$$

73. The angle is measured counterclockwise from the polar axis.
$$\theta = \frac{2}{3}(360°) = 240° \text{ or } \frac{4\pi}{3}.$$
The distance from the inner circle's center to the outer circle is
$$r = 6 + 3(3) = 6 + 9 = 15$$
The polar coordinates are $(r, \theta) = \left(15, \dfrac{4\pi}{3}\right)$.

75. (6.3, 50°) represents a sailing speed of 6.3 knots at an angle of 50° to the wind.

77. Out of the four points in this 10-knot-wind situation, you would recommend a sailing angle of 105°. A sailing speed of 7.5 knots is achieved at this angle.

79.–85. Answers may vary.

87.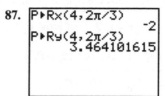
To three decimal places, the rectangular coordinates are (−2, 3.464).

89.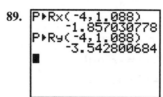
To three decimal places, the rectangular coordinates are (−1.857, −3.543).

91.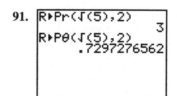
To three decimal places, the polar coordinates are $(r, \theta) = (3, 0.730)$.

93. Use the distance formula for rectangular coordinates, $d = \sqrt{(x_2 - x_1)^2 + (y_2 - y_1)^2}$.

Let $x_1 = r_1 \cos\theta_1, y_1 = r_1 \sin\theta_1,$
$x_2 = r_2 \cos\theta_2, y_2 = r_2 \sin\theta_2$

$$d = \sqrt{\left(r_2 \cos\theta_2 - r_1 \cos\theta_1\right)^2 + \left(r_2 \sin\theta_2 - r_1 \sin\theta_1\right)^2}$$

$$= \sqrt{r_2^2 \cos^2\theta_2 - 2r_1r_2 \cos\theta_1 \cos\theta_2 + r_1^2 \cos^2\theta_1 + r_2^2 \sin^2\theta_2 - 2r_1r_2 \sin\theta_1 \sin\theta_2 + r_1^2 \sin^2\theta_1}$$

$$= \sqrt{r_2^2\left(\cos^2\theta_2 + \sin^2\theta_2\right) + r_1^2\left(\cos^2\theta_1 + \sin^2\theta_1\right) - 2r_1r_2\left(\cos\theta_1 \cos\theta_2 + \sin\theta_1 \sin\theta_2\right)}$$

$$= \sqrt{r_2^2(1) + r_1^2(1) - 2r_1r_2\left(\cos\left(\theta_2 - \theta_1\right)\right)}$$

$$= \sqrt{r_1^2 + r_2^2 - 2r_1r_2 \cos\left(\theta_2 - \theta_1\right)}$$

95.

$$r = 4\cos\theta$$
$$r \cdot r = 4r\cos\theta$$
$$r^2 = 4r\cos\theta$$
$$x^2 + y^2 = 4x$$
$$x^2 - 4x + y^2 = 0$$
$$x^2 - 4x + 4 + y^2 = 0 + 4$$
$$(x - 2)^2 + y^2 = 4$$

The center is (2, 0), the radius is 2.

Section 2.4

Check Point Exercises

1. a. $z = 2 + 3i$ corresponds to the point (2, 3). Plot the complex number by moving two units to the right on the real axis and 3 units up parallel to the imaginary axis.

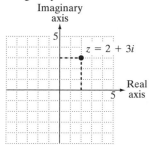

b. $z = -3 - 5i$ corresponds to the point (−3, −5). Plot the complex number by moving three units to the left on the real axis and five units down parallel to the imaginary axis.

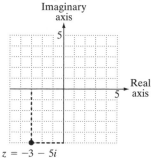

c. Because $z = -4 = -4 + 0i$, this complex number corresponds to the point (−4, 0). Plot the complex number by moving four units to the left on the real axis.

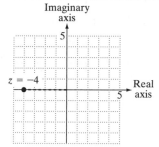

d. Because $z = -i = 0 - i$, this complex number corresponds to the point (0, −1). Plot the complex number by moving one unit down on the imaginary axis.

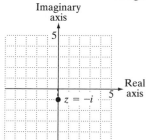

2. a. $z = 5 + 12i$

$a = 5, b = 12$

$|z| = \sqrt{5^2 + 12^2} = \sqrt{25 + 144} = \sqrt{169} = 13$

b. $z = 2 - 3i$

$a = 2, b = -3$

$|z| = \sqrt{2^2 + (-3)^2} = \sqrt{4 + 9} = \sqrt{13}$

3. $z = -1 - \sqrt{3}i$ corresponds to the point $\left(-1, -\sqrt{3}\right)$.

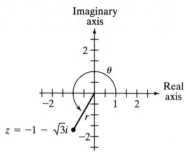

Use $r = \sqrt{a^2 + b^2}$ with $a = -1$ and $b = -\sqrt{3}$ to find r.

$$r = \sqrt{a^2 + b^2} = \sqrt{(-1)^2 + \left(-\sqrt{3}\right)^2}$$
$$= \sqrt{1+3} = \sqrt{4} = 2$$

Use $\tan\theta = \dfrac{b}{a}$ with $a = -1$ and $b = -\sqrt{3}$ to find θ.

$$\tan\theta = \frac{b}{a} = \frac{-\sqrt{3}}{-1} = \sqrt{3}$$

Because $\tan\dfrac{\pi}{3} = \sqrt{3}$ and θ lies in

quadrant III, $\theta = \pi + \dfrac{\pi}{3} = \dfrac{3\pi}{3} + \dfrac{\pi}{3} = \dfrac{4\pi}{3}$.

The polar form of $z = -1 - \sqrt{3}i$ is

$$z = r(\cos\theta + i\sin\theta) = 2\left(\cos\frac{4\pi}{3} + i\sin\frac{4\pi}{3}\right).$$

4. The complex number $z = 4(\cos 30° + i\sin 30°)$ is in polar form, with $r = 4$ and $\theta = 30°$. We use exact values for $\cos 30°$ and $\sin 30°$ to write the number in rectangular form.

$$4(\cos 30° + i\sin 30°) = 4\left(\frac{\sqrt{3}}{2} + i\frac{1}{2}\right) = 2\sqrt{3} + 2i$$

The rectangular form of $z = 4(\cos 30° + i\sin 30°)$ is $z = 2\sqrt{3} + 2i$.

5. $z_1 z_2 = [6(\cos 40° + i\sin 40°)][5(\cos 20° + i\sin 20°)] = (6 \cdot 5)[(\cos(40° + 20°) + i\sin(40° + 20°)]$
    $\qquad = 30(\cos 60° + i\sin 60°)$

6. $\dfrac{z_1}{z_2} = \dfrac{50\left(\cos\dfrac{4\pi}{3} + i\sin\dfrac{4\pi}{3}\right)}{5\left(\cos\dfrac{\pi}{3} + i\sin\dfrac{\pi}{3}\right)} = \dfrac{50}{5}\left[\cos\left(\dfrac{4\pi}{3} - \dfrac{\pi}{3}\right) + i\sin\left(\dfrac{4\pi}{3} - \dfrac{\pi}{3}\right)\right] = 10(\cos\pi + i\sin\pi)$

7. $\left[2(\cos 30° + i\sin 30°)\right]^5 = 2^5\left[\cos(5\cdot 30°) + i\sin(5\cdot 30°)\right] = 32(\cos 150° + i\sin 150°) = 32\left(-\dfrac{\sqrt{3}}{2} + i\dfrac{1}{2}\right)$

$$= -16\sqrt{3} + 16i$$

8. Write $1 + i$ in $r(\cos\theta + i\sin\theta)$ form.

$$r = \sqrt{a^2 + b^2} = \sqrt{1^2 + 1^2} = \sqrt{2}$$

$$\tan\theta = \dfrac{b}{a} = \dfrac{1}{1} = 1 \text{ and } \theta = \dfrac{\pi}{4}$$

$$1 + i = r(\cos\theta + i\sin\theta) = \sqrt{2}\left(\cos\dfrac{\pi}{4} + i\sin\dfrac{\pi}{4}\right)$$

Use DeMoivre's Theorem to raise $1 + i$ to the fourth power.

$$(1 + i)^4 = \left[\sqrt{2}\left(\cos\dfrac{\pi}{4} + i\sin\dfrac{\pi}{4}\right)\right]^4 = \left(\sqrt{2}\right)^4\left[\cos\left(4\cdot\dfrac{\pi}{4}\right) + i\sin\left(4\cdot\dfrac{\pi}{4}\right)\right] = 4(\cos\pi + i\sin\pi) = 4(-1 + 0i) = -4$$

9. From DeMoivre's Theorem for finding complex roots, the fourth roots of $16(\cos 60° + i\sin 60°)$ are

$$z_k = \sqrt[4]{16}\left[\cos\left(\dfrac{60° + 360°k}{4}\right) + i\sin\left(\dfrac{60° + 360°k}{4}\right)\right], \; k = 0, 1, 2, 3.$$

Substitute 0, 1, 2, and 3 for k in the above expression for z_k.

$$z_0 = \sqrt[4]{16}\left[\cos\left(\dfrac{60° + 360°\cdot 0}{4}\right) + i\sin\left(\dfrac{60° + 360°\cdot 0}{4}\right)\right] = \sqrt[4]{16}\left[\cos\dfrac{60°}{4} + i\sin\dfrac{60°}{4}\right] = 2(\cos 15° + i\sin 15°)$$

$$z_1 = \sqrt[4]{16}\left[\cos\left(\dfrac{60° + 360°\cdot 1}{4}\right) + i\sin\left(\dfrac{60° + 360°\cdot 1}{4}\right)\right] = \sqrt[4]{16}\left[\cos\dfrac{420°}{4} + i\sin\dfrac{420°}{4}\right]$$

$$= 2(\cos 105° + i\sin 105°)$$

$$z_2 = \sqrt[4]{16}\left[\cos\left(\dfrac{60° + 360°\cdot 2}{4}\right) + i\sin\left(\dfrac{60° + 360°\cdot 2}{4}\right)\right] = \sqrt[4]{16}\left[\cos\dfrac{780°}{4} + i\sin\dfrac{780°}{4}\right]$$

$$= 2(\cos 195° + i\sin 195°)$$

$$z_3 = \sqrt[4]{16}\left[\cos\left(\dfrac{60° + 360°\cdot 3}{4}\right) + i\sin\left(\dfrac{60° + 360°\cdot 3}{4}\right)\right] = \sqrt[4]{16}\left[\cos\dfrac{1140°}{4} + i\sin\dfrac{1140°}{4}\right]$$

$$= 2(\cos 285° + i\sin 285°)$$

10. First, write 27 in polar form. $27 = r(\cos\theta + i\sin\theta) = 27(\cos 0 + \sin 0)$. From DeMoivre's theorem for finding complex roots, the cube roots of 27 are

$$z_k = \sqrt[3]{27}\left[\cos\left(\frac{0+2\pi k}{3}\right) + i\sin\left(\frac{0+2\pi k}{3}\right)\right], \ k = 0, 1, 2.$$

$$z_0 = \sqrt[3]{27}\left[\cos\left(\frac{0+2\pi\cdot 0}{3}\right) + i\sin\left(\frac{0+2\pi\cdot 0}{3}\right)\right] = 3(\cos 0 + i\sin 0) = 3(1 + i\cdot 0) = 3$$

$$z_1 = \sqrt[3]{27}\left[\cos\left(\frac{0+2\pi\cdot 1}{3}\right) + i\sin\left(\frac{0+2\pi\cdot 1}{3}\right)\right] = 3\left(\cos\frac{2\pi}{3} + i\sin\frac{2\pi}{3}\right) = 3\left(-\frac{1}{2} + i\cdot\frac{\sqrt{3}}{2}\right) = -\frac{3}{2} + \frac{3\sqrt{3}}{2}i$$

$$z_2 = \sqrt[3]{27}\left[\cos\left(\frac{0+2\pi\cdot 2}{3}\right) + i\sin\left(\frac{0+2\pi\cdot 2}{3}\right)\right] = 3\left(\cos\frac{4\pi}{3} + i\sin\frac{4\pi}{3}\right) = 3\left(-\frac{1}{2} + i\cdot\left(-\frac{\sqrt{3}}{2}\right)\right) = -\frac{3}{2} - \frac{3\sqrt{3}}{2}i$$

Exercise Set 2.5

1. Because $z = 4i = 0 + 4i$, this complex number corresponds to the point (0, 4).

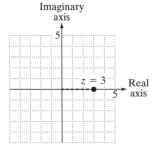

With $a = 0$ and $b = 4$, $|z| = \sqrt{0^2 + 4^2} = \sqrt{16} = 4$.

3. Because $z = 3 = 3 + 0i$, this complex number corresponds to the point (3, 0).

With $a = 3$ and $b = 0$, $|z| = \sqrt{3^2 + 0^2} = \sqrt{9} = 3$.

5. $z = 3 + 2i$ corresponds to the point (3, 2).

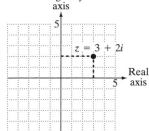

With $a = 3$ and $b = 2$,
$$|z| = \sqrt{3^2 + 2^2} = \sqrt{9 + 4} = \sqrt{13}.$$

7. $z = 3 - i$ corresponds to the point (3, –1).

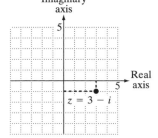

With $a = 3$ and $b = -1$,
$$|z| = \sqrt{3^2 + (-1)^2} = \sqrt{9 + 1} = \sqrt{10}.$$

9. $z = -3 + 4i$ corresponds to the point (–3, 4).

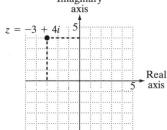

With $a = -3$ and $b = 4$,
$$|z| = \sqrt{(-3)^2 + 4^2} = \sqrt{9 + 16} = \sqrt{25} = 5.$$

11. $z = 2 + 2i$ corresponds to the point (2, 2).

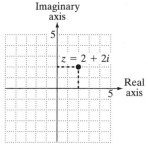

Use $r = \sqrt{a^2 + b^2}$ and $\tan\theta = \dfrac{b}{a}$, with $a = 2$ and $b = 2$, to find r and θ.
$$r = \sqrt{2^2 + 2^2} = \sqrt{4 + 4} = \sqrt{8} = 2\sqrt{2}$$
$$\tan\theta = \frac{2}{2} = 1$$

Because $\tan\dfrac{\pi}{4} = 1$ and θ lies in quadrant I,
$$\theta = \frac{\pi}{4}.$$

$$z = 2 + 2i = r(\cos\theta + i\sin\theta)$$
$$= 2\sqrt{2}\left(\cos\frac{\pi}{4} + i\sin\frac{\pi}{4}\right)$$
$$\text{or } 2\sqrt{2}(\cos 45° + i\sin 45°)$$

13. $z = -1 - i$ corresponds to the point (–1, –1).

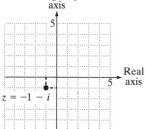

Use $r = \sqrt{a^2 + b^2}$ and $\tan\theta = \dfrac{b}{a}$, with $a = -1$ and $b = -1$, to find r and θ.

$r = \sqrt{(-1)^2 + (-1)^2} = \sqrt{1+1} = \sqrt{2}$

$\tan\theta = \dfrac{-1}{-1} = 1$

Because $\tan\dfrac{\pi}{4} = 1$ and θ lies in

quadrant III, $\theta = \pi + \dfrac{\pi}{4} = \dfrac{5\pi}{4}$.

$z = -1 - i = r(\cos\theta + i\sin\theta)$

$\quad = \sqrt{2}\left(\cos\dfrac{5\pi}{4} + i\sin\dfrac{5\pi}{4}\right)$

$\quad$ or $\sqrt{2}(\cos 225° + i\sin 225°)$

15. $z = -4i$ corresponds to the point $(0, -4)$.

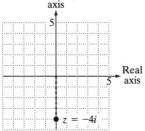

Use $r = \sqrt{a^2 + b^2}$ and $\tan\theta = \dfrac{b}{a}$, with

$a = 0$ and $b = -4$, to find r and θ.

$r = \sqrt{0^2 + (-4)^2} = \sqrt{16} = 4$

$\tan\theta = \dfrac{-4}{0}$ is undefined.

Because $\tan\dfrac{\pi}{2}$ is undefined and θ lies on

the negative y-axis, $\theta = \dfrac{\pi}{2} + \pi = \dfrac{3\pi}{2}$.

$z = -4i = r(\cos\theta + i\sin\theta)$

$\quad = 4\left(\cos\dfrac{3\pi}{2} + i\sin\dfrac{3\pi}{2}\right)$

$\quad$ or $4(\cos 270° + i\sin 270°)$

17. $z = 2\sqrt{3} - 2i$ corresponds to the point $\left(2\sqrt{3}, -2\right)$.

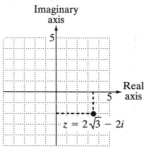

Use $r = \sqrt{a^2 + b^2}$ and $\tan\theta = \dfrac{b}{a}$, with

$a = 2\sqrt{3}$ and $b = -2$, to find r and θ.

$r = \sqrt{\left(2\sqrt{3}\right)^2 + (-2)^2} = \sqrt{12 + 4} = \sqrt{16} = 4$

$\tan\theta = \dfrac{-2}{2\sqrt{3}} = -\dfrac{1}{\sqrt{3}}$

Because $\tan\dfrac{\pi}{6} = \dfrac{1}{\sqrt{3}}$ and θ lies in

quadrant IV, $\theta = 2\pi - \dfrac{\pi}{6} = \dfrac{11\pi}{6}$.

$z = 2\sqrt{3} - 2i = r(\cos\theta + i\sin\theta)$

$\quad = 4\left(\cos\dfrac{11\pi}{6} + i\sin\dfrac{11\pi}{6}\right)$

$\quad$ or $4(\cos 330° + i\sin 330°)$

19. $z = -3$ corresponds to the point $(-3, 0)$.

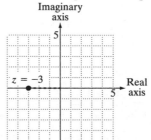

Use $r = \sqrt{a^2 + b^2}$ and $\tan\theta = \dfrac{b}{a}$, with $a = -3$ and $b = 0$, to find r and θ.

$r = \sqrt{(-3)^2 + 0^2} = \sqrt{9} = 3$

$\tan\theta = \dfrac{0}{-3} = 0$

Because $\tan 0 = 0$ and θ lies on the negative x-axis, $\theta = 0 + \pi = \pi$.

$z = -3 = r(\cos\theta + i\sin\theta)$

$\quad = 3\big(\cos\pi + i\sin\pi\big)$

$\quad$ or $3(\cos 180° + i\sin 180°)$

21. $z = -3\sqrt{2} - 3\sqrt{3}i$ corresponds to the point $\left(-3\sqrt{2}, -3\sqrt{3}\right)$.

Imaginary axis

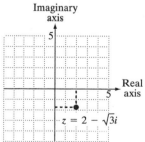

$z = -3\sqrt{2} - 3\sqrt{3}i$

Use $r = \sqrt{a^2 + b^2}$ and $\tan\theta = \dfrac{b}{a}$, with $a = -3\sqrt{2}$ and $b = -3\sqrt{3}$, to find r and θ.

$r = \sqrt{\left(-3\sqrt{2}\right)^2 + \left(-3\sqrt{3}\right)^2} = \sqrt{18 + 27}$

$\quad = \sqrt{45} = 3\sqrt{5}$

$\tan\theta = \dfrac{-3\sqrt{3}}{-3\sqrt{2}} = \dfrac{\sqrt{3}}{\sqrt{2}} = \dfrac{\sqrt{6}}{2}$

Because θ lies in quadrant III,

$\theta = 180° + \tan^{-1}\left(\dfrac{\sqrt{6}}{2}\right) \approx 180° + 50.8°$

$\quad = 230.8°$

$z = -3\sqrt{2} - 3\sqrt{3}i = r(\cos\theta + i\sin\theta)$

$\quad \approx 3\sqrt{5}(\cos 230.8° + i\sin 230.8°)$

23. $z = -3 + 4i$ corresponds to the point $(-3, 4)$.

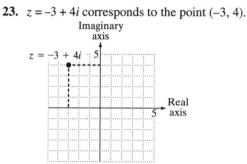

Use $r = \sqrt{a^2 + b^2}$ and $\tan\theta = \dfrac{b}{a}$, with $a = -3$ and $b = 4$, to find r and θ.

$r = \sqrt{(-3)^2 + (4)^2} = \sqrt{9 + 16} = \sqrt{25} = 5$

$\tan\theta = \dfrac{4}{-3} = -\dfrac{4}{3}$

Because θ lies in quadrant II,

$\theta = 180° - \tan^{-1}\left(\dfrac{4}{3}\right) \approx 180° - 53.1° = 126.9°.$

$z = -3 + 4i = r(\cos\theta + i\sin\theta)$

$\quad \approx 5(\cos 126.9° + i\sin 126.9°)$

25. $z = 2 - \sqrt{3}i$ corresponds to the point $\left(2, -\sqrt{3}\right)$.

Imaginary axis

$z = 2 - \sqrt{3}i$

Use $r = \sqrt{a^2 + b^2}$ and $\tan\theta = \dfrac{b}{a}$, with

$a = 2$ and $b = -\sqrt{3}$, to find r and θ.

$$r = \sqrt{2^2 + \left(-\sqrt{3}\right)^2} = \sqrt{4+3} = \sqrt{7}$$

$$\tan\theta = \frac{-\sqrt{3}}{2} = -\frac{\sqrt{3}}{2}$$

Because θ lies in quadrant IV,

$$\theta = 360° - \tan^{-1}\left(\frac{\sqrt{3}}{2}\right) \approx 360° - 40.9° = 319.1°$$

$$z = 2 - \sqrt{3}i = r(\cos\theta + i\sin\theta)$$

$$\approx \sqrt{7}(\cos 319.1° + i\sin 319.1°)$$

27. $6(\cos 30° + i\sin 30°) = 6\left(\dfrac{\sqrt{3}}{2} + i\,\dfrac{1}{2}\right)$

$$= 3\sqrt{3} + 3i$$

The rectangular form of

$z = 6(\cos 30° + i\sin 30°)$ is $z = 3\sqrt{3} + 3i$.

29. $4(\cos 240° + i\sin 240°) = 4\left(-\dfrac{1}{2} + i\left(-\dfrac{\sqrt{3}}{2}\right)\right)$

$$= -2 - 2\sqrt{3}i$$

The rectangular form of

$z = 4(\cos 240° + i\sin 240°)$ is $z = -2 - 2\sqrt{3}i$.

31. $8\left(\cos\dfrac{7\pi}{4} + i\sin\dfrac{7\pi}{4}\right) = 8\left(\dfrac{\sqrt{2}}{2} + i\left(-\dfrac{\sqrt{2}}{2}\right)\right)$

$$= 4\sqrt{2} - 4\sqrt{2}i$$

The rectangular form of

$8\left(\cos\dfrac{7\pi}{4} + i\sin\dfrac{7\pi}{4}\right)$ is $z = 4\sqrt{2} - 4\sqrt{2}i$.

33. $5\left(\cos\dfrac{\pi}{2} + i\sin\dfrac{\pi}{2}\right) = 5\left(0 + i(1)\right)$

$$= 5i$$

The rectangular form of

$z = 5\left(\cos\dfrac{\pi}{2} + i\sin\dfrac{\pi}{2}\right)$ is $z = 5i$.

35. $20\left(\cos 205° + i\sin 205°\right)$

$$\approx 20\left(-0.91 + i(-0.42)\right) = -18.2 - 8.4i$$

The rectangular form of

$z = 20\left(\cos 205° + i\sin 205°\right)$ is

$z \approx -18.2 - 8.4i$.

37. $z_1 z_2$

$$= \left[6(\cos 20° + i\sin 20°)\right]\left[5(\cos 50° + i\sin 50°)\right]$$

$$= (6\cdot 5)\left[\cos(20° + 50°) + i\sin(20° + 50°)\right]$$

$$= 30(\cos 70° + i\sin 70°)$$

39.

$z_1 z_2$

$$= \left[3\left(\cos\frac{\pi}{5} + i\sin\frac{\pi}{5}\right)\right]\left[4\left(\cos\frac{\pi}{10} + i\sin\frac{\pi}{10}\right)\right]$$

$$= (3\cdot 4)\left[\cos\left(\frac{\pi}{5} + \frac{\pi}{10}\right) + i\sin\left(\frac{\pi}{5} + \frac{\pi}{10}\right)\right]$$

$$= 12\left(\cos\frac{3\pi}{10} + i\sin\frac{3\pi}{10}\right)$$

41.

$$z_1 z_2 = \left[\cos\frac{\pi}{4} + i\sin\frac{\pi}{4}\right]\left[\cos\frac{\pi}{3} + i\sin\frac{\pi}{3}\right]$$

$$= \cos\left(\frac{\pi}{4} + \frac{\pi}{3}\right) + i\sin\left(\frac{\pi}{4} + \frac{\pi}{3}\right)$$

$$= \cos\left(\frac{3\pi}{12} + \frac{4\pi}{12}\right) + i\sin\left(\frac{3\pi}{12} + \frac{4\pi}{12}\right)$$

$$= \cos\frac{7\pi}{12} + i\sin\frac{7\pi}{12}$$

43. Begin by converting $z_1 = 1 + i$ and $z_2 = -1 + i$ to polar form.

For z_1: $a = 1$ and $b = 1$

$$r = \sqrt{a^2 + b^2} = \sqrt{1^2 + 1^2} = \sqrt{2}$$

$$\tan\theta = \frac{b}{a} = \frac{1}{1} = 1 \text{ and } \theta = \frac{\pi}{4}.$$

$$z_1 = r(\cos\theta + i\sin\theta) = \sqrt{2}\left(\cos\frac{\pi}{4} + i\sin\frac{\pi}{4}\right)$$

For z_2: $a = -1$ and $b = 1$

$$r = \sqrt{a^2 + b^2} = \sqrt{(-1)^2 + 1^2} = \sqrt{2}$$

$$\tan\theta = \frac{b}{a} = \frac{1}{-1} = -1$$

Because $\tan\frac{\pi}{4} = 1$ and θ lies in quadrant II, $\theta = \pi - \frac{\pi}{4} = \frac{3\pi}{4}$.

$$z_2 = r(\cos\theta + i\sin\theta) = \sqrt{2}\left(\cos\frac{3\pi}{4} + i\sin\frac{3\pi}{4}\right)$$

Now, find the product.

$$z_1 z_2 = (1+i)(-1+i)$$

$$= \left[\sqrt{2}\left(\cos\frac{\pi}{4} + i\sin\frac{\pi}{4}\right)\right]\left[\sqrt{2}\left(\cos\frac{3\pi}{4} + i\sin\frac{3\pi}{4}\right)\right] = \left(\sqrt{2}\cdot\sqrt{2}\right)\left[\cos\left(\frac{\pi}{4} + \frac{3\pi}{4}\right) + i\sin\left(\frac{\pi}{4} + \frac{3\pi}{4}\right)\right]$$

$$= 2\left(\cos\pi + i\sin\pi\right)$$

45. $\dfrac{z_1}{z_2} = \dfrac{20(\cos 75° + i\sin 75°)}{4(\cos 25° + i\sin 25°)} = \dfrac{20}{4}\left[\cos(75° - 25°) + i\sin(75° - 25°)\right]$

$$= 5(\cos 50° + i\sin 50°)$$

47. $\dfrac{z_1}{z_2} = \dfrac{3\left(\cos\frac{\pi}{5} + i\sin\frac{\pi}{5}\right)}{4\left(\cos\frac{\pi}{10} + i\sin\frac{\pi}{10}\right)} = \dfrac{3}{4}\left[\cos\left(\frac{\pi}{5} - \frac{\pi}{10}\right) + i\sin\left(\frac{\pi}{5} - \frac{\pi}{10}\right)\right] = \dfrac{3}{4}\left(\cos\frac{\pi}{10} + i\sin\frac{\pi}{10}\right)$

49. $\dfrac{z_1}{z_2} = \dfrac{\cos 80° + i\sin 80°}{\cos 200° + i\sin 200°} = \cos(80° - 200°) + i\sin(80° - 200°) = \cos(-120°) + i\sin(-120°)$

$$= \cos 240° + i\sin 240°$$

51. Begin by converting $z_1 = 2 + 2i$ and $z_2 = 1 + i$ to polar form.

For z_1: $a = 2$ and $b = 2$

$$r = \sqrt{a^2 + b^2} = \sqrt{2^2 + 2^2} = \sqrt{8} = 2\sqrt{2}$$

$$\tan\theta = \frac{b}{a} = \frac{2}{2} = 1 \text{ and } \theta = \frac{\pi}{4}$$

$$z_1 = r(\cos\theta + i\sin\theta) = 2\sqrt{2}\left(\cos\frac{\pi}{4} + i\sin\frac{\pi}{4}\right)$$

For z_2: $a = 1$ and $b = 1$

$$r = \sqrt{a^2 + b^2} = \sqrt{1^2 + 1^2} = \sqrt{2}$$

$$\tan\theta = \frac{b}{a} = \frac{1}{1} = 1 \text{ and } \theta = \frac{\pi}{4}$$

$$z_2 = r(\cos\theta + i\sin\theta) = \sqrt{2}\left(\cos\frac{\pi}{4} + i\sin\frac{\pi}{4}\right).$$

Now, find the quotient.

$$\frac{z_1}{z_2} = \frac{2 + 2i}{1 + i} = \frac{2\sqrt{2}\left(\cos\frac{\pi}{4} + i\sin\frac{\pi}{4}\right)}{\sqrt{2}\left(\cos\frac{\pi}{4} + i\sin\frac{\pi}{4}\right)} = 2\left[\cos\left(\frac{\pi}{4} - \frac{\pi}{4}\right) + i\sin\left(\frac{\pi}{4} - \frac{\pi}{4}\right)\right] = 2(\cos 0 + i\sin 0)$$

53. $\left[4(\cos 15° + i\sin 15°)\right]^3 = (4)^3\left[\cos(3\cdot 15°) + i\sin(3\cdot 15°)\right] = 64(\cos 45° + i\sin 45°) = 64\left(\frac{\sqrt{2}}{2} + i\frac{\sqrt{2}}{2}\right)$

$$= 32\sqrt{2} + 32\sqrt{2}i$$

55. $\left[2(\cos 80° + i\sin 80°)\right]^3 = (2)^3\left[\cos(3\cdot 80°) + i\sin(3\cdot 80°)\right] = 8(\cos 240° + i\sin 240°)$

$$= 8\left(-\frac{1}{2} + i\left(-\frac{\sqrt{3}}{2}\right)\right) = -4 - 4\sqrt{3}i$$

57. $\left[\frac{1}{2}\left(\cos\frac{\pi}{12} + i\sin\frac{\pi}{12}\right)\right]^6 = \left(\frac{1}{2}\right)^6\left[\cos\left(6\cdot\frac{\pi}{12}\right) + i\sin\left(6\cdot\frac{\pi}{12}\right)\right] = \frac{1}{64}\left(\cos\frac{\pi}{2} + i\sin\frac{\pi}{2}\right) = \frac{1}{64}(0 + i) = \frac{1}{64}i$

59.
$$\left[\sqrt{2}\left(\cos\frac{5\pi}{6}+i\sin\frac{5\pi}{6}\right)\right]^4 = \left(\sqrt{2}\right)^4\left[\cos\left(4\cdot\frac{5\pi}{6}\right)+i\sin\left(4\cdot\frac{5\pi}{6}\right)\right]$$

$$= 4\left(\cos\frac{20\pi}{6}+i\sin\frac{20\pi}{6}\right) = 4\left(\cos\frac{4\pi}{3}+i\sin\frac{4\pi}{3}\right)$$

$$= 4\left(-\frac{1}{2}+i\left(-\frac{\sqrt{3}}{2}\right)\right) = -2-2\sqrt{3}i$$

61. Write $1+i$ in $r(\cos\theta+i\sin\theta)$ form.

$$r = \sqrt{a^2+b^2} = \sqrt{1^2+1^2} = \sqrt{2}$$

$$\tan\theta = \frac{b}{a} = \frac{1}{1} = 1 \text{ and } \theta = \frac{\pi}{4}$$

$$1+i = r(\cos\theta+i\sin\theta) = \sqrt{2}\left(\cos\frac{\pi}{4}+i\sin\frac{\pi}{4}\right)$$

Use DeMoivre's Theorem to raise $1+i$ to the fifth power.

$$(1+i)^5 = \left[\sqrt{2}\left(\cos\frac{\pi}{4}+i\sin\frac{\pi}{4}\right)\right]^5 = \left(\sqrt{2}\right)^5\left[\cos\left(5\cdot\frac{\pi}{4}\right)+i\sin\left(5\cdot\frac{\pi}{4}\right)\right]$$

$$= 4\sqrt{2}\left(\cos\frac{5\pi}{4}+i\sin\frac{5\pi}{4}\right) = 4\sqrt{2}\left(-\frac{\sqrt{2}}{2}+i\left(-\frac{\sqrt{2}}{2}\right)\right) = -4-4i$$

63. Write $\sqrt{3}-i$ in $r(\cos\theta+i\sin\theta)$ form.

$$r = \sqrt{a^2+b^2} = \sqrt{\left(\sqrt{3}\right)^2+\left(-1\right)^2} = \sqrt{4} = 2$$

$$\tan\theta = \frac{b}{a} = \frac{-1}{\sqrt{3}} = -\frac{1}{\sqrt{3}}$$

Because $\tan 30° = \dfrac{1}{\sqrt{3}}$ and θ lies in quadrant IV, $\theta = 360° - 30° = 330°$.

$$\sqrt{3}-i = r(\cos\theta+i\sin\theta) = 2(\cos 330°+i\sin 330°)$$

Use DeMoivre's Theorem to raise $\sqrt{3}-i$ to the sixth power.

$$(\sqrt{3}-i)^6 = \left[2(\cos 330°+i\sin 330°)\right]^6 = (2)^6\left[\cos(6\cdot 330°)+i\sin(6\cdot 330°)\right]$$

$$= 64(\cos 1980°+i\sin 1980°) = 64(\cos 180°+i\sin 180°)$$

$$= 64(-1+0i) = -64$$

65. $9(\cos 30° + i \sin 30°)$

$$z_k = \sqrt[2]{9}\left[\cos\left(\frac{30° + 360°k}{2}\right) + i \sin\left(\frac{30° + 360°k}{2}\right)\right], \ k = 0,1$$

$$z_0 = \sqrt{9}\left[\cos\left(\frac{30° + 360° \cdot 0}{2}\right) + i \sin\left(\frac{30° + 360° \cdot 0}{2}\right)\right] = \sqrt{9}\left[\cos\left(\frac{30°}{2}\right) + i \sin\left(\frac{30°}{2}\right)\right] = 3(\cos 15° + i \sin 15°)$$

$$z_1 = \sqrt{9}\left[\cos\left(\frac{30° + 360° \cdot 1}{2}\right) + i \sin\left(\frac{30° + 360° \cdot 1}{2}\right)\right] = \sqrt{9}\left[\cos\left(\frac{390°}{2}\right) + i \sin\left(\frac{390°}{2}\right)\right] = 3(\cos 195° + i \sin 195°)$$

67. $8(\cos 210° + i \sin 210°)$

$$z_k = \sqrt[3]{8}\left[\cos\left(\frac{210° + 360°k}{3}\right) + i \sin\left(\frac{210° + 360°k}{3}\right)\right], \ k = 0,1,2$$

$$z_0 = \sqrt[3]{8}\left[\cos\left(\frac{210° + 360° \cdot 0}{3}\right) + i \sin\left(\frac{210° + 360° \cdot 0}{3}\right)\right] = \sqrt[3]{8}\left[\cos\left(\frac{210°}{3}\right) + i \sin\left(\frac{210°}{3}\right)\right]$$

$$= 2(\cos 70° + i \sin 70°)$$

$$z_1 = \sqrt[3]{8}\left[\cos\left(\frac{210° + 360° \cdot 1}{3}\right) + i \sin\left(\frac{210° + 360° \cdot 1}{3}\right)\right] = \sqrt[3]{8}\left[\cos\left(\frac{570°}{3}\right) + i \sin\left(\frac{570°}{3}\right)\right]$$

$$= 2(\cos 190° + i \sin 190°)$$

$$z_2 = \sqrt[3]{8}\left[\cos\left(\frac{210° + 360° \cdot 2}{3}\right) + i \sin\left(\frac{210° + 360° \cdot 2}{3}\right)\right] = \sqrt[3]{8}\left[\cos\left(\frac{930°}{3}\right) + i \sin\left(\frac{930°}{3}\right)\right]$$

$$= 2(\cos 310° + i \sin 310°)$$

69. $81\left(\cos\dfrac{4\pi}{3}+i\sin\dfrac{4\pi}{3}\right)$

$$z_k = \sqrt[4]{81}\left[\cos\left(\dfrac{\frac{4\pi}{3}+2\pi k}{4}\right)+i\sin\left(\dfrac{\frac{4\pi}{3}+2\pi k}{4}\right)\right], \; k = 0,1,2,3$$

$$z_0 = \sqrt[4]{81}\left[\cos\left(\dfrac{\frac{4\pi}{3}+2\pi\cdot 0}{4}\right)+i\sin\left(\dfrac{\frac{4\pi}{3}+2\pi\cdot 0}{4}\right)\right] = \sqrt[4]{81}\left(\cos\dfrac{\pi}{3}+i\sin\dfrac{\pi}{3}\right) = 3\left(\dfrac{1}{2}+i\dfrac{\sqrt{3}}{2}\right) = \dfrac{3}{2}+\dfrac{3\sqrt{3}}{2}i$$

$$z_1 = \sqrt[4]{81}\left[\cos\left(\dfrac{\frac{4\pi}{3}+2\pi\cdot 1}{4}\right)+i\sin\left(\dfrac{\frac{4\pi}{3}+2\pi\cdot 1}{4}\right)\right] = \sqrt[4]{81}\left(\cos\dfrac{5\pi}{6}+i\sin\dfrac{5\pi}{6}\right) = 3\left(-\dfrac{\sqrt{3}}{2}+i\dfrac{1}{2}\right) = -\dfrac{3\sqrt{3}}{2}+\dfrac{3}{2}i$$

$$z_2 = \sqrt[4]{81}\left[\cos\left(\dfrac{\frac{4\pi}{3}+2\pi\cdot 2}{4}\right)+i\sin\left(\dfrac{\frac{4\pi}{3}+2\pi\cdot 2}{4}\right)\right] = \sqrt[4]{81}\left(\cos\dfrac{4\pi}{3}+i\sin\dfrac{4\pi}{3}\right)$$

$$= 3\left(-\dfrac{1}{2}+i\left(-\dfrac{\sqrt{3}}{2}\right)\right) = -\dfrac{3}{2}-\dfrac{3\sqrt{3}}{2}i$$

$$z_3 = \sqrt[4]{81}\left[\cos\left(\dfrac{\frac{4\pi}{3}+2\pi\cdot 3}{4}\right)+i\sin\left(\dfrac{\frac{4\pi}{3}+2\pi\cdot 3}{4}\right)\right] = \sqrt[4]{81}\left(\cos\dfrac{11\pi}{6}+i\sin\dfrac{11\pi}{6}\right)$$

$$= 3\left(\dfrac{\sqrt{3}}{2}+i\left(-\dfrac{1}{2}\right)\right) = \dfrac{3\sqrt{3}}{2}-\dfrac{3}{2}i$$

119

71. $32 = 32(\cos 0° + i\sin 0°)$

$$z_k = \sqrt[5]{32}\left[\cos\left(\frac{0° + 360°k}{5}\right) + i\sin\left(\frac{0° + 360°k}{5}\right)\right], \; k = 0,1,2,3,4$$

$$z_0 = \sqrt[5]{32}\left[\cos\left(\frac{0° + 360° \cdot 0}{5}\right) + i\sin\left(\frac{0° + 360° \cdot 0}{5}\right)\right] = \sqrt[5]{32}(\cos 0° + i\sin 0°) = 2(1 + 0i) = 2$$

$$z_1 = \sqrt[5]{32}\left[\cos\left(\frac{0° + 360° \cdot 1}{5}\right) + i\sin\left(\frac{0° + 360° \cdot 1}{5}\right)\right] = \sqrt[5]{32}(\cos 72° + i\sin 72°) \approx 2(0.31 + i(0.95))$$

$$\approx 0.6 + 1.9i$$

$$z_2 = \sqrt[5]{32}\left[\cos\left(\frac{0° + 360° \cdot 2}{5}\right) + i\sin\left(\frac{0° + 360° \cdot 2}{5}\right)\right] = \sqrt[5]{32}(\cos 144° + i\sin 144°) \approx 2(-0.81 + i(0.59))$$

$$\approx -1.6 + 1.2i$$

$$z_3 = \sqrt[5]{32}\left[\cos\left(\frac{0° + 360° \cdot 3}{5}\right) + i\sin\left(\frac{0° + 360° \cdot 3}{5}\right)\right] = \sqrt[5]{32}(\cos 216° + i\sin 216°) \approx 2(-0.81 + i(-0.59))$$

$$\approx -1.6 - 1.2i$$

$$z_4 = \sqrt[5]{32}\left[\cos\left(\frac{0° + 360° \cdot 4}{5}\right) + i\sin\left(\frac{0° + 360° \cdot 4}{5}\right)\right] = \sqrt[5]{32}(\cos 288° + i\sin 288°) \approx 2(0.31 + i(-0.95))$$

$$\approx 0.6 - 1.9i$$

73. $1 = 1(\cos 0° + i\sin 0°)$

$$z_k = \sqrt[3]{1}\left[\cos\left(\frac{0° + 360°k}{3}\right) + i\sin\left(\frac{0° + 360°k}{3}\right)\right], \; k = 0,1,2$$

$$z_0 = \sqrt[3]{1}\left[\cos\left(\frac{0° + 360° \cdot 0}{3}\right) + i\sin\left(\frac{0° + 360° \cdot 0}{3}\right)\right] = \sqrt[3]{1}(\cos 0° + i\sin 0°) = 1(1 + 0i) = 1$$

$$z_1 = \sqrt[3]{1}\left[\cos\left(\frac{0° + 360° \cdot 1}{3}\right) + i\sin\left(\frac{0° + 360° \cdot 1}{3}\right)\right] = \sqrt[3]{1}(\cos 120° + i\sin 120°) = 1\left(-\frac{1}{2} + i\frac{\sqrt{3}}{2}\right) = -\frac{1}{2} + \frac{\sqrt{3}}{2}i$$

$$z_2 = \sqrt[3]{1}\left[\cos\left(\frac{0° + 360° \cdot 2}{3}\right) + i\sin\left(\frac{0° + 360° \cdot 2}{3}\right)\right] = \sqrt[3]{1}(\cos 240° + i\sin 240°) = 1\left(-\frac{1}{2} + i\left(-\frac{\sqrt{3}}{2}\right)\right)$$

$$= -\frac{1}{2} - \frac{\sqrt{3}}{2}i$$

75. $1 + i = \sqrt{2}\left(\cos 45° + i \sin 45°\right)$

$$z_k = \sqrt[4]{\sqrt{2}}\left[\cos\left(\frac{45° + 360°k}{4}\right) + i \sin\left(\frac{45° + 360°k}{4}\right)\right], \; k = 0, 1, 2, 3$$

$$z_0 = \sqrt[4]{\sqrt{2}}\left[\cos\left(\frac{45° + 360° \cdot 0}{4}\right) + i \sin\left(\frac{45° + 360° \cdot 0}{4}\right)\right] = \sqrt[4]{\sqrt{2}}\left(\cos 11.25° + i \sin 11.25°\right) \approx 1.1 + 0.2i$$

$$z_1 = \sqrt[4]{\sqrt{2}}\left[\cos\left(\frac{45° + 360° \cdot 1}{4}\right) + i \sin\left(\frac{45° + 360° \cdot 1}{4}\right)\right] = \sqrt[4]{\sqrt{2}}\left(\cos 101.25° + i \sin 101.25°\right) \approx -0.2 + 1.1i$$

$$z_2 = \sqrt[4]{\sqrt{2}}\left[\cos\left(\frac{45° + 360° \cdot 2}{4}\right) + i \sin\left(\frac{45° + 360° \cdot 2}{4}\right)\right] = \sqrt[4]{\sqrt{2}}\left(\cos 191.25° + i \sin 191.25°\right) \approx -1.1 - 0.2i$$

$$z_3 = \sqrt[4]{\sqrt{2}}\left[\cos\left(\frac{45° + 360° \cdot 3}{4}\right) + i \sin\left(\frac{45° + 360° \cdot 3}{4}\right)\right] = \sqrt[4]{\sqrt{2}}\left(\cos 281.25° + i \sin 281.25°\right) \approx 0.2 - 1.1i$$

77. $z = i$

    a.

$$z_1 = z = i$$
$$z_2 = z^2 + z = (i)^2 + i = -1 + i$$
$$z_3 = \left(z^2 + z\right)^2 + z = z_2^2 + z = \left(-1 + i\right)^2 + i = -i$$
$$z_4 = \left[\left(z^2 + z\right)^2 + z\right]^2 + z = z_3^2 + z = (-i)^2 + i = -1 + i$$
$$z_5 = z_4^2 + z = (-1 + i)^2 + i = -i$$
$$z_6 = z_5^2 + z = (-i)^2 + i = -1 + i$$

    b. $\left|-1 + i\right| = \sqrt{(-1)^2 + 1^2} = \sqrt{2}$

            $\left|i\right| = \sqrt{0^2 + 1^2} = 1$

The absolute values of the terms in the sequence are 1 and $\sqrt{2}$.
Choose a complex number with absolute value less than 1, and another with absolute value greater than $\sqrt{2}$. Complex numbers may vary.

79.–89. Answers may vary.

91. Exercise 27

```
P▶Rx(6,30)
        5.196152423
P▶Ry(6,30)
                  3
```

Exercise 29

```
P▶Rx(4,240)
                 -2
P▶Ry(4,240)
        -3.464101615
```

Exercise 31

```
P▶Rx(8,7π/4)
     5.656854249
P▶Ry(8,7π/4)
    -5.656854249
```

Exercise 33

```
P▶Rx(5,π/2)
                 0
P▶Ry(5,π/2)
                 5
```

93. $1 = 1\left(\cos 0° + i\sin 0°\right)$

$$z_k = \sqrt[4]{1}\left[\cos\left(\frac{0° + 360°k}{4}\right) + i\sin\left(\frac{0° + 360°k}{4}\right)\right], \ k = 0,1,2,3$$

$$z_0 = \sqrt[4]{1}\left[\cos\left(\frac{0° + 360° \cdot 0}{4}\right) + i\sin\left(\frac{0° + 360° \cdot 0}{4}\right)\right] = \sqrt[4]{1}\left(\cos 0° + i\sin 0\right) = 1(1 + 0i) = 1$$

$$z_1 = \sqrt[4]{1}\left[\cos\left(\frac{0° + 360° \cdot 1}{4}\right) + i\sin\left(\frac{0° + 360° \cdot 1}{4}\right)\right] = \sqrt[4]{1}\left(\cos 90° + i\sin 90°\right) = 1(0 + i(1)) = i$$

$$z_2 = \sqrt[4]{1}\left[\cos\left(\frac{0° + 360° \cdot 2}{4}\right) + i\sin\left(\frac{0° + 360° \cdot 2}{4}\right)\right] = \sqrt[4]{1}\left(\cos 180° + i\sin 180°\right) = 1(-1 + 0i) = -1$$

$$z_3 = \sqrt[4]{1}\left[\cos\left(\frac{0° + 360° \cdot 3}{4}\right) + i\sin\left(\frac{0° + 360° \cdot 3}{4}\right)\right] = \sqrt[4]{1}\left(\cos 270° + i\sin 270°\right) = 1(0 + i(-1)) = -i$$

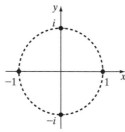

95. $x^3 - 8i = 0$

$\quad\quad x^3 = 8i$

We need to find the complex cube roots of $8i$.

$$8i = 8\left(\cos\frac{\pi}{2} + i\sin\frac{\pi}{2}\right)$$

$$z_k = \sqrt[3]{8}\left[\cos\left(\frac{\frac{\pi}{2} + 2\pi k}{3}\right) + i\sin\left(\frac{\frac{\pi}{2} + 2\pi k}{3}\right)\right],\ k = 0,\ 1,\ 2$$

$$z_0 = \sqrt[3]{8}\left[\cos\left(\frac{\frac{\pi}{2} + 2\pi \cdot 0}{3}\right) + i\sin\left(\frac{\frac{\pi}{2} + 2\pi \cdot 0}{3}\right)\right] = \sqrt[3]{8}\left(\cos\frac{\pi}{6} + i\sin\frac{\pi}{6}\right) = 2\left(\frac{\sqrt{3}}{2} + i\left(\frac{1}{2}\right)\right) = \sqrt{3} + i$$

$$z_1 = \sqrt[3]{8}\left[\cos\left(\frac{\frac{\pi}{2} + 2\pi \cdot 1}{3}\right) + i\sin\left(\frac{\frac{\pi}{2} + 2\pi \cdot 1}{3}\right)\right] = \sqrt[3]{8}\left(\cos\frac{5\pi}{6} + i\sin\frac{5\pi}{6}\right) = 2\left(-\frac{\sqrt{3}}{2} + i\left(\frac{1}{2}\right)\right) = -\sqrt{3} + i$$

$$z_2 = \sqrt[3]{8}\left[\cos\left(\frac{\frac{\pi}{2} + 2\pi \cdot 2}{3}\right) + i\sin\left(\frac{\frac{\pi}{2} + 2\pi \cdot 2}{3}\right)\right] = \sqrt[3]{8}\left(\cos\frac{3\pi}{2} + i\sin\frac{3\pi}{2}\right) = 2\left(0 + i(-1)\right) = -2i$$

Section 2.5

Check Point Exercises

1. First, we show that **u** and **v** have the same magnitude.

$$\|\mathbf{u}\| = \sqrt{(x_2 - x_1)^2 + (y_2 - y_1)^2}$$
$$= \sqrt{(-2 - (-5))^2 + (6 - 2)^2}$$
$$= \sqrt{3^2 + 4^2}$$
$$= \sqrt{9 + 16}$$
$$= \sqrt{25}$$
$$= 5$$

$$\|\mathbf{v}\| = \sqrt{(x_2 - x_1)^2 + (y_2 - y_1)^2}$$
$$= \sqrt{(5 - 2)^2 + (6 - 2)^2}$$
$$= \sqrt{3^2 + 4^2}$$
$$= \sqrt{9 + 16}$$
$$= \sqrt{25}$$
$$= 5$$

Thus, **u** and **v** have the same magnitude:
$$\|\mathbf{u}\| = \|\mathbf{v}\|.$$

Next, we show that **u** and **v** have the same direction. the line on which **u** lies has slope

$$m = \frac{y_2 - y_1}{x_2 - x_1} = \frac{6 - 2}{-2 - (-5)} = \frac{4}{3}.$$

The line on which **v** lies has slope

$$m = \frac{y_2 - y_1}{x_2 - x_1} = \frac{6 - 2}{5 - 2} = \frac{4}{3}.$$

Because **u** and **v** are both directed toward the upper right on lines having the same slope, $\frac{4}{3}$, they have the same direction. Thus, **u** and **v** have the same magnitude and direction, and **u** = **v**.

2. For the given vector $\mathbf{v} = 3\mathbf{i} - 3\mathbf{j}$, $a = 3$ and $b = -3$. The vector's initial point is the origin,

(0, 0). The vector's terminal point is $(a, b) = (3, -3)$. We sketch the vector by drawing an arrow from (0, 0) to (3, –3).

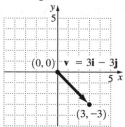

We determine the magnitude of the vector by using the distance formula. Thus, the magnitude is

$$\|\mathbf{v}\| = \sqrt{a^2 + b^2}$$
$$= \sqrt{3^2 + (-3)^2}$$
$$= \sqrt{9 + 9}$$
$$= \sqrt{18}$$
$$= 3\sqrt{2}.$$

3. We identify the values for the variables in the formula.

$$P_1 = (-1, 3) \quad P_2 = (2, 7)$$
$$\qquad \uparrow \ \uparrow \qquad\quad \uparrow \ \uparrow$$
$$\qquad x_1 \ y_1 \qquad\ x_2 \ y_2$$

Using these values, we write **v** in terms of **i** and **j** as follows:

$$\mathbf{v} = (x_2 - x_1)\mathbf{i} + (y_2 - y_1)\mathbf{j}$$
$$= (2 - (-1))\mathbf{i} + (7 - 3)\mathbf{j}$$
$$= 3\mathbf{i} + 4\mathbf{j}$$

4. a. $\mathbf{v} + \mathbf{w} = (7\mathbf{i} + 3\mathbf{j}) + (4\mathbf{i} - 5\mathbf{j})$
$$= (7 + 4)\mathbf{i} + (3 - 5)\mathbf{j}$$
$$= 11\mathbf{i} - 2\mathbf{j}$$

   b. $\mathbf{v} - \mathbf{w} = (7\mathbf{i} + 3\mathbf{j}) - (4\mathbf{i} - 5\mathbf{j})$
$$= (7 - 4)\mathbf{i} + (3 - (-5))\mathbf{j}$$
$$= 3\mathbf{i} + 8\mathbf{j}$$

5. a. $8\mathbf{v} = 8(7\mathbf{i} + 10\mathbf{j})$

$\qquad = (8 ? 7)\mathbf{i} + (8 ? 10)\mathbf{j}$

$\qquad = 56\mathbf{i} + 80\mathbf{j}$

b. $-5\mathbf{v} = -5(7\mathbf{i} + 10\mathbf{j})$

$\qquad = (-5 ? 7)\mathbf{i} + (-5 ? 10)\mathbf{j}$

$\qquad = -35\mathbf{i} - 50\mathbf{j}$

6. $6\mathbf{v} - 3\mathbf{w} = 6(7\mathbf{i} + 3\mathbf{j}) - 3(4\mathbf{i} - 5\mathbf{j})$

$\qquad = 42\mathbf{i} + 18\mathbf{j} - 12\mathbf{i} + 15\mathbf{j}$

$\qquad = (42 - 12)\mathbf{i} + (18 + 15)\mathbf{j}$

$\qquad = 30\mathbf{i} + 33\mathbf{j}$

7. First, find the magnitude of **v.**

$\|\mathbf{v}\| = \sqrt{a^2 + b^2}$

$\qquad = \sqrt{4^2 + (-3)^2}$

$\qquad = \sqrt{16 + 9}$

$\qquad = \sqrt{25}$

$\qquad = 5$

A unit vector in the same direction as **v** is

$\dfrac{\mathbf{v}}{\|\mathbf{v}\|} = \dfrac{4\mathbf{i} - 3\mathbf{j}}{5} = \dfrac{4}{5}\mathbf{i} - \dfrac{3}{5}\mathbf{j}$

Now, we must verify that the magnitude of the

vector is 1. The magnitude of $\dfrac{4}{5}\mathbf{i} - \dfrac{3}{5}\mathbf{j}$ is

$\sqrt{\left(\dfrac{4}{5}\right)^2 + \left(-\dfrac{3}{5}\right)^2} = \sqrt{\dfrac{16}{25} + \dfrac{9}{25}} = \sqrt{\dfrac{25}{25}} = 1.$

8. $60 \cos 45° \, \mathbf{i} + 60 \sin 45° \, \mathbf{j}$

$= 60 \cdot \dfrac{\sqrt{2}}{2}\mathbf{i} + 60 \cdot \dfrac{\sqrt{2}}{2}\mathbf{j}$

$= 30\sqrt{2}\mathbf{i} + 30\sqrt{2}\mathbf{j}$

9. We need to find $\|\mathbf{F}\|$ and θ.

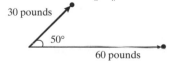

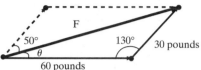

Use the Law of Cosines to find the magnitude of **F.**

$\|\mathbf{F}\|^2 = 60^2 + 30^2 - 2(60)(30)\cos 130° \approx 6814$

$\|\mathbf{F}\| \approx \sqrt{6814} \approx 82.5$

The magnitude of the resultant force is about 82.5 pounds.

To find θ, the direction of the resultant force, we use the Law of Sines.

$\dfrac{82.5}{\sin 130°} = \dfrac{30}{\sin \theta}$

$82.5 \sin \theta = 30 \sin 130°$

$\sin \theta = \dfrac{30 \sin 130°}{82.5}$

$\theta = \sin^{-1}\left(\dfrac{30 \sin 130°}{82.5}\right) \approx 16.2°$

The two given forces are equivalent to a single force of about 82.5 pounds in the direction of approximately 16.2° relative to the 60-pound force.

Exercise Set 2.5

1. a. $\|\mathbf{u}\| = \sqrt{(x_2 - x_1)^2 + (y_2 - y_1)^2}$

$\qquad = \sqrt{(4 - (-1))^2 + (6 - 2)^2}$

$\qquad = \sqrt{5^2 + 4^2}$

$\qquad = \sqrt{25 + 16}$

$\qquad = \sqrt{41}$

b. $\|\mathbf{v}\| = \sqrt{(x_2 - x_1)^2 + (y_2 - y_1)^2}$

$\quad = \sqrt{(5-0)^2 + (4-0)^2}$

$\quad = \sqrt{5^2 + 4^2}$

$\quad = \sqrt{25 + 16}$

$\quad = \sqrt{41}$

c. Since $\|\mathbf{u}\| = \|\mathbf{v}\|$, and $\mathbf{u}$ and $\mathbf{v}$ have the same direction, we can conclude that $\mathbf{u} = \mathbf{v}$.

3. a. $\|\mathbf{u}\| = \sqrt{(x_2 - x_1)^2 + (y_2 - y_1)^2}$

$\quad = \sqrt{(5-(-1))^2 + (1-1)^2}$

$\quad = \sqrt{6^2 + 0^2}$

$\quad = \sqrt{36 + 0}$

$\quad = \sqrt{36}$

$\quad = 6$

b. $\|\mathbf{v}\| = \sqrt{(x_2 - x_1)^2 + (y_2 - y_1)^2}$

$\quad = \sqrt{(4-(-2))^2 + (-1-(-1))^2}$

$\quad = \sqrt{6^2 + 0^2}$

$\quad = \sqrt{36 + 0}$

$\quad = \sqrt{36}$

$\quad = 6$

c. Since $\|\mathbf{u}\| = \|\mathbf{v}\|$, and $\mathbf{u}$ and $\mathbf{v}$ have the same direction, we can conclude that $\mathbf{u} = \mathbf{v}$.

5.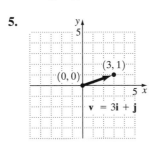

$\|\mathbf{v}\| = \sqrt{3^2 + 1^2} = \sqrt{9+1} = \sqrt{10}$

7.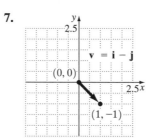

$\|\mathbf{v}\| = \sqrt{1^2 + (-1)^2} = \sqrt{1+1} = \sqrt{2}$

9.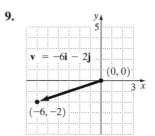

$\|\mathbf{v}\| = \sqrt{(-6)^2 + (-2)^2}$

$\quad = \sqrt{36 + 4}$

$\quad = \sqrt{40}$

$\quad = 2\sqrt{10}$

11.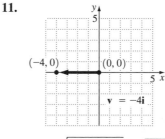

$\|\mathbf{v}\| = \sqrt{(-4)^2 + 0^2} = \sqrt{16+0} = \sqrt{16} = 4$

13. $\mathbf{v} = (x_2 - x_1)\mathbf{i} + (y_2 - y_1)\mathbf{j}$

$\mathbf{v} = (6-(-4))\mathbf{i} + (2-(-4))\mathbf{j} = 10\mathbf{i} + 6\mathbf{j}$

15. $\mathbf{v} = (x_2 - x_1)\mathbf{i} + (y_2 - y_1)\mathbf{j}$
$\mathbf{v} = (-2 - (-8))\mathbf{i} + (3 - 6)\mathbf{j} = 6\mathbf{i} - 3\mathbf{j}$

17. $\mathbf{v} = (x_2 - x_1)\mathbf{i} + (y_2 - y_1)\mathbf{j}$
$\mathbf{v} = (-7 - (-1))\mathbf{i} + (-7 - 7)\mathbf{j} = -6\mathbf{i} - 14\mathbf{j}$

19. $\mathbf{v} = (x_2 - x_1)\mathbf{i} + (y_2 - y_1)\mathbf{j}$
$\mathbf{v} = (6 - (-3))\mathbf{i} + (4 - 4)\mathbf{j} = 9\mathbf{i} + 0\mathbf{j} = 9\mathbf{i}$

21. $\begin{aligned} \mathbf{u} + \mathbf{v} &= (2\mathbf{i} - 5\mathbf{j}) + (-3\mathbf{i} + 7\mathbf{j}) \\ &= (2 - 3)\mathbf{i} + (-5 + 7)\mathbf{j} \\ &= -\mathbf{i} + 2\mathbf{j} \end{aligned}$

23. $\begin{aligned} \mathbf{u} - \mathbf{v} &= (2\mathbf{i} - 5\mathbf{j}) - (-3\mathbf{i} + 7\mathbf{j}) \\ &= 2\mathbf{i} - 5\mathbf{j} + 3\mathbf{i} - 7\mathbf{j} \\ &= (2 + 3)\mathbf{i} + (-5 - 7)\mathbf{j} \\ &= 5\mathbf{i} - 12\mathbf{j} \end{aligned}$

25. $\begin{aligned} \mathbf{v} - \mathbf{u} &= (-3\mathbf{i} + 7\mathbf{j}) - (2\mathbf{i} - 5\mathbf{j}) \\ &= -3\mathbf{i} + 7\mathbf{j} - 2\mathbf{i} + 5\mathbf{j} \\ &= (-3 - 2)\mathbf{i} + (7 + 5)\mathbf{j} \\ &= -5\mathbf{i} + 12\mathbf{j} \end{aligned}$

27. $5\mathbf{v} = 5(-3\mathbf{i} + 7\mathbf{j}) = -15\mathbf{i} + 35\mathbf{j}$

29. $-4\mathbf{w} = -4(-\mathbf{i} - 6\mathbf{j}) = 4\mathbf{i} + 24\mathbf{j}$

31. $\begin{aligned} 3\mathbf{w} + 2\mathbf{v} &= 3(-\mathbf{i} - 6\mathbf{j}) + 2(-3\mathbf{i} + 7\mathbf{j}) \\ &= -3\mathbf{i} - 18\mathbf{j} - 6\mathbf{i} + 14\mathbf{j} \\ &= (-3 - 6)\mathbf{i} + (-18 + 14)\mathbf{j} \\ &= -9\mathbf{i} - 4\mathbf{j} \end{aligned}$

33. $\begin{aligned} 3\mathbf{v} - 4\mathbf{w} &= 3(-3\mathbf{i} + 7\mathbf{j}) - 4(-\mathbf{i} - 6\mathbf{j}) \\ &= -9\mathbf{i} + 21\mathbf{j} + 4\mathbf{i} + 24\mathbf{j} \\ &= (-9 + 4)\mathbf{i} + (21 + 24)\mathbf{j} \\ &= -5\mathbf{i} + 45\mathbf{j} \end{aligned}$

35.
$$\begin{aligned} \left\| 2\mathbf{u} \right\| &= \left\| 2(2\mathbf{i} - 5\mathbf{j}) \right\| \\ &= \left\| 4\mathbf{i} - 10\mathbf{j} \right\| \\ &= \sqrt{4^2 + (-10)^2} \\ &= \sqrt{16 + 100} \\ &= \sqrt{116} \\ &= 2\sqrt{29} \end{aligned}$$

37.
$$\begin{aligned} \left\| \mathbf{w} - \mathbf{u} \right\| &= \left\| (-\mathbf{i} - 6\mathbf{j}) - (2\mathbf{i} - 5\mathbf{j}) \right\| \\ &= \left\| -\mathbf{i} - 6\mathbf{j} - 2\mathbf{i} + 5\mathbf{j} \right\| \\ &= \left\| (-1 - 2)\mathbf{i} + (-6 + 5)\mathbf{j} \right\| \\ &= \left\| -3\mathbf{i} - \mathbf{j} \right\| \\ &= \sqrt{(-3)^2 + (-1)^2} \\ &= \sqrt{9 + 1} \\ &= \sqrt{10} \end{aligned}$$

39. $\dfrac{\mathbf{v}}{\left\| \mathbf{v} \right\|} = \dfrac{6\mathbf{i}}{\sqrt{6^2 + 0^2}} = \dfrac{6\mathbf{i}}{\sqrt{36}} = \dfrac{6\mathbf{i}}{6} = \mathbf{i}$

41.

$$\begin{aligned} \dfrac{\mathbf{v}}{\left\| \mathbf{v} \right\|} &= \dfrac{3\mathbf{i} - 4\mathbf{j}}{\sqrt{3^2 + (-4)^2}} \\ &= \dfrac{3\mathbf{i} - 4\mathbf{j}}{\sqrt{9 + 16}} \\ &= \dfrac{3\mathbf{i} - 4\mathbf{j}}{\sqrt{25}} \\ &= \dfrac{3\mathbf{i} - 4\mathbf{j}}{5} \\ &= \dfrac{3}{5}\mathbf{i} - \dfrac{4}{5}\mathbf{j} \end{aligned}$$

43.

$$\frac{\mathbf{v}}{\|\mathbf{v}\|} = \frac{3\mathbf{i} - 2\mathbf{j}}{\sqrt{3^2 + (-2)^2}}$$

$$= \frac{3\mathbf{i} - 2\mathbf{j}}{\sqrt{9 + 4}}$$

$$= \frac{3\mathbf{i} - 2\mathbf{j}}{\sqrt{13}}$$

$$= \frac{3}{\sqrt{13}}\mathbf{i} - \frac{2}{\sqrt{13}}\mathbf{j}$$

45.

$$\frac{\mathbf{v}}{\|\mathbf{v}\|} = \frac{\mathbf{i} + \mathbf{j}}{\sqrt{1^2 + 1^2}}$$

$$= \frac{\mathbf{i} + \mathbf{j}}{\sqrt{2}}$$

$$= \frac{\mathbf{i}}{\sqrt{2}} + \frac{\mathbf{j}}{\sqrt{2}}$$

$$= \frac{\sqrt{2}}{2}\mathbf{i} + \frac{\sqrt{2}}{2}\mathbf{j}$$

47. $\mathbf{v} = \|\mathbf{v}\|\cos\theta\,\mathbf{i} + \|v\|\sin\theta\,\mathbf{j}$

$$= 6\cos 30°\mathbf{i} + 6\sin 30°\mathbf{j}$$

$$= 6\left(\frac{\sqrt{3}}{2}\right)\mathbf{i} + 6\left(\frac{1}{2}\right)\mathbf{j}$$

$$= 3\sqrt{3}\mathbf{i} + 3\mathbf{j}$$

49. $\mathbf{v} = \|\mathbf{v}\|\cos\theta\,\mathbf{i} + \|\mathbf{v}\|\sin\theta\,\mathbf{j}$

$$= 12\cos 225°\mathbf{i} + 12\sin 225°\mathbf{j}$$

$$= 12\left(-\frac{\sqrt{2}}{2}\right)\mathbf{i} + 12\left(-\frac{\sqrt{2}}{2}\right)\mathbf{j}$$

$$= -6\sqrt{2}\mathbf{i} - 6\sqrt{2}\mathbf{j}$$

51. $\mathbf{v} = \|\mathbf{v}\|\cos\theta\,\mathbf{i} + \|\mathbf{v}\|\sin\theta\,\mathbf{j}$

$$= \frac{1}{2}\cos 113°\mathbf{i} + \frac{1}{2}\sin 113°\mathbf{j}$$

$$\approx \frac{1}{2}(-0.39)\mathbf{i} + \frac{1}{2}(0.92)\mathbf{j}$$

$$\approx -0.20\mathbf{i} + 0.46\mathbf{j}$$

53. $\left\|\vec{v}\right\| = \sqrt{1^2 + 2^2}$

$$\left\|\vec{v}\right\| = \sqrt{5}$$

$$\theta = \tan^{-1}\left(\frac{2}{1}\right)$$

$$\theta = 63.4°$$

55. $\left\|\vec{v}\right\| = \sqrt{0^2 + (-5)^2}$

$$\left\|\vec{v}\right\| = 5$$

$$\theta = 270°$$

57. $\quad a = 5\cos 45°\quad\quad b = 5\sin 45°$
$\quad\quad\; a = 3.5 \quad\quad\quad\quad b = 3.5$

59. $\quad a = 6\cos 50°\quad\quad b = 6\sin 50°$
$\quad\quad\; a = 3.9 \quad\quad\quad\quad b = 4.6$

61. $\mathbf{v} = \|\mathbf{v}\|\cos\theta\,\mathbf{i} + \|\mathbf{v}\|\sin\theta\,\mathbf{j}$

$$= 44\cos 30°\mathbf{i} + 44\sin 30°\mathbf{j}$$

$$= 44\left(\frac{\sqrt{3}}{2}\right)\mathbf{i} + 44\left(\frac{1}{2}\right)\mathbf{j}$$

$$= 22\sqrt{3}\mathbf{i} + 22\mathbf{j}$$

$$\mathbf{v} = \|\mathbf{v}\|\cos\theta\,\mathbf{i} + \|\mathbf{v}\|\sin\theta\,\mathbf{j}$$

63. $\quad\; = 150\cos 8°\mathbf{i} + 150\sin 8°\mathbf{j}$

$$\approx 148.5\mathbf{i} + 20.9\mathbf{j}$$

65. $\mathbf{v} = \|\mathbf{v}\| \cos\theta \mathbf{i} + \|\mathbf{v}\| \sin\theta \mathbf{j}$

$\quad = 1.5\cos 25°\mathbf{i} + 1.5\sin 25°\mathbf{j}$

$\quad \approx 1.4\mathbf{i} + 0.6\mathbf{j}$

The length of the shadow is

$\left| 1.4 \right| = 1.4$ inches.

67. $\mathbf{F}_1 = \|\mathbf{F}_1\| \cos\_\mathbf{i} + \|\mathbf{F}_1\| \sin\_\mathbf{j}$

$\quad = 70\cos 326°\mathbf{i} + 70\sin 326°\mathbf{j}$

$\quad = 58\mathbf{i} - 39.1\mathbf{j}$

$\mathbf{F}_2 = \|\mathbf{F}_2\| \cos\_\mathbf{i} + \|\mathbf{F}_2\| \sin\_\mathbf{j}$

$\quad = 50\cos 18°\mathbf{i} + 50\sin 18°\mathbf{j}$

$\quad = 47.6\mathbf{i} + 15.5\mathbf{j}$

$\mathbf{F} = \mathbf{F}_1 + \mathbf{F}_2 = (58\mathbf{i} - 39.1\mathbf{j}) + (47.6\mathbf{i} + 15.5\mathbf{j})$
$\quad\quad = 105.6\mathbf{i} - 23.6\,\mathbf{j}$

$\| F \| = \sqrt{105.6^2 + (-23.6)^2} = 108.2$ pounds

$\cos\theta = \dfrac{a}{\| F \|}$

$\theta = \cos^{-1} \dfrac{105.6}{108.2} = 12.6°, 90 - 12.6 = \text{S}77.4°\text{E}$

69. $\mathbf{F}_1 = 70\cos 326°\mathbf{i} + 70\sin 326°\mathbf{j}$

$\quad = -100\mathbf{j}$

To find the length of the BC: $\quad \cos 18° = \dfrac{a}{100}$

$\quad\quad\quad\quad\quad\quad\quad\quad a \approx 95$

$\mathbf{F}_2 = 95\cos 2888° + 95\sin 288°$

$\quad = 29.4\mathbf{i} - 90.4\mathbf{j}$

$\mathbf{F} = \mathbf{F}_1 - \mathbf{F}_2 = (-100\mathbf{j}) - (29.4\mathbf{i} - 90.4\mathbf{j})$
$\quad\quad = -29.4\,\mathbf{i} - 9.6\,\mathbf{j}$

$\sqrt{(-29.4)^2 + (-9.6)^2} \approx 30.9$

The force required to pull the weight is 30.9 pounds.

71. a. $\mathbf{F}_1 + \mathbf{F}_2 = (3 + 6)\mathbf{i} + (-5 + 2)\mathbf{j} = 9\mathbf{i} - 3\mathbf{j}$

b. $-9\mathbf{i} + 3\mathbf{j}$

73. a. $\mathbf{F}_1 = -3\mathbf{i}\quad (-3, 0)$

$\quad\quad \mathbf{F}_2 = -\mathbf{i} + 4\mathbf{j}\quad (-1, 4)$

$\quad\quad \mathbf{F}_3 = 4\mathbf{i} - 2\mathbf{i}\quad (4, -2)$

$\quad\quad \mathbf{F}_4 = -4\mathbf{j}\quad (0, -4)$

$\quad\quad \mathbf{F}_1 + \mathbf{F}_2 + \mathbf{F}_2 + \mathbf{F}_2 = (-3 - 1 + 4)\mathbf{i}$

$\quad\quad\quad + (4 - 2 - 4)\mathbf{j} = -2\mathbf{j}$

b. $2\mathbf{j}$

75. a. $\mathbf{v} = 180\cos 40°\,\mathbf{i} + 180\sin 40°\,\mathbf{j}$

$\quad\quad = 137.88\mathbf{i} + 115.7\mathbf{j}$

$\quad\quad \mathbf{w} = 40\cos 0°\,\mathbf{i} + 40\sin 0^0\,\mathbf{j}$

$\quad\quad = 40\mathbf{i}$

b. $\mathbf{v} + \mathbf{w} = (137.88 + 40)\mathbf{i} + 115.7\mathbf{j}$

$\quad\quad\quad = 177.88\mathbf{i} + 115.7\mathbf{j}$

c. $\sqrt{177.88^2 + 115.7^2} \approx 212$ mph

d. $\cos\theta = \dfrac{177.88}{212}$

$\quad\quad \theta = 33°$

$\quad\quad 90° - 33° = \text{N}57°\text{E}$

77. $\mathbf{v} = 320\cos 20°\,\mathbf{i} + 320\sin 20°\,\mathbf{j}$

$\quad = 300.7\mathbf{i} + 109.5\mathbf{j}$

$\mathbf{w} = 370\cos 30°\,\mathbf{i} + 370\sin 30°\,\mathbf{j}$

$\quad = 320.4\mathbf{i} + 185\mathbf{j}$

$\mathbf{w} - \mathbf{v} = (320.4 - 300.7)\mathbf{i}$

$\quad\quad\quad + (115.7 - 109.5)\mathbf{j}$

$\quad = 19.7\mathbf{i} + 75.6\mathbf{j}$

$\sqrt{19.7^2 + 75.6^2} \approx 78$ mph

$\quad \cos\theta = \dfrac{19.7}{78}$

$\quad\quad \theta = 75.4°$

79.–95. Answers may vary.

97.

$$\frac{\mathbf{v}}{\|\mathbf{v}\|} = \frac{a\mathbf{i} + b\mathbf{j}}{\|a\mathbf{i} + b\mathbf{j}\|} = \frac{a\mathbf{i} + b\mathbf{j}}{\sqrt{a^2 + b^2}}$$

$$= \frac{a}{\sqrt{a^2 + b^2}}\mathbf{i} + \frac{b}{\sqrt{a^2 + b^2}}\mathbf{j}$$

$$\left\|\frac{\mathbf{v}}{\|\mathbf{v}\|}\right\|^2 = \left(\frac{a}{\sqrt{a^2 + b^2}}\right)^2 + \left(\frac{b}{\sqrt{a^2 + b^2}}\right)^2$$

$$= \frac{a^2}{a^2 + b^2} + \frac{b^2}{a^2 + b^2} = \frac{a^2 + b^2}{a^2 + b^2} = 1$$

$$\left\|\frac{\mathbf{v}}{\|\mathbf{v}\|}\right\| = 1$$

Since $\left\|\dfrac{\mathbf{v}}{\|\mathbf{v}\|}\right\|$ is 1, $\dfrac{\mathbf{v}}{\|\mathbf{v}\|}$ is a unit vector.

99.

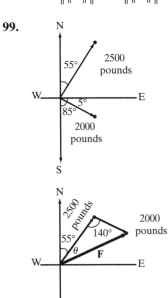

To find the magnitude of **F**, we use the Law of Cosines.

$$\|\mathbf{F}\|^2 = 2500^2 + 2000^2 - 2(2500)(2000)\cos 140°$$

$$\approx 17,910,444.4$$

$$\|\mathbf{F}\| \approx \sqrt{17,910,444.4} \approx 4232.1$$

To find the compass direction of the resultant force, use the Law of Sines.

$$\frac{4232.1}{\sin 140°} = \frac{2000°}{\sin\theta}$$

$$4232.1\sin\theta = 2000\sin 140°$$

$$\sin\theta = \frac{2000\sin 140°}{4232.1}$$

$$\theta = \sin^{-1}\left(\frac{2000\sin 140°}{4232.1}\right)$$

$$\theta \approx 17.7°$$

The compass direction of the resultant force is $55° + 17.7° = 72.7°$.

Section 2.6

Check Point Exercises

1. a. $\mathbf{v \cdot w} = 7(2) + (-4)(-1) = 14 + 4 = 18$

b. $\mathbf{w \cdot v} = 2(7) + (-1)(-4) = 14 + 4 = 18$

c. $\mathbf{w \cdot w} = 2(2) + (-1)(-1) = 4 + 1 = 5.$

2. $\cos\theta = \dfrac{\mathbf{v \cdot w}}{\|\mathbf{v}\| \ \|\mathbf{w}\|}$

$$= \frac{(4\mathbf{i} - 3\mathbf{j}) \cdot (\mathbf{i} + 2\mathbf{j})}{\sqrt{4^2 + (-3)^2}\sqrt{1^2 + 2^2}}$$

$$= \frac{4(1) + (-3)(2)}{\sqrt{25}\sqrt{5}}$$

$$= \frac{2}{\sqrt{125}}$$

The angle θ between the vector is

$$\theta = \cos^{-1}\left(-\frac{2}{\sqrt{125}}\right) \approx 100.3°.$$

3. $\mathbf{v \cdot w} = (6\mathbf{i} - 3\mathbf{j}) \cdot (\mathbf{i} + 2\mathbf{j})$
$= 6(1) + (-3)(2) = 6 - 6 = 0$

The dot product is zero. Thus, the given vectors are orthogonal.

4. $\operatorname{proj}_{\mathbf{w}}\mathbf{v} = \dfrac{\mathbf{v}\cdot\mathbf{w}}{\|\mathbf{w}\|^2}\,\mathbf{w}$

$\qquad = \dfrac{(2\mathbf{i}-5\mathbf{j})\cdot(\mathbf{i}-\mathbf{j})}{\left(\sqrt{1^2+(-1)^2}\right)^2}\,\mathbf{w}$

$\qquad = \dfrac{2(1)+(-5)(-1)}{\left(\sqrt{2}\right)^2}\,\mathbf{w}$

$\qquad = \dfrac{7}{2}\,\mathbf{w}$

$\qquad = \dfrac{7}{2}(\mathbf{i}-\mathbf{j})$

$\qquad = \dfrac{7}{2}\mathbf{i} - \dfrac{7}{2}\mathbf{j}$

5. $\mathbf{v}_1 = \operatorname{proj}_{\mathbf{w}}\mathbf{v} = \dfrac{7}{2}\mathbf{i} - \dfrac{7}{2}\mathbf{j}$

$\quad \mathbf{v}_2 = \mathbf{v} - \mathbf{v}_1$

$\qquad = (2\mathbf{i}-5\mathbf{j}) - \left(\dfrac{7}{2}\mathbf{i} - \dfrac{7}{2}\mathbf{j}\right)$

$\qquad = -\dfrac{3}{2}\mathbf{i} - \dfrac{3}{2}\mathbf{j}$

6. $W = \|\mathbf{F}\|\,\left\|\overrightarrow{AB}\right\|\cos\theta = (20)(150)\cos 30°$

$\qquad \approx 2598$

The work done is approximately 2598 foot-pounds.

Exercise Set 2.6

1. a. $\mathbf{v}\cdot\mathbf{w} = 3(1) + 1(3) = 3 + 3 = 6$

   b. $\mathbf{v}\cdot\mathbf{w} = 3(3) + 1(1) = 9 + 1 = 10$

3. a. $\mathbf{v}\cdot\mathbf{w} = 5(-2) + (-4)(-1) = -10 + 4 = -6$

   b. $\mathbf{v}\cdot\mathbf{w} = 5(5) + (-4)(-4) = 25 + 16 = 41$

5. a. $\mathbf{v}\cdot\mathbf{w} = -6(-10) + (-5)(-8) = 60 + 40$
$\qquad\qquad = 100$

   b. $\mathbf{v}\cdot\mathbf{w} = -6(-6) + (-5)(-5) = 36 + 25 = 61$

7. a. $\mathbf{v}\cdot\mathbf{w} = 5(0) + 0(1) = 0 + 0 = 0$

   b. $\mathbf{v}\cdot\mathbf{w} = 5(5) + 0(0) = 25 + 0 = 25$

9. $\mathbf{v}\cdot(\mathbf{v}+\mathbf{w}) = (2\mathbf{i}-\mathbf{j})[(3\mathbf{i}+\mathbf{j})+(\mathbf{i}+4\mathbf{j})]$

$\qquad\qquad = (2\mathbf{i}-\mathbf{j})[(3+1)\mathbf{i}+(1+4)\mathbf{j})]$

$\qquad\qquad = (2\mathbf{i}-\mathbf{j})(4\mathbf{i}+5\mathbf{j})$

$\qquad\qquad = 2(4)+(-1)(5)$

$\qquad\qquad = 8-5$

$\qquad\qquad = 3$

11. $\mathbf{u}\cdot\mathbf{v}+\mathbf{u}\cdot\mathbf{w}$
$\quad = (2\mathbf{i}-\mathbf{j})\cdot(3\mathbf{i}+\mathbf{j})+(2\mathbf{i}-\mathbf{j})(\mathbf{i}+4\mathbf{j})$

$\quad = (2)(3)+(-1)(1)+2(1)+(-1)(4)$

$\quad = 6-1+2-4$

$\quad = 3$

13. $(4\mathbf{u})\cdot\mathbf{v}$
$\quad = [(4(2\mathbf{i}-\mathbf{j})]\cdot(3\mathbf{i}+\mathbf{j})$

$\quad = (8\mathbf{i}-4\mathbf{j})\cdot(3\mathbf{i}+\mathbf{j})$

$\quad = (8)(3)+(-4)(1)$

$\quad = 24-4$

$\quad = 20$

15. $4(\mathbf{u}\cdot\mathbf{v})$
$\quad = 4[(2\mathbf{i}-\mathbf{j})\cdot(3\mathbf{i}+\mathbf{j})]$

$\quad = 4[2(3)+(-1)1]$

$\quad = 4[6-1]$

$\quad = 4[5]$

$\quad = 20$

17. $\cos\theta \dfrac{\mathbf{v}\cdot\mathbf{w}}{\|\mathbf{v}\|\ \|\mathbf{w}\|}$

$=\dfrac{(2\mathbf{i}-\mathbf{j})\cdot(3\mathbf{i}+4\mathbf{j})}{\sqrt{2^2+\left(-1\right)^2}\ \sqrt{3^2+4^2}}$

$=\dfrac{2(3)+(-1)(4)}{\sqrt{5}\sqrt{25}}$

$=\dfrac{6-4}{\sqrt{125}}$

$=\dfrac{2}{\sqrt{125}}$

The angle θ between the vectors is

$\theta=\cos^{-1}\left(\dfrac{2}{\sqrt{125}}\right)\approx 79.7°.$

19. $\cos\theta \dfrac{\mathbf{v}\cdot\mathbf{w}}{\|\mathbf{v}\|\ \|\mathbf{w}\|}$

$=\dfrac{(-3\mathbf{i}+2\mathbf{j})\cdot(4\mathbf{i}-\mathbf{j})}{\sqrt{(-3)^2+2^2}\ \sqrt{4^2+(-1)^2}}$

$=\dfrac{-3(4)+2(-1)}{\sqrt{13}\sqrt{17}}$

$=\dfrac{-14}{\sqrt{221}}$

The angle θ between the vectors is

$\theta=\cos^{-1}\left(-\dfrac{14}{\sqrt{221}}\right)\approx 160.3°.$

21. $\cos\theta \dfrac{\mathbf{v}\cdot\mathbf{w}}{\|\mathbf{v}\|\ \|\mathbf{w}\|}$

$=\dfrac{(6\mathbf{i}+0\mathbf{j})\cdot(5\mathbf{i}+4\mathbf{j})}{\sqrt{6^2+0^2}\ \sqrt{5^2+4^2}}$

$=\dfrac{6(5)+0(4)}{\sqrt{36}\sqrt{41}}$

$=\dfrac{30}{\sqrt{1476}}$

The angle θ between the vectors is

$\theta=\cos^{-1}\left(\dfrac{30}{\sqrt{1476}}\right)\approx 38.7°.$

23. $\mathbf{v}\cdot\mathbf{w}=(\mathbf{i}+\mathbf{j})\cdot(\mathbf{i}-\mathbf{j})=(1)(1)+1(-1)=1-1=0$
The dot product is zero. Thus, the given vectors are orthogonal.

25. $\mathbf{v}\cdot\mathbf{w}=(2\mathbf{i}+8\mathbf{j})\cdot(4\mathbf{i}-\mathbf{j})$
$=2(4)+(8)(-1)$
$=8-8$
$=0$
The dot product is zero. Thus, the given vectors are orthogonal.

27. $\mathbf{v}\cdot\mathbf{w}=(2\mathbf{i}-2\mathbf{j})\cdot(-\mathbf{i}+\mathbf{j})$
$=2(-1)+(-2)(1)$
$=-2-2$
$=-4$
The dot product is not zero. Thus, the given vectors are not orthogonal.

29. $\mathbf{v}\cdot\mathbf{w}=(3\mathbf{i}+0\mathbf{j})\cdot(-4\mathbf{i}+0\mathbf{j})$
$=3(-4)+0(0)$
$=-12+0$
$=-12$
The dot product is not zero. Thus, the given vectors are not orthogonal.

31. $\mathbf{v}\cdot\mathbf{w}=(3\mathbf{i}+0\mathbf{j})\cdot(0\mathbf{i}-4\mathbf{j})$
$=3(0)+(0)(-4)$
$=0+0$
$=0$
The dot product is zero. Thus, the given vectors are orthogonal.

33. $\text{proj}_{\mathbf{w}}\mathbf{v} = \dfrac{\mathbf{v}\cdot\mathbf{w}}{\|\,\mathbf{w}\,\|^2}\,\mathbf{w}$

$\qquad = \dfrac{(3\mathbf{i}-2\mathbf{j})\cdot(\mathbf{i}-\mathbf{j})}{\left(\sqrt{1^2+(-1)^2}\right)^2}\,\mathbf{w}$

$\qquad = \dfrac{3(1)+(-2)(-1)}{\left(\sqrt{2}\right)^2}$

$\qquad = \dfrac{5}{2}\,\mathbf{w}$

$\qquad = \dfrac{5}{2}(\mathbf{i}-\mathbf{j})$

$\qquad = \dfrac{5}{2}\mathbf{i}-\dfrac{5}{2}\mathbf{j}$

$\mathbf{v}_1 = \text{proj}_{\mathbf{w}}\mathbf{v} = \dfrac{5}{2}\mathbf{i}-\dfrac{5}{2}\mathbf{j}$

$\mathbf{v}_2 = \mathbf{v}-\mathbf{v}_1 = (3\mathbf{i}-2\mathbf{j})-\left(\dfrac{5}{2}\mathbf{i}-\dfrac{5}{2}\mathbf{j}\right)$

$\qquad = \dfrac{1}{2}\mathbf{i}+\dfrac{1}{2}\mathbf{j}$

35. $\text{proj}_{\mathbf{w}}\mathbf{v} = \dfrac{\mathbf{v}\cdot\mathbf{w}}{\|\,\mathbf{w}\,\|}\,\mathbf{w}$

$\qquad = \dfrac{(\mathbf{i}+3\mathbf{j})\cdot(-2\mathbf{i}+5\mathbf{j})}{\sqrt{1^2+(-1)^2}}\,\mathbf{w}$

$\qquad = \dfrac{1(-2)+3(5)}{\left(\sqrt{(-2)^2+5^2}\right)^2}\,\mathbf{w}$

$\qquad = \dfrac{13}{\left(\sqrt{29}\right)^2}\,\mathbf{w}$

$\qquad = \dfrac{13}{29}\,\mathbf{w}$

$\qquad = \dfrac{13}{29}(-2\mathbf{i}+5\mathbf{j})$

$\qquad = \dfrac{-26}{29}\mathbf{i}+\dfrac{65}{29}\mathbf{j}$

$\mathbf{v}_1 = \text{proj}_{\mathbf{w}}\mathbf{v} = -\dfrac{26}{29}\mathbf{i}+\dfrac{65}{29}\mathbf{j}$

$\mathbf{v}_2 = \mathbf{v}-\mathbf{v}_1$

$\qquad = (\mathbf{i}+3\mathbf{j})-\left(-\dfrac{26}{29}\mathbf{i}+\dfrac{65}{29}\mathbf{j}\right)$

$\qquad = \dfrac{55}{29}\mathbf{i}+\dfrac{22}{29}\mathbf{j}$

37. $\text{proj}_{\mathbf{w}}\mathbf{v} = \dfrac{\mathbf{v}\cdot\mathbf{w}}{\|\,\mathbf{w}\,\|^2}\,\mathbf{w}$

$\qquad = \dfrac{(\mathbf{i}+2\mathbf{j})\cdot(3\mathbf{i}+6\mathbf{j})}{\left(\sqrt{3^2+6^2}\right)^2}\,\mathbf{w}$

$\qquad = \dfrac{1(3)+2(6)}{\sqrt{45}}$

$\qquad = \dfrac{15}{45}\,\mathbf{w}$

$\qquad = \dfrac{1}{3}\,\mathbf{w}$

$\qquad = \dfrac{1}{3}(3\mathbf{i}+6\mathbf{j})$

$\qquad = \mathbf{i}+2\mathbf{j}$

$\mathbf{v}_1 = \text{proj}_{\mathbf{w}}\mathbf{v} = \mathbf{i}+2\mathbf{j}$

$\mathbf{v}_2 = \mathbf{v}-\mathbf{v}_1$

$\qquad = (\mathbf{i}+2\mathbf{j})-(\mathbf{i}+2\mathbf{j})$

$\qquad = 0\mathbf{i}+0\mathbf{j}$

$\qquad = \mathbf{0}$

39. $\mathbf{v}\cdot\mathbf{w} = (240\mathbf{i}+300\mathbf{j})\cdot(1.90\mathbf{i}+2.07\mathbf{j})$

$\qquad = 240(1.90)+300(2.07)$

$\qquad = 456+621$

$\qquad = 1077$

$\mathbf{v}\cdot\mathbf{w} = 1007$ means \$1077 in revenue was generated on Monday by the sale of 240 gallons of regular gas at \$1.90 per gallon and 300 gallons of premium gas at \$2.07 per gallon.

41. Since the car is pushed along a level road, the angle between the force and the direction of motion is $\theta = 0$. The work done

$$W = \left\| \mathbf{F} \right\| \left\| \overrightarrow{AB} \right\| \cos \theta$$

$$= (95)(80) \cos 0°$$

$$= 7600.$$

The work done is 7600 foot-pounds.

43. $W = \left\| \mathbf{F} \right\| \left\| \overrightarrow{AB} \right\| \cos \theta$

$$= (40)(100) \cos 32°$$

$$\approx 3392$$

The work done is approximately 3392 foot-pounds.

45. $w = \mathbf{F} \cdot \overrightarrow{\mathbf{AB}}$

$$= 60(20) \cos(38° - 12°)$$

$$= 1200 \cos 26°$$

$$\approx 1079 \text{ foot - pounds}$$

47. $w = \mathbf{F} \cdot \overrightarrow{\mathbf{AB}}$
$$= (3,2) \cdot [(10,20) - (4,9)]$$

$$= (3,2) \cdot (6,11)$$

$$= 18 + 22$$

$$= 40 \text{ foot - pounds}$$

49. $w = \mathbf{F} \cdot \overrightarrow{\mathbf{AB}}$
$$= (4 \cos 50°, 4 \sin 50°) \cdot [(8,10) - (3,7)]$$

$$= (4 \cos 50°, 4 \sin 50°) \cdot (5,3)$$

$$= 20 \cos 50° + 12 \sin 50°$$

$$\approx 22.05 \text{ foot - pounds}$$

51. a. $\cos 30°\mathbf{i} + \sin 30°\mathbf{j} = \dfrac{\sqrt{3}}{2}\mathbf{i} + \dfrac{1}{2}\mathbf{j}$

b. $\text{proj}_{\mathbf{u}} \mathbf{F} = \dfrac{(0,-700) \cdot \left(\dfrac{\sqrt{3}}{2}, \dfrac{1}{2} \right)}{\left\| \mathbf{u} \right\|^2} \left(\dfrac{\sqrt{3}}{2}, \dfrac{1}{2} \right)$

$$= -350 \left(\dfrac{\sqrt{3}}{2}, \dfrac{1}{2} \right) = -175\sqrt{3}\mathbf{i} - 175\mathbf{j}$$

c. $\sqrt{(-175\sqrt{3})^2 + (-175)^2}$

$$= \sqrt{122,500} = 350$$

A force of 350 pounds is required to keep the boat from rolling down the ramp.

53-61. Answers will vary.

63. $\mathbf{u} \cdot \mathbf{v} = (a_1\mathbf{i} + b_1\mathbf{j}) \cdot (a_2\mathbf{i} + b_2\mathbf{j})$

$\qquad = a_1a_2 + b_1b_2$

$\qquad = a_2a_1 + b_2b_1$

$\qquad = (a_2\mathbf{i} + b_2\mathbf{j}) \cdot (a_1\mathbf{i} + b_1\mathbf{j})$

$\qquad = \mathbf{v} \cdot \mathbf{u}$

Thus $\mathbf{u} \cdot \mathbf{v} = \mathbf{v} \cdot \mathbf{u}$.

65. $\mathbf{u} \cdot (\mathbf{v} + \mathbf{w}) = (a_1\mathbf{i} + b_1\mathbf{j}) \cdot [(a_2\mathbf{i} + b_2\mathbf{j}) + (a_3\mathbf{i} + a_3\mathbf{j})]$

$\qquad = (a_1\mathbf{i} + b_1\mathbf{j}) \cdot [(a_2 + a_3)\mathbf{i} + (b_2 + b_3)\mathbf{j}]$

$\qquad = a_1(a_2 + a_3) + b_1(b_2 + b_3)$

$\qquad = a_1a_2 + a_1a_3 + b_1b_2 + b_1b_3$

$\qquad = a_1a_2 + b_1b_2 + a_1a_3 + b_1b_3$

$\qquad = (a_1\mathbf{i} + b_1\mathbf{j}) \cdot (a_2\mathbf{i} + b_2\mathbf{j}) + (a_1\mathbf{i} + b_1\mathbf{j}) \cdot (a_3\mathbf{i} + b_3\mathbf{j})$

$\qquad = \mathbf{u} \cdot \mathbf{v} + \mathbf{u} \cdot \mathbf{w}$

67. Let $\mathbf{v} = 15\mathbf{i} - 3\mathbf{j}$ and $\mathbf{w} = -4\mathbf{i} + b\mathbf{j}$. The vectors $\mathbf{v}$ and $\mathbf{w}$ are orthogonal if $\mathbf{u} \cdot \mathbf{w} = 0$.

$\mathbf{v} \cdot \mathbf{w} = (15\mathbf{i} - 3\mathbf{j}) \cdot (-4\mathbf{i} + b\mathbf{j}) = 15(-4) + (-3)b = -60 - 3b$

$\mathbf{v} \cdot \mathbf{w} = 0$ if $-60 - 3b = 0$. Solving the equation for b, we find $b = -20$.

69. We know that $\text{proj}_{\mathbf{w}}\mathbf{v} = \dfrac{\mathbf{v} \cdot \mathbf{w}}{\| \mathbf{w} \|^2}\mathbf{w}$ If the projection of $\mathbf{v}$ onto $\mathbf{w}$ is $\mathbf{v}$, then $\mathbf{v} = \dfrac{\mathbf{v} \cdot \mathbf{w}}{\| \mathbf{w} \|^2}\mathbf{w}$.

Since $\dfrac{\mathbf{v} \cdot \mathbf{w}}{\| \mathbf{w} \|^2}$ is a scalar for all $\mathbf{v}$ and $\mathbf{w}$, let $k = \dfrac{\mathbf{v} \cdot \mathbf{w}}{\| \mathbf{w} \|^2}$. Substituting, we have $\mathbf{v} = k\mathbf{w}$.

When one vector can be expressed as a scalar multiple of another, the vectors have the same direction. Thus, the projection of $\mathbf{v}$ onto $\mathbf{w}$ is $\mathbf{v}$ only if $\mathbf{v}$ and $\mathbf{w}$ have the same direction. Thus, any two vectors, $\mathbf{v}$ and $\mathbf{w}$, having the same direction will satisfy the condition that the projection of $\mathbf{v}$ onto $\mathbf{w}$ is $\mathbf{v}$.

Chapter 3

Check Point Exercises

1. Substitute 60 for x and evaluate the function at 60. $f(60) = 13.49(0.967)^{-60} - 1 \approx 1$
   Thus, one O-ring is expected to fail at a temperature of 60°F.

2. Begin by setting up a table of coordinates.

x	$f(x) = 3^x$
-3	$f(-3) = 3^{-3} = \frac{1}{27}$
-2	$f(-2) = 3^{-2} = \frac{1}{9}$
-1	$f(-1) = 3^{-1} = \frac{1}{3}$
0	$f(0) = 3^0 = 1$
1	$f(1) = 3^1 = 3$
2	$f(2) = 3^2 = 9$
3	$f(3) = 3^3 = 27$

   Plot these points, connecting them with a continuous curve.

   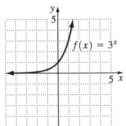

3. Note that the function $g(x) = 3^{x-1}$ has the general form $g(x) = b^{x+c}$ where $c = -1$. Because $c < 0$, we graph $g(x) = 3^{x-1}$ by shifting the graph of $f(x) = 3^x$ one unit to the right. Construct a table showing some of the coordinates for f and g.

x	$f(x) = 3^x$	$g(x) = 3^{x-1}$
-2	$3^{-2} = \frac{1}{9}$	$3^{-2-1} = 3^{-3} = \frac{1}{27}$
-1	$3^{-1} = \frac{1}{3}$	$3^{-1-1} = 3^{-2} = \frac{1}{9}$
0	$3^0 = 1$	$3^{0-1} = 3^{-1} = \frac{1}{3}$
1	$3^1 = 3$	$3^{1-1} = 3^0 = 1$
2	$3^2 = 9$	$3^{2-1} = 3^1 = 3$

   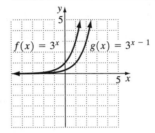

4. Note that the function $g(x) = 2^x + 1$ has the general form $g(x) = b^x + c$ where $c = 1$. Because $c > 0$, we graph $g(x) = 2^x + 1$ by shifting the graph of $f(x) = 2^x$ up one unit. Construct a table showing some of the coordinates for f and g.

x	$f(x) - 2^x$	$g(x) = 2^x + 1$
-2	$2^{-2} = \frac{1}{4}$	$2^{-2} + 1 = \frac{1}{4} + 1 = \frac{5}{4}$
-1	$2^{-1} = \frac{1}{2}$	$2^{-1} + 1 = \frac{1}{2} + 1 = \frac{3}{2}$
0	$2^0 = 1$	$2^0 + 1 = 1 + 1 = 2$
1	$2^1 = 2$	$2^1 + 1 = 2 + 1 = 3$
2	$2^2 = 4$	$2^2 + 1 = 4 + 1 = 5$

   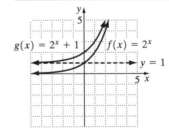

5. Because 2050 is 50 years after 2000, substitute 50 for x.

$$f(50) = 6e^{0.013(50)} = 6e^{0.65} \approx 11.49$$

The world population is 2050 will be approximately 11.49 billion.

6. a. $A = 10,000\left(1 + \dfrac{0.08}{4}\right)^{4 \cdot 5} \approx 14,859.47$

The balance in this account after 5 years is \$14,859.47.

b. $A = 10,000e^{0.08(5)} \approx 14,918.25$

The balance in this account after 5 years is \$14,918.25.

Exercise Set 3.1

1. $2^{3.4} \approx 10.556$

3. $3^{\sqrt{5}} \approx 11.665$

5. $4^{-1.5} = 0.125$

7. $e^{2.3} \approx 9.974$

9. $e^{-0.95} \approx 0.387$

11.

x	$f(x) = 4^x$
-2	$4^{-2} = \frac{1}{16}$
-1	$4^{-1} = \frac{1}{4}$
0	$4^0 = 1$
1	$4^1 = 4$
2	$4^2 = 16$

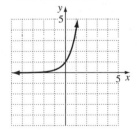

13.

x	$g(x) = \left(\frac{3}{2}\right)^x$
-2	$\left(\frac{3}{2}\right)^{-2} = \frac{4}{9}$
-1	$\left(\frac{3}{2}\right)^{-1} = \frac{2}{3}$
0	$\left(\frac{3}{2}\right)^0 = 1$
1	$\left(\frac{3}{2}\right)^1 = \frac{3}{2}$
2	$\left(\frac{3}{2}\right)^2 = \frac{9}{4}$

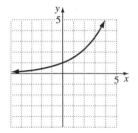

15.

x	$h(x) = \left(\frac{1}{2}\right)^x$
-2	$\left(\frac{1}{2}\right)^{-2} = 4$
-1	$\left(\frac{1}{2}\right)^{-1} = 2$
0	$\left(\frac{1}{2}\right)^0 = 1$
1	$\left(\frac{1}{2}\right)^1 = \frac{1}{2}$
2	$\left(\frac{1}{2}\right)^2 = \frac{1}{4}$

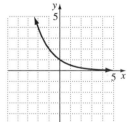

17.

x	$f(x) = (0.6)^x$
-2	$(0.6)^{-2} = 2.\overline{7}$
-1	$(0.6)^{-1} = 1.\overline{6}$
0	$(0.6)^0 = 1$
1	$(0.6)^1 = 0.6$
2	$(0.6)^2 = 0.36$

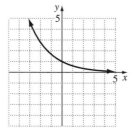

19. This is the graph of $f(x) = 3^x$ reflected about the x-axis and about the y-axis, so the function is $H(x) = -3^{-x}$.

21. This is the graph of $f(x) = 3^x$ reflected about the x-axis, so the function is $F(x) = -3^x$.

23. This is the graph of $f(x) = 3^x$ shifted one unit downward, so the function is $h(x) = 3^x - 1$.

25. The graph of $g(x) = 2^{x+!}$ can be obtained by shifting the graph of $f(x) = 2^x$ one unit to the left.

x	$g(x) = 2^{x+1}$
-2	$2^{-2+1} = 2^{-1} = \frac{1}{2}$
-1	$2^{-1+1} = 2^0 = 1$
0	$2^{0+1} = 2^1 = 2$
1	$2^{1+1} = 2^2 = 4$
2	$2^{2+1} = 2^3 = 8$

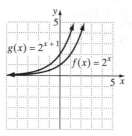

27. The graph of $g(x) = 2^x - 1$ can be obtained by shifting the graph of $f(x) = 2^x$ downward one unit.

x	$g(x) = 2^x - 1$
-2	$2^{-2} - 1 = \frac{1}{4} - 1 = -\frac{3}{4}$
-1	$2^{-1} - 1 = \frac{1}{2} - 1 = -\frac{1}{2}$
0	$2^0 - 1 = 1 - 1 = 0$
1	$2^1 - 1 = 2 - 1 = 1$
2	$2^2 - 1 = 4 - 1 = 3$

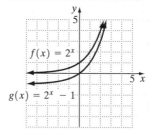

29. The graph of $h(x) = 2^{x+1} - 1$ can be obtained by shifting the graph of $f(x) = 2^x$ one unit to the left and one unit downward.

x	$h(x) = 2^{x+1} - 1$
-2	$2^{-2+1} - 1 = 2^{-1} - 1 = \frac{1}{2} - 1 = -\frac{1}{2}$
-1	$2^{-1+1} - 1 = 2^0 - 1 = 1 - 1 = 0$
0	$2^{0+1} - 1 = 2^1 - 1 = 2 - 1 = 1$
1	$2^{1+1} - 1 = 2^2 - 1 = 4 - 1 = 3$
2	$2^{2+1} - 1 = 2^3 - 1 = 8 - 1 = 7$

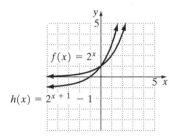

31. The graph of $g(x) = -2^x$ can be obtained by reflecting the graph of $f(x) = 2^x$ about the x-axis.

x	$g(x) = -2^x$
-2	$-2^{-2} = -\frac{1}{4}$
-1	$-2^{-1} = -\frac{1}{2}$
0	$-2^0 = -1$
1	$-2^1 = -2$
2	$-2^2 = -4$

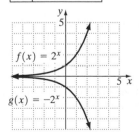

33. The graph of $g(x) = 2 \cdot 2^x$ can be obtained by vertically stretching the graph of

$f(x) = 2^x$ by a factor of two.

x	$g(x) = 2 \cdot 2^x$
-2	$2 \cdot 2^{-2} = 2 \cdot \frac{1}{4} = \frac{1}{2}$
-1	$2 \cdot 2^{-1} = 2 \cdot \frac{1}{2} = 1$
0	$2 \cdot 2^0 = 2 \cdot 1 = 2$
1	$2 \cdot 2^1 = 2 \cdot 2 = 4$
2	$2 \cdot 2^2 = 2 \cdot 4 = 8$

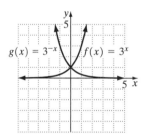

35. The graph of $g(x)$ can be obtained by reflecting $f(x)$ about the y-axis.

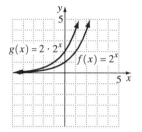

37. The graph of $g(x)$ can be obtained by horizontally stretching $f(x)$.

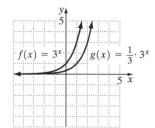

39. The graph of $g(x)$ can be obtained by moving the graph of $f(x)$ one space to the right and one space up.

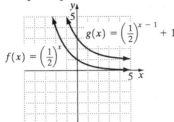

$$g(x) = \left(\tfrac{1}{2}\right)^{x-1} + 1$$

$$f(x) = \left(\tfrac{1}{2}\right)^{x}$$

41. a. $A = 10,000\left(1 + \dfrac{0.055}{2}\right)^{2(5)}$

   $\approx 13,116.51$

b. $A = 10,000\left(1 + \dfrac{0.055}{4}\right)^{4(5)}$

   $\approx \$13,140.67$

c. $A = 10,000\left(1 + \dfrac{0.055}{12}\right)^{12(5)}$

   $\approx 13,157.04$

d. $A = 10,000e^{0.055(5)}$

   $\approx 13,165.31$

43. $A = 12,000\left(1 + \dfrac{0.07}{12}\right)^{12(3)}$

   $\approx 14,795.11$ (7% yield)

   $A = 12,000e^{0.0685(3)}$

   $\approx 14,737.67$ (6.85% yield)

   Investing \$12,000 for 3 years at 7% compounded monthly yields the greatest return.

45. a. $f(0) = 67.38(1.026)^{0} = 67.38$

   67.38 million

b. $f(27) = 67.38(1.026)^{27}$

   ≈ 134.7441 million

c. $f(54) = 67.38(1.026)^{254}$

   ≈ 269.4564 million

d. $f(81) = 67.38(1.026)^{81}$

   ≈ 538.8492 million

e. The population appears to double every 27 years.

47. $f(10) = \dfrac{400}{1 + 399(.67)^{10}} \approx 48$

   At ten minutes after 8:00, 48 have heard the rumor.

49. $\$65,000(1 + 0.06)^{10} \approx 116,405.10$

   The house will be worth \$116,405.10.

51. $2^{1.7} \approx 3.249009585$

   $2^{1.73} \approx 3.317278183$

   $2^{1.732} \approx 3.321880096$

   $2^{1.73205} \approx 3.321995226$

   $2^{1.7320508} \approx 3.321997068$

   $2^{\sqrt{3}} \approx 3.321997085$

   The closer the exponent is to $\sqrt{3}$, the closer the value is to $2^{\sqrt{3}}$.

53. $2006 - 1992 = 14$

   $f(14) = 36.1e^{0.113(14)} \approx 175.6$ million

   In the year 2006, approximately 175.6 million Americans will be enrolled in HMOs.

55. a. $f(0) = 80e^{-0.5(0)} + 20$

   $= 80e^{0} + 20$

   $= 80(1) + 20$

   $= 100$

   100% of the material is remembered at the moment it is first learned.

b. $f(1) = 80e^{-0.5(1)} + 20 \approx 68.5$

   68.5% of the material is remembered 1 week after it is first learned.

c. $f(4) = 80e^{-0.5(4)} + 20 \approx 30.8$

30.8% of the material is remembered 4 week after it is first learned.

d. $f(52) = 80e^{-0.5(52)} + 20 \approx 20$

20% of the material is remembered 1 year after it is first learned.

57. a. $N(0) = \dfrac{30,000}{1 + 20e^{-1.5(0)}} = 1428.57$

About 1429 people became ill.

b. $N(3) = \dfrac{30,000}{1 + 20e^{-1.5(3)}} \approx 24,546.30$

About 24,546 people were ill by the end of the third week.

c. The growth of the epidemic is limited by the size of the population. The horizontal asymptote shows that the epidemic will grow to the limiting size of the population, so that the entire population will eventually become ill.

59.–63. Answers may vary.

65.

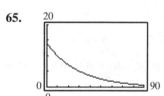

When $x = 31, y \approx 3.77$. NASA would not have launched the *Challenger*, since nearly 4 O-rings are expected to fail.

67. a.

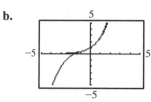

b.

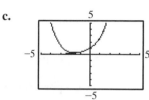

c.

d. Answers may vary.

69. $y = 3^x$ is (d). y increases as x increases, but not as quickly as $y = 5^x$. $y = 5^x$ is (c).
$y = \left(\frac{1}{3}\right)^x$ is (a). $y = \left(\frac{1}{3}\right)^x$ is the same as $y = 3^{-x}$, so it is (d) reflected about the y-axis. $y = \left(\frac{1}{5}\right)^x$ is (b). $y = \left(\frac{1}{5}\right)^x$ is the same as $y = 5^{-x}$, so it is (c) reflected about the y-axis.

71.
$$(\cosh x)^2 - (\sinh x)^2 = 1$$
$$\left(\frac{e^x + e^{-x}}{2}\right)^2 - \left(\frac{e^x - e^{-x}}{2}\right)^2 =$$
$$\frac{e^{2x} + 2 + e^{-2x}}{4} - \frac{e^{2x} - 2 + e^{-2x}}{4} =$$
$$\frac{e^{2x} + 2 + e^{-2x} - e^{2x} + 2 - e^{-2x}}{4} =$$
$$\frac{4}{4} =$$
$$1 = 1$$

Section 3.2

Check Point Exercises

1. a. $3 = \log_7 x$ means $7^3 = x$.

141

b. $2 = \log_b 25$ means $b^2 = 25$.

c. $\log_4 26 = y$ means $4^y = 26$.

2. a. $2^5 = x$ means $5 = \log_2 x$.

b. $b^3 = 27$ means $3 = \log_b 27$.

c. $e^y = 33$ means $y = \log_e 33$.

3. a.   Question: 10 to what power gives 100?
$\log_{10} 100 = 2$ because $10^2 = 100$.

b.   Question: 3 to what power gives 3?
$\log_3 3 = 1$ because $3^1 = 3$.

c.   Question: 36 to what power gives 6?
$\log_{36} 6 = \dfrac{1}{2}$ because $36^{\frac{1}{2}} = \sqrt{36} = 6$

4. a.   Because $\log_b b = 1$, we conclude
$\log_9 9 = 1$.

b.   Because $\log_b 1 = 0$, we conclude
$\log_8 1 = 0$.

5. a.   Because $\log_b b^x = x$, we conclude
$\log_7 7^8 = 8$.

b.   Because $b^{\log_b x} = x$, we conclude
$3^{\log_3 17} = 17$.

6.   First, set up a table of coordinates for
$f(x) = 3^x$.

x	-2	-1	0	1	2	3
$f(x) = 3^x$	$\frac{1}{9}$	$\frac{1}{3}$	1	3	9	27

Reversing these coordinates gives the
coordinates for the inverse function
$g(x) = \log_3 x$.

x	$\frac{1}{9}$	$\frac{1}{3}$	1	3	9	27
$g(x) = \log_3 x$	-2	-1	0	1	2	3

The graph of the inverse can also be drawn

by reflecting the graph of $f(x) = 3^x$ about
the line $y = x$.

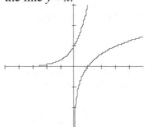

7.   The domain of h consists of all x for which
$x - 5 > 0$. Solving this inequality for x, we
obtain $x > 5$. Thus, the domain of h is
$(5, \infty)$.

8.   Substitute the boy's age, 10, for x and
evaluate the function at 10.
$f(10) = 29 + 48.8 \ \log(10 + 1)$
$= 29 + 48.8 \ \log(11)$
≈ 80
Thus, a 10-year-old boy is approximately
80% of his adult height.

9.   Because $I = 10{,}000 \ I_0$,
$R = \log \dfrac{10{,}000 I_0}{I_0}$
$= \log \ 10{,}000$
$= 4$
The earthquake registered 4.0 on the Richter
scale.

10. a.   The domain of f consists of all x for
which $4 - x > 0$. Solving this inequality
for x, we obtain $x < 4$. Thus, the
domain of f is $(-\infty, 4)$

b.   The domain of g consists of all x for
which $x^2 > 0$. Solving this inequality
for x, we obtain $x < 0$ or $x > 0$. Thus the
domain of g is $(-\infty, 0)$ or $(0, \infty)$.

11. a.   Because $\ln e^x = x$, we conclude
$\ln e^{25x} = 25x$.

b. Because $e^{\ln x} = x$, we conclude
$$e^{\ln \sqrt{x}} = \sqrt{x}.$$

12. Substitute 197 for P, the population in thousands. $W = 0.35 \ln 197 + 2.74 \approx 4.6$ The average walking speed in Jackson, Mississippi is approximately 4.6 feet per second.

Exercise Set 3.2

1. $2^4 = 16$

3. $3^2 = x$

5. $b^5 = 32$

7. $6^y = 216$

9. $\log_2 8 = 3$

11. $\log_2 \dfrac{1}{16} = -4$

13. $\log_8 2 = \dfrac{1}{3}$

15. $\log_{13} x = 2$

17. $\log_b 1000 = 3$

19. $\log_7 200 = y$

21. $\log_4 16 = 2$ because $4^2 = 16$.

23. $\log_2 64 = 6$ because $2^6 = 64$.

25. $\log_7 \sqrt{7} = \dfrac{1}{2}$ because $7^{\frac{1}{2}} = \sqrt{7}$.

27. $\log_2 \dfrac{1}{8} = -3$ because $2^{-3} = \dfrac{1}{8}$.

29. $\log_{64} 8 = \dfrac{1}{2}$ because $64^{\frac{1}{2}} = \sqrt{64} = 8$.

31. Because $\log_b b = 1$, we conclude $\log_5 5 = 1$.

33. Because $\log_b 1 = 0$, we conclude $\log_4 1 = 0$.

35. Because $\log_b b^x = x$, we conclude $\log_5 5^7 = 7$.

37. Because $b^{\log_b x} = x$, we conclude $8^{\log_8 19} = 19$.

39. First, set up a table of coordinates for $f(x) = 4^x$.

x	-2	-1	0	1	2	3
$f(x) = 4x$	$\frac{1}{16}$	$\frac{1}{4}$	1	4	16	64

Reversing these coordinates gives the coordinates for the inverse function $g(x) = \log_4 x$.

x	$\frac{1}{16}$	$\frac{1}{4}$	1	4	16	64
$g(x) = \log_{4x}$	-2	-1	0	1	2	3

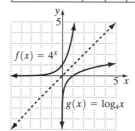

41. First, set up a table of coordinates for $f(x) = \left(\dfrac{1}{2}\right)^x$.

x	-2	-1	0	1	2	3
$f(x) = \left(\frac{1}{2}\right)^x$	4	2	1	$\frac{1}{2}$	$\frac{1}{4}$	$\frac{1}{8}$

Reversing these coordinates gives the coordinates for the inverse function $g(x) = \log_{1/2} x$.

x	4	2	1	$\frac{1}{2}$	$\frac{1}{4}$	$\frac{1}{8}$
$g(x) = \log_{1/2} x$	-2	-1	0	1	2	3

51.

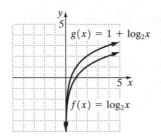

x-intercept: (0.5,0)
vertical asymptote: $x = 0$

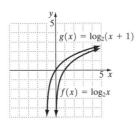

43. This is the graph of $f(x) = \log_3 x$ reflected about the *x*-axis and shifted up one unit, so the function is $H(x) = 1 - \log^x$.

45. This is the graph of $f(x) = \log_3 x$ shifted down one unit, so the function is $h(x) = \log_3 x - 1$.

47. This is the graph of $f(x) = \log_3 x$ shifted right one unit, so the function is $g(x) = \log_3(x - 1)$.

49.

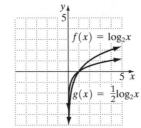

x-intercept: (0,0)
vertical asymptote: $x = -1$

53.

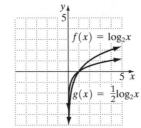

x-intercept: (1,0)
vertical asymptote: $x = 0$

55. The domain of *f* consists of all *x* for which $x + 4 > 0$. Solving this inequality for *x*, we obtain $x > -4$. Thus, the domain of *f* is $(-4, \infty)$.

57. The domain of *f* consists of all *x* for which $2 - x > 0$. Solving this inequality for *x*, we obtain $x < 2$. Thus, the domain of *f* is $(-\infty, 2)$.

59. The domain of *f* consists of all *x* for which $(x - 2)^2 > 0$. Solving this inequality for *x*, we obtain $x < 2$ or $x > 2$. Thus, the domain of *f* is $(-\infty, 2)$ or $(2, -\infty)$.

61. $\log 100 = \log_{10} 100 = 2$ because $10^2 = 100$.

63. Because $\log 10^x = x$, we conclude $\log 10^7 = 7$.

65. Because $10^{\log x} = x$, we conclude $10^{\log 33} = 33$.

67. $\ln 1 = 0$ because $e^0 = 1$.

69. Because $\ln e^x = x$, we conclude $\ln e^6 = 6$.

71. $\ln \dfrac{1}{e^6} = \ln e^{-6}$

Because $\ln e^x = x$ we conclude $\ln e^{-6} = -6$, so $\ln \dfrac{1}{e^6} = -6$.

73. Because $e^{\ln x} = x$, we conclude $e^{\ln 125} = 125$.

75. Because $\ln e^x = x$, we conclude $\ln e^{9x} = 9x$.

77. Because $e^{\ln x} = x$, we conclude $e^{\ln 5x^2} = 5x^2$.

79. Because $10^{\log x} = x$, we conclude $10^{\log \sqrt{x}} = \sqrt{x}$.

81. $f(13) = 62 + 35\log(13{-}4) \approx 95.4$
She is approximately 95.4% of her adult height.

83. $f(16) = 2.05 + 1.3\ln(16) \approx 5.65$ billion
Approximately \$5.65 billion was spent in 2000.

85. $D = 10\log\left[10^{12}(6.3\times10^6)\right] \approx 188$

Yes, the sound can rupture the human eardrum.

87. **a.** $f(0) = 88{-}15\ln(0 + 1) = 88$
The average score on the original exam was 88.

    b. $f(2) = 88{-}15\ln(2 + 1) = 71.5$
$f(4) = 88{-}15\ln(4 + 1) = 63.9$

$f(6) = 88{-}15\ln(6 + 1) = 58.8$
$f(8) = 88{-}15\ln(8 + 1) = 55$
$f(10) = 88{-}15\ln(10 + 1) = 52$
$f(12) = 88{-}15\ln(12 + 1) = 49.5$

The average score after 2 months was about 71.5, after 4 months was about 63.9, after 6 months was about 58.8, after 8 months was about 55, after 10 months was about 52, and after one year was about 49.5.

c.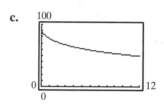

Material retention decreases as time passes.

89.–95. Answers may vary.

97.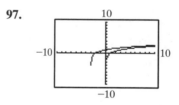

$g(x)$ is $f(x)$ shifted 3 units left.

99.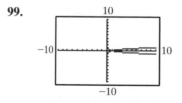

$g(x)$ is $f(x)$ reflected about the x-axis.

101.

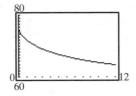

The score falls below 65 after 9 months.

103.

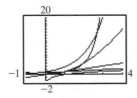

$$y = \ln x, \ y = \sqrt{x}, \ y = x,$$
$$y = x^2, y = e^x, y = x^x$$

105. $\dfrac{\log_3 81 - \log_\pi 1}{\log_{2\sqrt{2}} 8 - \log 0.001} = \dfrac{4 - 0}{2 - (-3)} = \dfrac{4}{5}$

107. $\log_4 60 < \log_4 64 = 3$ so $\log_4 60 < 3$.
$\log_3 40 > \log_3 27 = 3$ so $\log_3 40 > 3$.
$\log_4 60 < 3 < \log_3 40$
$\log_3 40 > \log_4 60$

Section 3.3

Check Point Exercises

1. a. $\log_6 (7 \cdot 11) = \log_6 7 + \log_6 11$

b. $\log(100x) = \log 100 + \log x$
$\qquad = 2 + \log x$

2. a. $\log_8\left(\dfrac{23}{x}\right) = \log_8 23 - \log_8 x$

b. $\ln\left(\dfrac{e^5}{11}\right) = \ln e^5 - \ln 11$
$\qquad = 5 - \ln 11$

3. a. $\log_6 3^9 = 9\log_6 3$

b. $\ln \sqrt[3]{x} = \ln x^{1/3}$
$\qquad = \dfrac{1}{3}\ln x$

4. a. $\log_b x^4 \sqrt[3]{y}$
$\qquad = \log_b x^4 y^{1/3}$
$\qquad = \log_b x^4 + \log_b y^{1/3}$
$\qquad = 4\log_b x + \dfrac{1}{3}\log_b y$

b. $\log_5 \dfrac{\sqrt{x}}{25y^3}$
$\qquad = \log_5 \dfrac{x^{1/2}}{25y^3}$
$\qquad = \log_5 x^{1/2} - \log_5 25y^3$
$\qquad = \log_5 x^{1/2} - \left(\log_5 25 + \log_5 y^3\right)$
$\qquad = \dfrac{1}{2}\log_5 x - \left(\log_5 25 + 3\log_5 y\right)$
$\qquad = \dfrac{1}{2}\log_5 x - \log_5 25 - 3\log_5 y$
$\qquad = \dfrac{1}{2}\log_5 x - 2 - 3\log_5 y$

5. a. $\log 25 + \log 4 = \log(25 \cdot 4)$
$\qquad = \log 100$
$\qquad = 2$

b. $\log(7x + 6) - \log x = \log \dfrac{7x + 6}{x}$

6. a. $\ln x^2 + \dfrac{1}{3}\ln(x + 5)$
$\qquad = \ln x^2 + \ln(x + 5)^{1/3}$
$\qquad = \ln x^2 (x + 5)^{1/3}$
$\qquad = \ln x^2 \sqrt[3]{x + 5}$

b. $2\log(x - 3) - \log x$
$\qquad = \log(x - 3)^2 - \log x$
$\qquad = \log \dfrac{(x - 3)^2}{x}$

146

c. $\dfrac{1}{4}\log_b x - 2\log_b 5 + 10\log_b y$

$= \log_b x^{1/4} - \log_b 5^2 + \log_b y^{10}$

$= \log_b \dfrac{x^{1/4}\,y^{10}}{25}$

7. $\log_7 2506 = \dfrac{\log 2506}{\log 7}$

≈ 4.02

8. $\log_7 2506 = \dfrac{\ln 2506}{\ln 7}$

≈ 4.02

Exercise Set 3.3

1. $\log_5(7 \cdot 3) = \log_5 7 + \log_5 3$

3. $\log_7(7x) = \log_7 7 + \log_7 x$

$= 1 + \log_7 x$

5. $\log(1000x) = \log 1000 + \log x$

$= 3 + \log x$

7. $\log_7\left(\dfrac{7}{x}\right) = \log_7 7 - \log_7 x$

$= 1 - \log_7 x$

9. $\log\left(\dfrac{x}{100}\right) = \log x - \log 100$

$= \log_x - 2$

11. $\log_4\left(\dfrac{64}{y}\right) = \log_4 64 - \log_4 y$

$= 3 - \log_4 y$

13. $\ln\left(\dfrac{e^2}{5}\right) = \ln e^2 - \ln 5$

$= 2\ln e - \ln 5$

$= 2 - \ln 5$

15. $\log_b x^3 = 3\log_b x$

17. $\log N^{-6} = -6\log N$

19. $\ln \sqrt[5]{x} = \ln x^{(1/5)}$

$= \dfrac{1}{5}\ln x$

21. $\log_b x^2 y = \log_b x^2 + \log_b y$

$= 2\log_b x + \log_b y$

23. $\log_4\left(\dfrac{\sqrt{x}}{64}\right) = \log_4 x^{1/2} - \log_4 64$

$= \dfrac{1}{2}\log_4 x - 3$

25. $\log_6\left(\dfrac{36}{\sqrt{x+1}}\right) = \log_6 36 - \log_6(x+1)^{1/2}$

$= 2 - \dfrac{1}{2}\log_6(x+1)$

27. $\log_b\left(\dfrac{x^2 y}{z^2}\right) = \log_b\left(x^2 y\right) - \log_b z^2$

$= \log_b x^2 + \log_b y - \log_b z^2$

$= 2\log_b x + \log_b y - 2\log_b z$

29. $\log\sqrt{100x} = \log(100x)^{1/2}$

$= \dfrac{1}{2}\log(100x)$

$= \dfrac{1}{2}(\log 100 + \log x)$

$= \dfrac{1}{2}(2 + \log x)$

$= 1 + \dfrac{1}{2}\log x$

31. $\log\sqrt[3]{\dfrac{x}{y}} = \log\left(\dfrac{x}{y}\right)^{1/3}$

$= \dfrac{1}{3}\left[\log\left(\dfrac{x}{y}\right)\right]$

$= \dfrac{1}{3}(\log x - \log y)$

$= \dfrac{1}{3}\log x - \dfrac{1}{3}\log y$

33.

$$\log_b \frac{\sqrt{x}y^3}{z^3}$$

$$= \log_b x^{1/2} + \log_b y^3 - \log_b z^3$$

$$= \frac{1}{2}\log_b x + 3\log_b y - 3\log_b z$$

35.

$$\log_5 \sqrt[3]{\frac{x^2 y}{25}}$$

$$= \log_5 x^{2/3} + \log_5 y^{1/3} - \log_5 25^{1/3}$$

$$= \frac{2}{3}\log_5 x + \frac{1}{3}\log_5 y - \log_5 5^{2/3}$$

$$= \frac{2}{3}\log_5 x + \frac{1}{3}\log_5 y - \frac{2}{3}$$

37.

$$\ln\left[\frac{x^3\sqrt{x^2+1}}{(x+1)^4}\right]$$

$$= \ln x^3 + \ln\sqrt{x^2+1} - \ln(x+1)^4$$

$$= 3\ln x + \frac{1}{2}\ln(x^2+1) - 4\ln(x+1)$$

39.

$$\log\left[\frac{10x^2\sqrt[3]{1-x}}{7(x+1)^2}\right]$$

$$= \log 10 + \log x^2 + \log\sqrt[3]{1-x} - \log 7 - \log(x+1)^2$$

$$= 1 + 2\log x + \frac{1}{3}\log(1-x) - \log 7 - 2\log(x+1)$$

41. $\log 5 + \log 2 = \log(5\cdot2)$
$$= \log 10$$
$$= 1$$

43. $\ln x + \ln 7 = \ln(7x)$

45. $\log_2 96 - \log_2 3 = \log_2\left(\frac{96}{3}\right)$
$$= \log_2 32$$
$$= 5$$

47. $\log(2x+5) - \log x = \log\left(\frac{2x+5}{x}\right)$

49. $\log x + 3\log y = \log x + \log y^3$
$$= \log(xy^3)$$

51. $\frac{1}{2}\ln x + \ln y = \ln x^{1/2} + \ln y$
$$= \ln\left(x^{\frac{1}{2}}y\right) \text{ or } \ln\left(\sqrt{x}y\right)$$

53. $2\log_b x + 3\log_b y = \log_b x^2 + \log_b y^3$
$$= \log_b(x^2y^3)$$

55. $5\ln x - 2\ln y = \ln x^5 - \ln y^2$
$$= \ln\left(\frac{x^5}{y^2}\right)$$

57. $3\ln x - \frac{1}{3}\ln y = \ln x^3 - \ln y^{1/3}$
$$= \ln\left(\frac{x^3}{y^{1/3}}\right) \text{ or } \ln\left(\frac{x^3}{\sqrt[3]{y}}\right)$$

59. $4\ln(x+6) - 3\ln x = \ln(x+6)^4 - \ln x^3$
$$= \ln\frac{(x+6)^4}{x^3}$$

61. $3\ln x + 5\ln y - 6\ln z$
$$= \ln x^3 + \ln y^5 - \ln z^6$$
$$= \ln\frac{x^3 y^5}{z^6}$$

63. $\frac{1}{2}\left(\log x + \log y\right)$
$$= \frac{1}{2}(\log xy)$$
$$= \log(xy)^{1/2}$$
$$= \log\sqrt{xy}$$

65.
$$\frac{1}{2}(\log_5 x + \log_5 y) - 2\log_5(x+1)$$
$$= \frac{1}{2}\log_5 xy - \log_5(x+1)^2$$
$$= \log_5(xy)^{1/2} - \log_5(x+1)^2$$
$$= \log_5 \frac{(xy)^{1/2}}{(x+1)^2}$$
$$= \log_5 \frac{\sqrt{xy}}{(x+1)^2}$$

67.
$$\frac{1}{3}[2\ln(x+5) - \ln x - \ln(x^2-4)]$$
$$= \frac{1}{3}[\ln(x+5)^2 - \ln x - \ln(x^2-4)]$$
$$= \frac{1}{3}\left[\ln \frac{(x+5)^2}{x(x^2-4)}\right]$$
$$= \ln\left[\frac{(x+5)^2}{x(x^2-4)}\right]^{1/3}$$
$$= \ln \sqrt[3]{\frac{(x+5)^2}{x(x^2-4)}}$$

69.
$$\log x + \log 7 + \log(x^2-1) - \log(x+1)$$
$$= \log \frac{7x(x^2-1)}{(x+1)}$$
$$= \log \frac{7x(x-1)(x+1)}{x+1}$$
$$= \log[7x(x-1)]$$

71. $\log_5 13 = \dfrac{\log 13}{\log 5} \approx 1.5937$

73. $\log_{14} 87.5 = \dfrac{\ln 87.5}{\ln 14} \approx 1.6944$

75. $\log_{0.1} 17 = \dfrac{\log 17}{\log 0.1} \approx -1.2304$

77. $\log_\pi 63 = \dfrac{\ln 63}{\ln \pi} \approx 3.6193$

79.

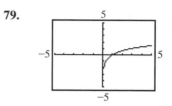

81.

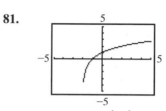

83. a. $D = 10\log\left(\dfrac{I}{I_0}\right)$

    b. $D_1 = 10\log\left(\dfrac{100I}{I_0}\right)$
$$= 10\log(100I - I_0)$$
$$= 10\log 100 + 10\log I - 10\log I_0$$
$$= 10(2) + 10\log I - 10\log I_0$$
$$= 20 + 10\log\left(\dfrac{I}{I_0}\right)$$

This is 20 more than the loudness level of the softer sound. This means that the 100 times louder sound will be 20 decibels louder.

85.–91. Answers may vary.

93. a. $y = \log_3 x = \dfrac{\ln x}{\ln 3}$

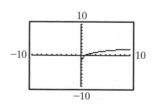

b.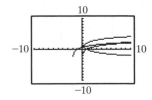

To obtain the graph of $y = 2 + \log_3 x$, shift the graph of $y = \log_3 x$ two units upward. To obtain the graph of $y = \log_3(x + 2)$, shift the graph of $y = \log_3 x$ two units left. To obtain the graph of $y = -\log_3 x$, reflect the graph of $y = \log_3 x$ about the *x*-axis.

95.
$$\log_3 x = \frac{\log x}{\log 3};$$

$$\log_{25} x = \frac{\log x}{\log 25};$$

$$\log_{100} x = \frac{\log x}{\log 100}$$

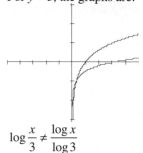

a. top graph: $y = \log_{100} x$
bottom graph: $y = \log_3 x$

b. top graph: $y = \log_3 x$
bottom graph: $y = \log_{100} x$

c. Comparing graphs of $\log_b x$ for $b > 1$, the graph of the equation with the largest b will be on the top in the interval $(0, 1)$ and on the bottom in the interval $(1, \infty)$.

97. a. Values of y may vary.

b. For $y = 3$, the graphs are:

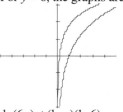

$$\log \frac{x}{3} \neq \frac{\log x}{\log 3}$$

99. a. Values of y may vary.
b. For $y = 6$, the graphs are:

$$\ln(6x) \neq (\ln x)(\ln 6)$$

101. a. False;
$$\log_7 49 - \log_7 7 = \log_7 \frac{49}{7} = \log_7 7 = 1$$
$$\frac{\log_7 49}{\log_7 7} = \frac{2}{1} = 2$$

b. False;
$$3\log_b x + 3\log_b y = \log_b(xy)^3$$
$$\neq \log_b\!\left(x^3 + y^3\right)$$

c. False;
$$\log_b(xy)^5 = 5\log_b(xy)$$
$$= 5(\log_b x + \log_b y)$$
$$\neq (\log_b x + \log_b y)^5$$

d. True;
$$\ln \sqrt{2} = \ln 2^{1/2}$$
$$= \frac{1}{2}\ln 2 = \frac{\ln 2}{2}$$

(d) is true.

103. $\log_7 9 = \dfrac{\log 9}{\log 7} = \dfrac{\log 3^2}{\log 7} = \dfrac{2\log 3}{\log 7}$

$\quad\quad = \dfrac{2A}{B}$

105.

$\dfrac{\log_b(x+h) - \log_b x}{h}$

$= \dfrac{\log_b \dfrac{x+h}{x}}{h}$

$= \dfrac{\log_b\left(1 + \dfrac{h}{x}\right)}{h}$

$= \dfrac{1}{h}\log_b\left(1 + \dfrac{h}{x}\right)$

$= \log_b\left(1 + \dfrac{x}{h}\right)^{1/h}$

Section 3.4

Check Point Exercises

1. $5^x = 134$

$\ln 5^x = \ln 134$

$x \ln 5 = \ln 134$

$x = \dfrac{\ln 134}{\ln 5} \approx 3.04$

The solution set is $\left\{\dfrac{\ln 134}{\ln 5}\right\}$, approximately 3.04.

2. $7e^{2x} = 63$

$e^{2x} = 9$

$\ln e^{2x} = \ln 9$

$2x = \ln 9$

$x = \dfrac{\ln 9}{2} \approx 1.10$

The solution set is $\left\{\dfrac{\ln 9}{2}\right\}$, approximately 1.10.

3. $6^{3x-4} - 7 = 2081$

$6^{3x-4} = 2088$

$\ln 6^{3x-4} = \ln 2088$

$(3x - 4)\ln 6 = \ln 2088$

$3x \ln 6 - 4 \ln 6 = \ln 2088$

$3x \ln 6 = \ln 2088 + 4 \ln 6$

$x = \dfrac{\ln 2088 + 4 \ln 6}{3 \ln 6} \approx 2.76$

The solution set is $\left\{\dfrac{\ln 2088 + 4 \ln 6}{3 \ln 6}\right\}$, approximately 2.76.

4. $e^{2x} - 8e^x + 7 = 0$

$\left(e^x - 7\right)\left(e^x - 1\right) = 0$

$e^x - 7 = 0 \quad$ or $\quad e^x - 1 = 0$

$\quad e^x = 7 \quad\quad\quad\quad e^x = 1$

$\ln e^x = \ln 7 \quad\quad \ln e^x = \ln 1$

$\quad x = \ln 7 \quad\quad\quad\quad x = 0$

The solution set is $\{0, \ln 7\}$. The solutions are 0 and (approximately) 1.95.

5. $\log_2(x - 4) = 3$

$2^3 = x - 4$

$8 = x - 4$

$12 = x$

Check:

$\log_2(x - 4) = 3$

$\log_2(12 - 4) = 3$

$\log_2 8 = 3$

$3 = 3$

The solution set is $\{12\}$.

6. $\log x + \log(x - 3) = 1$

$\log x(x - 3) = 1$

$10^1 = x(x - 3)$

$10 = x^2 - 3x$

$0 = x^2 - 3x - 10$

$0 = (x - 5)(x + 2)$

$x - 5 = 0 \quad$ or $\quad x + 2 = 0$

$\quad x = 5 \quad$ or $\quad\quad x = -2$

Check

Checking 5:

$$\log 5 + \log(5-3) = 1$$
$$\log 5 + \log 2 = 1$$
$$\log(5 \cdot 2) = 1$$
$$\log 10 = 1$$
$$1 = 1$$

Checking -2:
$$\log x + \log(x-3) = 1$$
$$\log(-2) + \log(-2-3) \overset{?}{=} 1$$

Negative numbers do not have logarithms so -2 does not check.
The solution set is $\{5\}$.

7. $4 \ln 3x = 8$
$$\ln 3x = 2$$
$$e^{\ln 3x} = e^2$$
$$3x = e^2$$
$$x = \frac{e^2}{3} \approx 2.46$$

Check
$$4 \ln 3x = 8$$
$$4 \ln 3\left(\frac{e^2}{3}\right) = 8$$
$$4 \ln e^2 = 8$$
$$4(2) = 8$$
$$8 = 8$$

The solution set is $\left\{\dfrac{e^2}{3}\right\}$,

approximately 2.46.

8.   For a risk of 7%, let $R = 7$ in
$$R = 6e^{12.77x}$$
$$6e^{12.77x} = 7$$
$$e^{12.77x} = \frac{7}{6}$$
$$\ln e^{12.77x} = \ln\left(\frac{7}{6}\right)$$
$$12.77x = \ln\left(\frac{7}{6}\right)$$
$$x = \frac{\ln\left(\frac{7}{6}\right)}{12.77} \approx 0.01$$

For a blood alcohol concentration of 0.01, the risk of a car accident is 7%.

9. $A = P\left(1 + \dfrac{r}{n}\right)^{nt}$

$$3600 = 1000\left(1 + \frac{0.08}{4}\right)^{4t}$$
$$1000\left(1 - \frac{0.08}{4}\right)^{4t} = 3600$$
$$1000(1 + 0.02)^{4t} = 3600$$
$$1000(1.02)^{4t} = 3600$$
$$(1.02)^{4t} = \ln 3.6$$
$$4t \ln(1.02) = \ln 3.6$$
$$t = \frac{\ln 3.6}{4 \ln 1.02}$$
$$\approx 16.2$$

After approximately 16.2 years, the $1000 will grow to an accumulated value of $3600.

10.
$$N = 461.87 + 299.4 \ln x$$
$$2000 = 461.87 + 299.4 \ln x$$
$$461.87 + 299.4 \ln x = 2000$$
$$299.4 \ln x = 1538.13$$
$$\ln x = \frac{1538.13}{299.4}$$
$$e^{\ln x} = e^{1538.13/299.4}$$
$$x = e^{1538.13/299.4}$$
$$\approx 170$$

Approximately 170 years after 1979, in 2149, there will be 2 million U.S. workers in the environmental industry.

Exercise Set 3.4

1. $10^x = 3.91$
$$\ln 10^x = \ln 3.91$$
$$x \ln 10 = \ln 3.91$$
$$x = \frac{\ln 3.91}{\ln 10} \approx 0.59$$

The solution set is $\left\{\dfrac{\ln 3.91}{\ln 10}\right\}$,

approximately 0.59.

3. $e^x = 5.7$

$\ln e^x = 5.7$

$x = \ln 5.7 \approx 1.74$

The solution set is $\{\ln 5.7\}$,

approximately 1.74.

5. $5^x = 17$

$\ln 5^x = \ln 17$

$x \ln 5 = \ln 17$

$x = \dfrac{\ln 17}{\ln 5} \approx 1.76$

The solution set is $\left\{\dfrac{\ln 17}{\ln 5}\right\}$,

approximately 1.76.

7. $5e^x = 23$

$e^x = \dfrac{23}{5}$

$\ln e^x = \ln \dfrac{23}{5}$

$x = \ln \dfrac{23}{5} \approx 1.53$

The solution set is $\left\{\ln \dfrac{23}{5}\right\}$,

approximately 1.53.

9. $3e^{5x} = 1977$

$e^{5x} = 659$

$\ln e^{5x} = \ln 659$

$x = \dfrac{\ln 659}{5} \approx 1.30$

The solution set is $\left\{\dfrac{\ln 659}{5}\right\}$,

approximately 1.30.

11. $e^{1-5x} = 793$

$\ln e^{1-5x} = \ln 793$

$(1-5x)(\ln e) = \ln 793$

$1-5x = \ln 793$

$5x = 1 - \ln 793$

$x = \dfrac{1 - \ln 793}{5} \approx -1.14$

The solution set is $\left\{\dfrac{1 - \ln 793}{5}\right\}$,

approximately -1.14.

13. $e^{5x-3} - 2 = 10,476$

$e^{5x-3} = 10,478$

$\ln e^{5x-3} = \ln 10,478$

$(5x-3)\ln e = \ln 10,478$

$5x - 3 = \ln 10,478$

$5x = \ln 10,478 + 3$

$x = \dfrac{\ln 10,478 + 3}{5} \approx 2.45$

The solution set is $\left\{\dfrac{\ln 10,478 + 3}{5}\right\}$,

approximately 2.45.

15. $7^{x+2} = 410$

$\ln 7^{x+2} = \ln 410$

$(x+2)\ln 7 = \ln 410$

$x + 2 = \dfrac{\ln 410}{\ln 7}$

$x = \dfrac{\ln 410}{\ln 7} - 2 \approx 1.09$

The solution set is $\left\{\dfrac{\ln 410}{\ln 7} - 2\right\}$,

approximately 1.09.

17. $7^{0.3x} = 813$

$\ln 7^{0.3x} = \ln 813$

$0.3x \ln 7 = \ln 813$

$x = \dfrac{\ln 813}{0.3 \ln 7} \approx 11.48$

The solution set is $\left\{\dfrac{\ln 813}{0.3 \ln 7}\right\}$,

approximately 11.48.

19.
$$5^{2x+3} = 3^{x-1}$$
$$\ln 5^{2x+3} = \ln 3^{x-1}$$

$$(2x+3)\ln 5 = (x-1)\ln 3$$

$$2x \ln 5 + 3 \ln 5 = x \ln 3 - \ln 3$$

$$3 \ln 5 + \ln 3 = x \ln 3 - 2x \ln 5$$

$$3 \ln 5 + \ln 3 = x(\ln 3 - 2 \ln 5)$$

$$\frac{3 \ln 5 + \ln 3}{\ln 3 - 2 \ln 5} = x$$
$$-2.80 \approx x$$

The solution set is $\left\{\dfrac{3 \ln 5 + \ln 3}{\ln 3 - 2 \ln 5}\right\}$,

approximately -2.80.

21.
$$e^{2x} - 3e^x + 2 = 0$$
$$\left(e^x - 2\right)\left(e^x - 1\right) = 0$$

$$e^x - 2 = 0 \quad \text{or} \quad e^x - 1 = 0$$
$$e^x = 2 \qquad\qquad e^x = 1$$
$$\ln e^x = \ln 2 \qquad \ln e^x = \ln 1$$
$$x = \ln 2 \qquad\qquad x = 0$$

The solution set is {0, ln 2}. The solutions are 0 and (approximately) 0.69.

23.
$$e^{4x} + 5e^{2x} - 24 = 0$$
$$\left(e^{2x} + 8\right)\left(e^{2x} - 3\right) = 0$$

$$e^{2x} + 8 = 0 \qquad \text{or } e^{2x} - 3 = 0$$
$$e^{2x} = -8 \qquad\qquad e^{2x} = 3$$
$$\ln e^{2x} = \ln(-8) \qquad \ln e^{2x} = \ln 3$$
$$2x = \ln(-8) \qquad\qquad 2x = \ln 3$$
$$\ln(-8) \text{ does not exist} \qquad x = \frac{\ln 3}{2}$$

$$x = \frac{\ln 3}{2} \approx 0.55$$

The solution set is $\left\{\dfrac{\ln 3}{2}\right\}$,

approximately 0.55.

25.
$$3^{2x} + 3^x - 2 = 0$$
$$(3^x + 2)(3^x - 1) = 0$$

$$3^x + 2 = 0 \qquad\qquad 3^x - 1 = 0$$
$$3^x = -2 \qquad\qquad 3^x = 1$$
$$\log 3^x = \log(-2) \qquad \log 3^x = \log 1$$
$$\text{can't do} \qquad\qquad x \log 3 = 0$$

$$x = \frac{0}{\log 3}$$
$$x = 0$$

The solution set is {0}.

27. $\log_3 x = 4$
$$x = 3^4$$
$$x = 81$$
The solution set is {81}.

29. $\log_4(x+5) = 3$
$$x + 5 = 4^3$$
$$x + 5 = 64$$
$$x = 59$$
The solution set is {59}.

31. $\log_3(x-4) = -3$
$$x - 4 = 3^{-3}$$
$$x - 4 = \frac{1}{27}$$
$$x = \frac{109}{27}$$

The solution set is $\left\{\dfrac{109}{27}\right\}$.

33. $\log_4(3x+2) = 3$
$$3x + 2 = 4^3$$
$$3x + 2 = 64$$
$$3x = 62$$
$$x = \frac{62}{3}$$

The solution set is $\left\{\dfrac{62}{3}\right\}$.

35.
$$\log_5 x + \log_5(4x-1) = 1$$
$$\log_5\left(4x^2 - x\right) = 1$$
$$4x^2 - x = 5$$
$$4x^2 - x - 5 = 0$$
$$(4x-5)(x+1) = 0$$
$$x = \frac{5}{4} \text{ or } x = -1$$

$x = -1$ does not check because $\log_5(-1)$ does not exist.

The solution set is $\left\{\dfrac{5}{4}\right\}$.

37.
$$\log_3(x-5) + \log_3(x+3) = 2$$
$$\log_3\left[(x-5)(x+3)\right] = 2$$
$$(x-5)(x+3) = 3^2$$
$$x^2 - 2x - 15 = 9$$
$$x^2 - 2x - 24 = 0$$
$$(x-6)(x+4) = 0$$
$$x = 6 \text{ or } x = -4$$

$x = -4$ does not check because $\log_3(-4-5)$ does not exist. The solution set is $\{6\}$.

39.
$$\log_2(x+2) - \log_2(x-5) = 3$$
$$\log_2\left(\frac{x+2}{x-5}\right) = 3$$
$$\frac{x+2}{x-5} = 2^3$$
$$\frac{x+2}{x-5} = 8$$
$$x+2 = 8(x-5)$$
$$x+2 = 8x - 40$$
$$7x = 42$$
$$x = 6$$

The solution set is $\{6\}$.

41.
$$2\log_3(x+4) = \log_3 9 + 2$$
$$2\log_3(x+4) = 2 + 2$$
$$2\log_3(x+4) = 4$$
$$\log_3(x+4) = 2$$
$$3^2 = x + 4$$
$$9 = x + 4$$
$$5 = x$$

The solution set is $\{5\}$.

43.
$$\log_2(x-6) + \log_2(x-4) - ???_2 x = 2$$
$$\log_2 \frac{(x-6)(x-4)}{x} = 2$$
$$\frac{(x-6)(x-4)}{x} = 2^2$$
$$x^2 - 10x + 24 = 4x$$
$$x^2 - 14x + 24 = 0$$
$$(x-12)(x-2) = 0$$
$$x - 12 = 0 \qquad x - 2 = 0$$
$$x = 12 \qquad\quad x = 2$$

The solution set is $\{12\}$ since $\log_2(2\_6) = \log_2(\_4)$ is not possible.

45.
$$\ln x = 2$$
$$e^{\ln x} = e^2$$
$$x = e^2 \approx 7.39$$

The solution set is $\left\{e^2\right\}$, approximately 7.39.

47.
$$5\ln 2x = 20$$
$$\ln 2x = 4$$
$$e^{\ln 2x} = e^4$$
$$2x = e^4$$
$$x = \frac{e^4}{2} \approx 27.30$$

The solution set is $\left\{\dfrac{e^4}{2}\right\}$, approximately 27.30.

49.
$$6 + 2\ln x = 5$$
$$2\ln x = -1$$
$$\ln x = -\frac{1}{2}$$
$$e^{\ln x} = e^{-1/2}$$
$$x = e^{-1/2} \approx 0.61$$

The solution set is $\left\{e^{-1/2}\right\}$, approximately 0.61.

51. $\ln \sqrt{x+3} = 1$

$e^{\ln \sqrt{x+3}} = e^1$

$\sqrt{x+3} = e$

$x + 3 = e^2$

$x = e^2 - 3 \approx 4.39$

The solution set is $\{e^2 - 3\}$, approximately 4.39.

53. $25 = 6e^{12.77x}$

$\dfrac{25}{6} = e^{12.77x}$

$\ln \dfrac{25}{6} = \ln e^{12.77x}$

$\ln \dfrac{25}{6} = 12.77x$

$\dfrac{\ln \dfrac{25}{6}}{12.77} = x$

$0.112 \approx x$

A blood alcohol level of about 0.112 corresponds to a 25% risk of a car accident.

55. **a.** $A = 18.9e^{0.005(0)}$

$A = 18.9$ million

b. $19.6 = 18.9e^{0.0055t}$

$\dfrac{19.6}{18.9} = e^{0.0055t}$

$\ln \dfrac{19.6}{18.9} = \ln e^{0.0055t}$

$\ln \dfrac{19.6}{18.9} = 0.0055t$

$\dfrac{\ln \dfrac{19.6}{18.9}}{0.0055} = t$

$6.6 \approx t$

In 2007 the population of New York will reach 19.6 million.

57. $20,000 = 12,500\left(1 + \dfrac{0.0575}{4}\right)^{4t}$

$12,500(1.014375)^{4t} = 20,000$

$(1.014375)^{4t} = 1.6$

$\ln(1.014375)^{4t} = \ln 1.6$

$4t \ln(1.014375) = \ln 1.6$

$t = \dfrac{\ln 1.6}{4 \ln 1.014375} \approx 8$

8 years

59. $1400 = 1000\left(1 + \dfrac{r}{360}\right)^{360 \cdot 2}$

$\left(1 + \dfrac{r}{360}\right)^{720} = 1.4$

$\ln\left(1 + \dfrac{r}{360}\right)^{720} = \ln 1.4$

$720 \ln\left(1 + \dfrac{r}{360}\right) = \ln 1.4$

$\ln\left(1 + \dfrac{r}{360}\right) = \dfrac{\ln 1.4}{720}$

$e^{\ln(1 + r/360)} = e^{(\ln 1.4)/720}$

$1 + \dfrac{r}{360} = e^{(\ln 1.4)/720} - 1$

$r = 360(e^{(\ln 1.4)/720}) - 1$

≈ 0.168

16.8%

61. accumulated amount $= 2(8000) = 16,000$

$16,000 = 8000e^{0.08t}$

$e^{0.08t} = 2$

$\ln e^{0.08t} = \ln 2$

$0.08t = \ln 2$

$t = \dfrac{\ln 2}{0.08}$

$t \approx 8.7$

The amount would double in 8.7 years.

63. accumulated amount = 3(2350) = 7050

$$7050 = 2350e^{r \cdot 7}$$

$$e^{7r} = 3$$

$$\ln e^{7r} = \ln 3$$

$$7r = \ln 3$$

$$r = \frac{\ln 3}{7} \approx 0.157$$

15.7%

65. $25,000 = 15,557 + 5259 \ln x$

$$5259 \ln x = 9443$$

$$\ln x = \frac{9443}{5259}$$

$$e^{\ln x} = e^{9443/5259}$$

$$x = e^{9443/5259} \approx 6$$

The average cost was $25,000 6 years after 1989, in 1995.

67. $30 \log_2 x = 45$

$$\log_2 x = 1.5$$

$$x = 2^{1.5} \approx 2.8$$

Only half the students recall the important features of the lecture after 2.8 days. (2.8, 50)

69. $2.4 = -\log x$

$$\log x = -2.4$$

$$x = 10^{-2.4} \approx 0.004$$

The hydrogen ion concentration was $10^{-2.4}$, approximately 0.004 moles per liter.

71.–73. Answers may vary.

75.

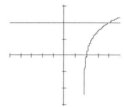

The intersection point is (2, 8).

Verify : $x = 2$

$$2^{x+1} = 8$$

$$2^{2+1} = 2$$

$$2^3 = 8$$

$$8 = 8$$

The solution set is {2}.

77.

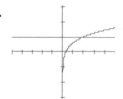

The intersection point is (4, 2).

Verify : $x = 4$

$$\log_3 (4 \cdot 4 - 7) = 2$$

$$\log_3 9 = 2$$

$$2 = 2$$

The solution set is {4}.

79.

The intersection point is (2, 1).

Verity :$x = 2$

$$\log(2 + 3) + \log 2 = 1$$

$$\log 5 + \log 2 = 1$$

$$\log(5 \cdot 2) = 1$$

$$\log 10 = 1$$

$$1 = 1$$

The solution set is {2}.

81.

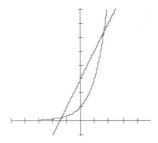

There are 2 points of intersection, approximately
(−1.391606, 0.21678798) and
(1.6855579, 6.3711158).
Verify $x \approx \_1.391606$
　　　$3^x = 2x + 3$
$3^{-1.391606} \approx 2(-1.391606) + 3$
$0.2167879803 \approx 0.216788$
Verify $x \approx 1.6855579$
　　　$3^x = 2x + 3$
$3^{1.6855579} \approx 2(1.6855579) + 3$
$6.37111582 \approx 6.371158$
The solution set is $\{-1.391606, 1.6855579\}$.

83.

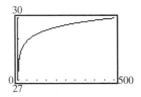

As the distance from the eye increases, barometric air pressure increases, leveling off at about 30 inches of mercury.

85.

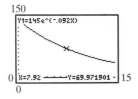

When $P = 70$, $t \approx 7.9$, so it will take about 7.9 minutes.
Verify:

$70 = 45e^{-0.092(7.9)}$
$70 \approx 70.10076749$
The runner's pulse will be 70 beats per minute after about 7.9 minutes.

87. a. False; $\log(x + 3) = 2$ means
　　　　$x + 3 = 10^2$

b. False; $\log(7x + 3) - \log(2x + 5) = 4$
　　　means $\log\dfrac{7x + 3}{2x + 5} = 4$ which means
　　　$\dfrac{7x + 3}{2x + 5} = 10^4$

c. True; $x = \dfrac{1}{k}\ln y$

$$kx = \ln y$$
$$e^{kx} = e^{\ln y}$$
$$e^{kx} = y$$

d. False; The equation $x^{10} = 5.71$ has no variable in an exponent so is not an exponential equation.

(c) is true

89.
$$(\ln x)^2 = \ln x^2$$
$$(\ln x)^2 = 2\ln x$$
$$(\ln x)^2 - 2\ln x = 0$$
$$\ln x(\ln x - 2) = 0$$
$$\ln x = 2$$
$$e^{\ln x} = e^2 \quad \text{or} \quad \begin{array}{c} \ln x = 0 \\ x = 1 \end{array}$$
$$x = e^2$$

The solution set is $\{1, e^2\}$.
Check with graphing utility:

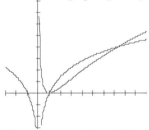

There are two points of intersection: (1, 0) and approximately (7.3890561, 4). Since $e^2 \approx 7.3890566099$, the graph verifies $x = 1$ and $x = e^2$, so the solution set is $\{1, e^2\}$ as determined algebraically.

91. $\ln(\ln x) = 0$
$$e^{\ln(\ln x)} = e^0$$
$$\ln x = 1$$
$$e^{\ln x} = e^1$$
$$x = e$$
The solution set is $\{e\}$.

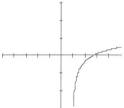

The graph of $\ln(\ln(x))$ crosses the graph $y = 0$ at approximately 2.718.

Section 3.5

Check Point Exercises

1. a. Use the exponential growth model $A = A_0 e^{kt}$ with 1990 corresponding to $t = 0$ when the population was 643 million:
$$A = 643e^{kt}$$

Substitute $t = 2000 - 1990 = 10$ when the population was 813 million, so $A = 813$, to find k.
$$813 = 643e^{k10}$$
$$\frac{813}{643} = e^{k10}$$
$$\ln\frac{813}{643} = \ln e^{k10}$$
$$\ln\frac{813}{643} = 10k$$
$$\frac{\ln\dfrac{813}{643}}{10} = k$$
$$0.023 \approx k$$

So the exponential growth function is $A = 643e^{0.023t}$

b. Substitute 2000 for A in the model from part (a) and solve for t.

$$2000 = 643e^{0.023t}$$

$$\frac{2000}{643} = e^{0.023t}$$

$$\ln\frac{2000}{643} = \ln e^{0.023t}$$

$$\ln\frac{2000}{643} = 0.023t$$

$$\frac{\ln\frac{2000}{643}}{0.023} = t$$

$$49 \approx t$$

The population will reach 2000 million, or two billion, about 49 years after 1990, in 2039.

2. a. In the exponential decay model $A = A_0e^{kt}$, substitute $\frac{A_0}{2}$ for A since the amount present after 28 years is half the original amount.

$$\frac{A_0}{2} = A_0e^{k\cdot28}$$

$$e^{28k} = \frac{1}{2}$$

$$\ln e^{28k} = \ln\frac{1}{2}$$

$$28k = \ln\frac{1}{2}$$

$$k = \frac{\ln^{1/2}}{28} \approx -0.0248$$

So the exponential decay model is
$$A = A_0e^{-0.0248t}$$

b. Substitute 60 for A_0 and 10 for A in the model from part (a) and solve for t.

$$10 = 60e^{-0.0248t}$$

$$e^{-0.0248t} = \frac{1}{6}$$

$$\ln e^{-0.0248t} = \ln\frac{1}{6}$$

$$-0.0248t = \ln\frac{1}{6}$$

$$t = \frac{\ln\frac{1}{6}}{-0.0248} \approx 72$$

The strontium-90 will decay to a level of 10 grams about 72 years after the accident.

3. a. The time prior to learning trials corresponds to $t = 0$.
$$f(0) = \frac{0.8}{1+e^{-0.2(0)}} = 0.4$$
The proportion of correct responses prior to learning trials was 0.4.

b. Substitute 10 for t in the model:
$$f(10) = \frac{0.8}{1+e^{-0.2(10)}} \approx 0.7$$
The proportion of correct responses after 10 learning trials was 0.7.

c. In the logistic growth model,
$$f(t) = \frac{c}{1+ae^{-bt}},$$ the constant c represents the limiting size that $f(t)$ can attain. The limiting size of the proportion of correct responses as continued learning trials take place is 0.8.

4. $y = ab^x$ is equivalent to $y = ae^{(\ln b)x}$.
For $y = 4(7.8)^x$, $a = 4$, $b = 7.8$.
Thus, $y = 4(7.8)^x$ is equivalent to $y = 4e^{(\ln 7.8)x}$ in terms of a natural logarithm. Rounded to three decimal places, the model is approximately equivalent to $y = 4e^{2.054x}$.

Exercise Set 3.5

1. 1970 corresponds to $t = 0$.

$A = 203e^{0.011(0)}$

$A = 203$

In 1970, the population was 203 million.

3. Solve for t when $A = 300$.

$$300 = 203e^{0.011t}$$

$$\frac{300}{203} = e^{0.011t}$$

$$\ln\frac{300}{203} = \ln e^{0.011t}$$

$$\ln\frac{300}{203} = 0.011t$$

$$\frac{\ln\frac{300}{203}}{0.011} = t$$

$$36 \approx t$$

The population will be 300 million about 36 years after 1970, in 2006.

5. In the exponential growth model,
$A = A_0 e^{kt}$, k represents the growth rate.
The population was increasing by about 2.6% each year.

7. $1624 = 574e^{0.026t}$

$$\frac{116}{41} = e^{0.026t}$$

$$\ln\frac{116}{41} = \ln e^{0.026t}$$

$$\ln\frac{116}{41} = 0.026t$$

$$t = \frac{\ln\frac{116}{41}}{0.026} \approx 40$$

The population will be 1624 million about 40 years after 1974, in 2014.

9. a.

$$A_0 = 158700$$

$$A = 158700e^{kt} \text{ for 2000,}$$

$$t = 5, A = 207200$$

$$207200 = 158700e^{k5}$$

$$\frac{207200}{158700} = e^{5k}$$

$$\ln\frac{207200}{158700} = \ln e^{5k}$$

$$\ln\frac{207200}{158700} = 5k$$

$$\frac{\ln\frac{207200}{158700}}{5} = k$$

$$0.0533 \approx k$$

b.

$$300000 = 158700e^{0.0533t}$$

$$\frac{300000}{158700} = e^{0.0533t}$$

$$\ln\frac{300000}{158700} = ??e^{0.0533t}$$

$$\ln\frac{300000}{158700} = 0.0533t$$

$$\frac{\ln\frac{300000}{158700}}{0.0533} = t$$

$$12 \approx t$$

In 12 years after 1995, 2007, the price will
Be $300,000.

11. $A_0 = 6.04$, in 2050, $t = 50$ and $A = 10$

$$10 = 6.04e^{k50}$$

$$\frac{10}{6.04} = e^{50k}$$

$$\ln\frac{10}{6.04} = \ln e^{50k}$$

$$\ln\frac{10}{6.04} = 50k$$

$$\frac{\ln\dfrac{10}{6.04}}{50} = k$$

$$0.01 \approx k$$

$$A = 6.04e^{0.01k}$$

13. $A = 16e^{-0.000121(5715)} \approx 8.01$
In 5715 years, 8.01 grams of carbon-14 will be present.

15. After 10 seconds, $\dfrac{16}{2}$ or 8 grams;

After 20 seconds, $\dfrac{8}{2}$ or 4 grams;

After 30 seconds, $\dfrac{4}{2}$ or 2 grams;

After 40 seconds, $\dfrac{2}{2}$ or 1 gram;

After 50 seconds, $\dfrac{1}{2}$ or 0.5 gram.

17. For an original amount of A_0, for the amount remaining is $A = 0.15A_0$.

$$0.15A_0 = A_0e^{-0.000121t}$$

$$0.15 = e^{-0.000121t}$$

$$\ln 0.15 = \ln e^{-0.000121t}$$

$$\ln 0.15 = -0.000121t$$

$$t = \ln\frac{0.15}{-0.000121} \approx 15{,}679$$

The paintings were about 15,679 years old.

19. a. Half the original amount corresponds to an amount remaining of $A = \dfrac{1}{2}A_0$. This amount corresponds to $t = 1.31$.

$$\frac{1}{2}A_0 = A_0e^{1.31k}$$

$$\frac{1}{2} = e^{1.31k}$$

$$\ln\frac{1}{2} = \ln e^{1.31k}$$

$$k = \frac{\ln\frac{1}{2}}{1.31} \approx -0.52912$$

The decay model is given by
$$A = A_0e^{-0.52912t}$$

b.
$$0.945A_0 = A_0e^{-0.52912t}$$

$$0.945 = e^{-0.52912t}$$

$$\ln 0.945 = -0.52912t$$

$$t = \frac{\ln 0.945}{-0.52912} \approx 0.107$$

The bones of the dinosaur were about 0.107 billion, or 107 million years old.

21. The doubling of the original population corresponds to $A = 2A$.

$$2A_0 = A_0e^{kt}$$

$$2 = e^{kt}$$

$$\ln 2 = \ln e^{kt}$$

$$\ln 2 = kt$$

$$t = \frac{\ln 2}{k}$$

23. $t = \dfrac{\ln 2}{0.011} \approx 63$

It will take China about 63 years to double its population.

25. a. When the epidemic began, $t = 0$.
$$f(0) = \frac{100{,}000}{1 + 5000e^0} \approx 20$$
Twenty people became ill when the epidemic began.

b. $f(4) = \dfrac{100{,}000}{1 + 5{,}000e^{-4}} \approx 1080$

About 1080 people were ill at the end of the fourth week.

c. In the logistic growth model,

$$f(t) = \frac{c}{1 + ae^{-bt}},$$

the constant c represents the limiting size that $f(t)$ can attain. The limiting size of the population that becomes ill is 100,000 people.

27. $P(20) = \dfrac{0.9}{1 + 271e^{-0.122(20)}} \approx 0.037$

The probability that a 20-year-old has some coronary heart disease is about 3.7%.

29.

$$0.5 = \frac{1.9}{1 + 271e^{-0.122t}}$$

$$0.5\left(1 + 271e^{-0.122t}\right) = 0.9$$

$$1 + 271e^{-0.122t} = 1.8$$

$$271e^{-0.122t} = 0.8$$

$$e^{-0.122t} = \frac{0.8}{271}$$

$$\ln e^{-0.122t} = \ln \frac{0.8}{271}$$

$$-0.122t = \ln \frac{0.8}{271}$$

$$t = \frac{\ln \frac{0.8}{271}}{-0.122} \approx 48$$

The probability of some coronary heart disease is 0.5 at about age 48.

31. $y = 100(4.6)^x$ is equivalent to

$y = 100e^{(\ln 4.6)x}$;

Using $\ln 4.6 \approx 1.526$,

$y = 100e^{1.526x}$.

33. $y = 2.5(0.7)^x$ is equivalent to

$y = 2.5e^{(\ln 0.7)x}$;

Using $\ln 0.7 \approx -0.357$,

$y = 2.5e^{-0.357x}$.

35.–43. Answers may vary.

45. $y = 1.74(1.037)^x$

The correlation coefficient,

$r = 0.97$, is somewhat close to 1, indicating that the model is a good fit.

47. $y = 1.547 + 0.112x$

The correlation coefficient, $r = 0.99$, is close to 1, indicating that the model is a good fit.

49. $y = 1.547 + 0.112x$

The correlation coefficient, $r = 0.99$, is close to 1, indicating that the model is the best fit.

$7.5 = 1.547 + 0.112x$

$5.953 = 0.112x$

$53.15 = x$

$1969 + 53 = 2022$

51. $y = 0.06x^4 - 1.7x^3 + 14.2x^2 + 34x + 153;\ r = .9979$

53. Answers will vary.

Review Exercises

1. This is the graph of $f(x) = 4^x$ reflected about the y-axis, so the function is $g(x) = 4^{-x}$.

2. This is the graph of $f(x) = 4^x$ reflected about the x-axis and about the y-axis, so the function is $h(x) = -4^{-x}$.

3. This is the graph of $f(x) = 4^x$ reflected about the x-axis and about the y-axis then shifted upward 3 units, so the function is $r(x) = -4^{-x} + 3$.

4. This is the graph of $f(x) = 4^x$.

5.

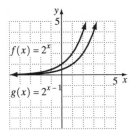

x	$f(x) = 2x$	$g(x) = 2^{x-1}$
-2	$2^{-2} = \frac{1}{4}$	$2^{-2-1} = 2^{-3} = \frac{1}{8}$
-1	$2^{-1} = \frac{1}{2}$	$2^{-1-1} = 2^{-2} = \frac{1}{4}$
0	$2^0 = 1$	$2^{0-1} = 2^{-1} = \frac{1}{2}$
1	$2^1 = 2$	$2^{1-1} = 2^0 = 1$
2	$2^2 = 4$	$2^{2-1} = 2^1 = 2$

The graph of $g(x)$ shifts the graph of $f(x)$ one unit to the right.

6.

x	$f(x) = 3^x$	$g(x) = 3^x - 1$
-2	$3^{-2} = \frac{1}{9}$	$3^{-2} - 1 = -\frac{8}{9}$
-1	$3^{-1} = \frac{1}{3}$	$3^{-1} - 1 = -\frac{2}{3}$
0	$3^0 = 1$	$3^0 - 1 = 0$
1	$3^1 = 3$	$3^1 - 1 = 2$
2	$3^2 = 9$	$3^2 - 1 = 8$

The graph of $g(x)$ reflects the graph of $f(x)$ about the x-axis.

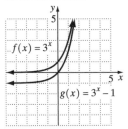

7.

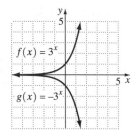

x	$f(x) = 3^x$	$g(x) = -3^x$
-2	$3^{-2} = \frac{1}{9}$	$-3^{-2} = -\frac{1}{9}$
-1	$3^{-1} = \frac{1}{3}$	$-3^{-1} = -\frac{1}{3}$
0	$3^0 = 1$	$-3^0 = -1$
1	$3^1 = 3$	$-3^1 = -3$
2	$3^2 = 9$	$-3^2 = -9$

The graph of $g(x)$ reflects the graph of $f(x)$ about the y – axis.

8.

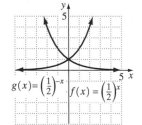

x	$f(x)=\left(\frac{1}{2}\right)^x$	$g(x)=\left(\frac{1}{2}\right)^{-x}$
-2	$\left(\frac{1}{2}\right)^{-2}=4$	$\left(\frac{1}{2}\right)^{-(-2)}=\left(\frac{1}{2}\right)^2=\frac{1}{4}$
-1	$\left(\frac{1}{2}\right)^{-1}=2$	$\left(\frac{1}{2}\right)^{-1(-1)}=\left(\frac{1}{2}\right)^1=\frac{1}{2}$
0	$\left(\frac{1}{2}\right)^0=1$	$\left(\frac{1}{2}\right)^{-(0)}=\left(\frac{1}{2}\right)^0=1$
1	$\left(\frac{1}{2}\right)^1=\frac{1}{2}$	$\left(\frac{1}{2}\right)^{-1(1)}=\left(\frac{1}{2}\right)^{-1}=2$
2	$\left(\frac{1}{2}\right)^2=\frac{1}{4}$	$\left(\frac{1}{2}\right)^{-2(2)}=\left(\frac{1}{2}\right)^{-2}=4$

The graph of $g(x)$ reflects the graph of $f(x)$ about the y-axis.

9. 5.5% compounded semiannually:
$$A=5000\left(1+\frac{0.055}{2}\right)^{2\cdot5}\approx6558.26$$
5.25% compounded monthly:
$$A=5000\left(1+\frac{0.0525}{12}\right)^{12\cdot5}\approx6497.16$$
5.5% compounded semiannually yields the greater return.

10. 7% compounded monthly:
$$A=14,000\left(1+\frac{0.07}{12}\right)^{12\cdot10}\approx28,135.26$$
6.85% compounded continuously:
$$A=14,000e^{0.0685(10)}\approx27,772.81$$
7% compounded monthly yields the greater return.

11. a. When first taken out of the microwave, the temperature of the coffee was 200°.

    b. After 20 minutes, the temperature of the coffee was about 120°.
$$T=70+130e^{-0.04855(20)}\approx119.23$$
Using a calculator, the temperature is about 119°.

    c. The coffee will cool to about 70°;
The temperature of the room is 70°.

12. $49^{1/2}=7$

13. $4^3=x$

14. $3^y=81$

15. $\log_6 216=3$

16. $\log_b 625=4$

17. $\log_{13} 874=y$

18. $\log_4 64=3$ because $4^3=64$.

19. $\log_5 \dfrac{1}{25}=-2$ because $5^{-2}=\dfrac{1}{25}$.

20. $\log_3(-9)$ cannot be evaluated since $\log_b x$ is defined only for $x>0$.

21. $\log_{16} 4=\dfrac{1}{2}$ because $16^{1/2}=\sqrt{16}=4$.

22. Because $\log_b b=1$,
we conclude $\log_{17} 17=1$.

23. Because $\log_b b^x=x$,
we conclude $\log_3 3^8=8$.

24. Because $\ln e^x=x$,
we conclude $e^5=5$.

25. Because $\log_b=1$,
we conclude $\log_8 8=1$.
So, $\log_3(\log_8 8)=\log_3 1$.
Because $\log_b 1=0$
we conclude $\log_3 1=0$.
Therefore, $\log_3(\log_8 8)=0$.

26.

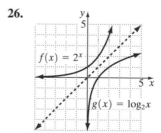

27.

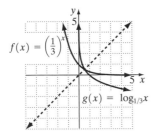

$f(x) = \left(\frac{1}{3}\right)^x$

$g(x) = \log_{1/3} x$

28. This is the graph of $f(x) = \log x$ reflected about the *y*-axis, so the function is $g(x) = \log(-x)$.

29. This is the graph of $f(x) = \log x$ shifted left 2 units, reflected about the *y*-axis, then shifted upward one unit, so the function is $r(x) = 1 + \log(2 - x)$.

30. This is the graph of $f(x) = \log x$ shifted left 2 units then reflected about the *y*-axis, so the function is $h(x) = \log(2 - x)$.

31. This is the graph of $f(x) = \log x$.

32.

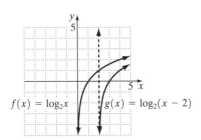

$f(x) = \log_2 x$ $g(x) = \log_2(x - 2)$

x-intercept: (3, 0)
vertical asymptote: $x = 2$

33.

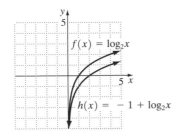

$f(x) = \log_2 x$

$h(x) = -1 + \log_2 x$

x-intercept: (2, 0)
vertical asymptote: $x = 0$

34.

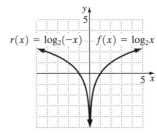

$r(x) = \log_2(-x)$ $f(x) = \log_2 x$

x-intercept: (−1, 0)
vertical asymptote: $x = 0$

35. The domain of *f* consists of all *x* for which $x + 5 > 0$.
Solving this inequality for *x*, we obtain $x > -5$.
Thus the domain of *f* is $(-5, \infty)$

36. The domain of *f* consists of all *x* for which $3 - x > 0$.
Solving this inequality for *x*, we obtain $x < 3$.
Thus, the domain of *f* is $(-\infty, 3)$.

37. The domain of *f* consists of all *x* for which $(x - 1)^2 > 0$.
Solving this inequality for *x*, we obtain $x < 1$ or $x > 1$. Thus, the domain of *f* is $(-\infty, 1)$ or $(1, \infty)$.

38. Because $\ln e^x = x$, we conclude $\ln e^{6x} = 6x$.

39. Because $e^{\ln x} = x$, we conclude $e^{\ln \sqrt{x}} = \sqrt{x}$.

40. Because $10^{\log x} = x$, we conclude $10^{\log 4x^2} = 4x^2$.

41. $R = \log \dfrac{1000 I_0}{I_0} = \log 1000 = 3$

The Richter scale magnitude is 3.0.

42. a. $f(0) = 76 - 18\log(0+1) = 76$
When first given, the average score was 76.

    b. $f(2) = 76 - 18\log(2+1) \approx 67$
$f(4) = 76 - 18\log(4+1) \approx 63$
$f(6) = 76 - 18\log(6+1) \approx 61$
$f(8) = 76 - 18\log(8+1) \approx 59$
$f(12) = 76 - 18\log(12+1) \approx 56$
After 2, 4, 6, 8, and 12 months, the average scores are about 67, 63, 61, 59, and 56, respectively.

    c.

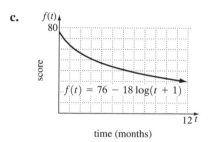

Retention decreases as time passes.

43. $t = \dfrac{1}{0.06}\ln\!\left(\dfrac{12}{12-5}\right) \approx 8.98$
It will take about 9 weeks.

44. $\log_6\!\left(36x^3\right)$
$= \log_6 36 + \log_6 x^3$
$= \log_6 36 + 3\log_6 x$
$= 2 + 3\log_6 x$

45. $\log_4 \dfrac{\sqrt{x}}{64} = \log_4 x^{1/2} - \log_4 64$
$= \dfrac{1}{2}\log_4 x - 3$

46. $\log_2 \dfrac{xy^2}{64} = \log_2 xy^2 - \log_2 64$
$= \log_2 x + \log_2 y^2 - \log_2 64$
$= \log_2 x + 2\log_2{}^{y-6}$

47. $\ln 3\sqrt[3]{\dfrac{x}{e}}$
$= \ln\!\left(\dfrac{x}{e}\right)^{1/3}$
$= \dfrac{1}{3}[\ln x - \ln e]$
$= \dfrac{1}{3}\ln x - \dfrac{1}{3}\ln e$
$= \dfrac{1}{3}\ln x - \dfrac{1}{3}$

48. $\log_b 7 + \log_b 3$
$= \log_b(7\cdot 3)$
$= \log_b 21$

49. $\log 3 - 3\log x$
$= \log 3 - \log x^3$
$= \log \dfrac{3}{x^3}$

50. $3\ln x + 4\ln y$
$= \ln x^3 + \ln y^4$
$= \ln\!\left(x^3 y^4\right)$

51. $\dfrac{1}{2}\ln x - \ln y$
$= \ln x^{1/2} - \ln y$
$= \ln \dfrac{\sqrt{x}}{y}$

52. $\log_6 72{,}348 = \dfrac{\log 72{,}348}{\log 6} \approx 6.2448$

53. $\log_4 0.863 = \dfrac{\ln 0.863}{\ln 4} \approx -0.1063$

54. $8^x = 12{,}143$
$\ln 8^x = \ln 12{,}143$

$x \ln 8 = \ln 12{,}143$

$x = \dfrac{\ln 12{,}143}{\ln 8} \approx 4.523$

The solution set is $\left\{ \dfrac{\ln 12{,}143}{\ln 8} \right\}$,

approximately 4.52.

55. $9e^{5x} = 1269$

$e^{5x} = 141$

$\ln e^{5x} = \ln 141$

$5x = \ln 141$

$x = \dfrac{\ln 141}{5}$

The solution set is $\left\{ \dfrac{\ln 141}{5} \right\}$, approximately

0.99.

56. $e^{12-5x} - 7 = 123$

$e^{12-5x} = 130$

$\ln e^{12-5x} = \ln 130$

$12 - 5x = \ln 130$

$5x = 12 - \ln 130$

$x = \dfrac{12 - \ln 130}{5} \approx 1.426$

The solution set is $\{1.43\}$.

57. $5^{4x+2} = 37{,}500$

$\ln 5^{4x+2} = \ln 37{,}500$

$(4x+2)\ln 5 = \ln 37{,}500$

$4x \ln 5 + 2 \ln 5 = \ln 37{,}500$

$4x \ln 5 = \ln 37{,}500 - 2 \ln 5$

$x = \dfrac{\ln 37{,}500 - 2 \ln 5}{4 \ln 5}$

The solution set is $\left\{ \dfrac{\ln 37{,}500 - 2 \ln 5}{4 \ln 5} \right\}$,

approximately 1.14.

58. $e^{2x} - e^x - 6 = 0$

$(e^x - 3)(e^x + 2) = 0$

$e^x - 3 = 0$ or $e^x + 2 = 0$

$e^x = 3 \qquad e^x = -2$

$\ln e^x = \ln 3 \qquad \ln e^x - \ln(-2)$

$x = \ln 3 \qquad x = \ln(-2)$

$x = \ln 3 \approx 1.099 \quad \ln(-2)$ does not exist.

The solution set is $\{\ln 3\}$,

approximately 1.10.

59. $\log_4(3x - 5) = 3$

$3x - 5 = 4^3$

$3x - 5 = 64$

$3x = 69$

$x = 23$

The solutions set is $\{23\}$.

60. $\log_2(x+3) + \log_2(x-3) = 4$

$\log_2(x+3)(x-3) = 4$

$\log_2(x^2 - 9) = 4$

$x^2 - 9 = 2^4$

$x^2 - 9 = 16$

$x^2 = 25$

$x = \pm 5$

$x = -5$ does not check because $\log_2(-5+3)$

does not exist.

The solution set is $\{5\}$.

61. $\log_3(x-1) - \log_3(x+2) = 2$

$\log_3 \dfrac{x-1}{x+2} = 2$

$\dfrac{x-1}{x-2} = 3^2$

$\dfrac{x-1}{x+2} = 9$

$x - 1 = 9(x+2)$

$x - 1 = 9x + 18$

$8x = -19$

$x = -\dfrac{19}{8}$

$x = -\dfrac{19}{8}$ does not check because

$\log_3\left(-\dfrac{19}{8}-1\right)$ does not exist.

The solution set is $\varnothing$.

62. $\ln x = -1$

$x = e^{-1} = \dfrac{1}{e} \approx 0.368$

The solution set is $\left\{\dfrac{1}{e}\right\}$,

approximately 0.368.

63. $3 + 4\ln 2x = 15$

$4\ln 2x = 12$

$\ln 2x = 3$

$2^x = e^3$

$x = \dfrac{e^3}{2} \approx 10.043$

The solution set is $\left\{\dfrac{e^3}{2}\right\}$,

approximately 10.043

64. $13 = 10.1e^{0.005t}$

$e^{0.005t} = \dfrac{13}{10.1}$

$\ln e^{0.005t} = \ln\dfrac{13}{10.1}$

$0.005t = \ln\dfrac{13}{10.1}$

$t = \dfrac{\ln\dfrac{13}{10.1}}{0.005} \approx 50$

The population will reach 13 million about 50 years after 1992, in 2042.

65. $280\cdot 2 = 364(1.005)^t$

$364(1.005)^t = 560$

$1.005^t = \dfrac{20}{13}$

$\ln 1.005^t = \ln\dfrac{20}{13}$

$t\ln 1.005 = \ln\dfrac{20}{13}$

$t = \dfrac{\ln\dfrac{20}{13}}{\ln 1.005} \approx 86$

The carbon dioxide concentration will be double the pre-industrial level about 86 years after 2000, in 2086.

66. $30,000 = 15,557 + 5259\ln x$

$5259\ln x = 14,443$

$\ln x = \dfrac{14,443}{5259}$

$x = e^{14,443/5259} \approx 16$

The average cost of a new car will reach $30,000 about 16 years after 1989, in 2005.

67. $20,000 = 12,500\left(1 + \dfrac{0.065}{4}\right)^{4t}$

$12,500(1.01625)^{4t} = 20,000$

$(1.01625)^{4t} = 1.6$

$\ln(1.01625)^{4t} = \ln 1.6$

$4t\ln 1.01625 = \ln 1.6$

$t = \dfrac{\ln 1.6}{4\ln 1.01625} \approx 7.3$

It will take about 7.3 years.

68. $3\cdot 50,000 = 50,000e^{0.075t}$

$50,000e^{0.075t} = 150,000$

$e^{0.075} = 3$

$\ln e^{0.075t} = \ln 3$

$0.075t = \ln 3$

$t = \dfrac{\ln 3}{0.075} \approx 14.6$

It will take about 14.6 years.

69. When an investment value triples, $A = 3P$.

$3P = Pe^{5r}$

$e^{5r} = 3$

$\ln e^{5r} = \ln 3$

$5r = \ln 3$

$r = \dfrac{\ln 3}{5} \approx 0.2197$

The interest rate would need to be about 21.97%

70.   **a.** $35.3 = 22.4e^{k10}$

$$\frac{35.3}{22.4} = e^{10k}$$

$$\ln \frac{35.3}{22.4} = ??e^{10k}$$

$$\ln \frac{35.3}{22.4} = 10k$$

$$\frac{\ln \frac{35.3}{22.4}}{10} = k$$

$$0.045 \approx k$$

$$A = 22.4e^{0.045t}$$

b. $A = 22.4e^{0.045(20)} \approx 55.1$

In 2010, the population will be about 55.1 million.

c. $60 = 22.4e^{0.045t}$

$$\frac{60}{22.4} = e^{0.045t}$$

$$\ln \frac{60}{22.4} = \ln e^{0.045t}$$

$$\ln \frac{60}{22.4} = 0.045t$$

$$\frac{\ln \frac{60}{22.4}}{0.045} = t$$

$$22 \approx t$$

The population will reach 60 million about 22 years after 1990, in 2012.

71. If the remaining amount is 15% of the original amount, them $A = 0.15A_0$.

$$0.15A_0 = A_0 e^{-0.000121t}$$

$$e^{-0.00121t} = 0.15$$

$$\ln e^{-0.00121t} = \ln 0.15$$

$$-0.0012t = \ln 0.15$$

$$t = \frac{\ln 0.15}{-0.00121} \approx 15,679$$

At the time of discovery, the paintings were about 15,679 years old.

72.   **a.** $f(0) = \dfrac{500,000}{1 + 2499e^{-0.92(0)}} = 200$

200 people became ill when the epidemic began.

b. $f(6) = \dfrac{500,000}{1 + 2499e^{-0.92(6)}} = 45,410$

45,410 were ill after 6 weeks.

c. 500,000

73. $y = 73(2.6)^x$ is equivalent to

$y = 73e^{(\ln 2.6)x}$; Using $\ln 2.6 \approx 0.956$;

$y = 73e^{0.956x}$.

74. $y = 6.5(0.43)^x$ is equivalent to

$y = 6.5e^{(\ln 0.43)x}$; Using $\ln 0.43 \approx -0.844$;

$y = 6.5e^{-0.844x}$.

75. The high projection might be best modeled by an exponential function, the medium projection by a linear function, and the low projection by a quadratic function; If the low projection is modeled by a quadratic function, the leading coefficient would be negative since the parabola opens downward.

76. linear model:

$y = 0.5055x - 8.5905$

$r = 0.9451995388$

quadratic model:
$$y = 0.0042934712x^2 - 0.1041729153x$$
$$+ 5.038408856$$
$$R^2 = 0.9883582557$$

exponential model:
$$y = 3.38051786(1.0235357)^x$$
$$r = 0.9945619484$$

logarithmic model:
$$y = -20.94062012 + 12.53110237\ln x$$
$$r = 0.6748503469$$

The exponential model best fits the given data. 2050 is 151 years after 1899.
$$y = 3.38051786(1.0235357)^{151} \approx 113.4$$
In 2050, the projected U.S. population age 65 and over will be about 113.4 million.

Chapter 3 Test

1.

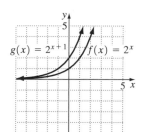

$$g(x) = 2^{x+1} \quad f(x) = 2^x$$

2.

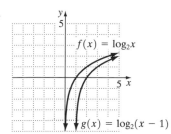

$$f(x) = \log_2 x$$
$$g(x) = \log_2(x-1)$$

3. $125 = 5^3$

4. $\log_{36} 6 = \dfrac{1}{2}$

5. The domain of f consists of all x for which $3 - x > 0$. Solving this inequality for x, we obtain $x < 3$.
Thus, the domain of f is $(-\infty, 3)$.

6. $\log_4\left(64x^5\right) = \log_4 64 + \log_4 x^5$
$$= 3 + 5\log_4 x$$

7. $\log_3 \dfrac{\sqrt[3]{x}}{81} = \log_3 x^{\frac{1}{3}} - \log_3 81$
$$= \dfrac{1}{3}\log_3 x - 4$$

8. $6\log x + 2\log y = \log x^6 + \log y^2$
$$= \log\left(x^6 y^2\right)$$

9. $\ln 7 - 3\ln x = \ln 7 - \ln x^3$
$$= \ln \dfrac{7}{x^3}$$

10. $\log_{15} 71 = \dfrac{\log 71}{\log 15} \approx 1.5741$

11.
$$5^x = 1.4$$
$$\ln 5^x = \ln 1.4$$
$$x\ln 5 = \ln 1.4$$
$$x = \dfrac{\ln 1.4}{\ln 5} \approx 0.2091$$
The solution set is $\left\{\dfrac{\ln 1.4}{\ln 5}\right\}$, approximately 0.2091.

12. $400e^{0.005x} = 1600$
$$e^{0.005x} = 4$$
$$\ln e^{0.005x} = \ln 4$$
$$0.005x = \ln 4$$
$$x = \dfrac{\ln 4}{0.005} \approx 277.2589$$
The solution set is $\left\{\dfrac{\ln 4}{0.005}\right\}$, approximately 277.2589.

13. $e^{2x} - 6e^x + 5 = 0$

$(e^x - 5)(e^x - 1) = 0$

$e^x - 5 = 0 \quad$ or $\quad e^x - 1 = 0$

$\qquad e^x = 5 \qquad\qquad e^x = 1$

$\quad \ln e^x = \ln 5 \qquad \ln e^x = \ln 1$

$\qquad x = \ln 5 \qquad\qquad x = \ln 1$

$\qquad x \approx 1.6094 \qquad\quad x = 0$

The solution set is $\{0, \ln 5\};\ \ln \approx 1.6094.$

14. $\log_6(4x - 1) = 3$

$\qquad 4x - 1 = 6^3$

$\qquad 4x - 1 = 216$

$\qquad\quad 4x = 217$

$\qquad\quad\ x = \dfrac{217}{4}$

The solution set is $\left\{\dfrac{217}{4}\right\}.$

15. $\log x + \log(x + 15) = 2$

$\qquad \log\!\left(x^2 + 15x\right) = 2$

$\qquad\quad x^2 + 15x = 10^2$

$\qquad x^2 + 15x - 100 = 0$

$\qquad (x + 20)(x - 5) = 0$

$\qquad\qquad x + 20 = 0$ or $x - 5 = 0$

$x = -20 \qquad x = 5$

$x = -20$ does not check because $\log(-20)$
does not exist.
The solution set is $\{5\}.$

16. $2 \ln 3x = 8$

$\quad \ln 3x = 4$

$\qquad 3x = e^4$

$\qquad\ x = \dfrac{e^4}{3} \approx 18.1994$

The solution set is $\left\{\dfrac{e^4}{3}\right\},$

approximately 18.1994.

17. 6.5% compounded semiannually:

$$A = 3,000\left(1 + \frac{0.065}{2}\right)^{2(10)} \approx \$5,687.51$$

6% compounded continuously:

$\quad A = 3,000e^{0.06(10)} \approx \$5,466.36$

6.5% compounded semiannually yields
about \$221 more than 6% compounded
continuously.

18. $D = 10 \log \dfrac{10^{12} I_0}{I_0}$

$\qquad = 10 \log 10^{12}$

$\qquad = 10 \cdot 12$

$\qquad = 120$

The loudness of the sound is 120 decibels.

19. a. In 1959, $t = 0$.

$\quad 89.18e^{-0.004(0)} = 89.18$

In 1959, about 89% of married men
were employed.

b. The percentage is decreasing since
$k = -0.004 < 1.$

c. $\qquad\qquad 77 = 89.18e^{-0.004t}$

$\qquad e^{-0.004t} = \dfrac{77}{89.18}$

$\quad \ln e^{-0.004t} = \ln \dfrac{77}{89.18}$

$\qquad -0.004t = \ln \dfrac{77}{89.18}$

$\qquad\qquad t = \dfrac{\ln \frac{77}{89.18}}{-0.004} \approx 37$

77% of U.S. married men were
employed about 37 years after 1959, in
1996.

20. In 1990, $t = 0$ and $A_0 = 509$
In 2000, $t = 2000 - 1990 = 10$ and

$A = 729$.

$$729 = 509e^{k10}$$

$$\frac{729}{509} = e^{10k}$$

$$\ln\frac{729}{509} = \ln e^{10k}$$

$$\ln\frac{729}{509} = 10k$$

$$\frac{\ln\frac{729}{509}}{10} = k$$

$$0.036 \approx k$$

The exponential growth function is
$A = 509e^{0.036t}$.

21. When the amount remaining is 5%,
$A = 0.05A_0$.

$$0.05A_0 = A_0e^{-0.000121t}$$

$$e^{-0.000121t} = 0.05$$

$$\ln e^{-0.000121t} = \ln 0.05$$

$$-0.000121t = \ln 0.05$$

$$t = \frac{\ln 0.05}{-0.000121} \approx 24,758$$

The man died about 24,758 years ago.

22. a. $f(0) = \dfrac{140}{1 + 9e^{-0.165(0)}} = 14$

Fourteen elk were initially introduced to the habitat.

b. $f(10) = \dfrac{140}{1 + 9e^{-0.165(10)}} \approx 51$

After 10 years, about 51 elk are expected.

c. In the logistic growth model,

$$f(t) = \frac{c}{1 + ae^{-bt}},$$

the constant c represents the limiting size that $f(t)$ can attain. The limiting size of the elk population is 140 elk.

Chapter 4

Section 4.1

Check Point Exercises

1. **a.** $a_n = 2n + 5$

$a_1 = 2(1) + 5 = 7$

$a_2 = 2(2) + 5 = 9$

$a_3 = 2(3) + 5 = 11$

$a_4 = 2(4) + 5 = 13$

The first four terms are 7, 9, 11, and 13.

b.

$a_n = \dfrac{(-1)^n}{2^n + 1}$

$a_1 = \dfrac{(-1)^1}{2^1 + 1} = \dfrac{-1}{3} = -\dfrac{1}{3}$

$a_2 = \dfrac{(-1)^2}{2^2 + 1} = \dfrac{1}{5}$

$a_3 = \dfrac{(-1)^3}{2^3 + 1} = \dfrac{-1}{9} = -\dfrac{1}{9}$

$a_4 = \dfrac{(-1)^4}{2^4 + 1} = \dfrac{1}{17}$

The first four terms are $-\dfrac{1}{3}, \dfrac{1}{5}, -\dfrac{1}{9},$

and $\dfrac{1}{17}$.

2. $a_1 = 3$ and $a_n = 2a_{n-1} + 5$ for $n \geq 2$

$a_2 = 2a_1 + 5$

$\quad = 2(3) + 5 = 11$

$a_3 = 2a_2 + 5$

$\quad = 2(11) + 5 = 27$

$a_4 = 2a_3 + 5$

$\quad = 2(27) + 5 = 59$

The first four terms are 3, 11, 27, and 59.

3.

$a_n = \dfrac{20}{(n+1)!}$

$a_1 = \dfrac{20}{(1+1)!} = \dfrac{20}{2!} = 10$

$a_2 = \dfrac{20}{(2+1)!} = \dfrac{20}{3!} = \dfrac{20}{6} = \dfrac{10}{3}$

$a_3 = \dfrac{20}{(3+1)!} = \dfrac{20}{4!} = \dfrac{20}{24} = \dfrac{5}{6}$

$a_4 = \dfrac{20}{(4+1)!} = \dfrac{20}{5!} = \dfrac{20}{120} = \dfrac{1}{6}$

The first four terms are $10, \dfrac{10}{3}, \dfrac{5}{6},$ and $\dfrac{1}{6}$.

4. **a.** $\dfrac{14!}{2!\,12!} = \dfrac{14 \cdot 13 \cdot 12!}{2!\,12!} = \dfrac{14 \cdot 13}{2 \cdot 1} = 91$

b. $\dfrac{n!}{(n-1)!} = \dfrac{n \cdot (n-1)!}{(n-1)!} = n$

5. **a.** $\displaystyle\sum_{i=1}^{6} 2i^2$

$= 2(1)^2 + 2(2)^2 + 2(3)^2$

$\quad + 2(4)^2 + 2(5)^2 + 2(6)^2$

$= 2 + 8 + 18 + 32 + 50 + 72$

$= 182$

b. $\displaystyle\sum_{k=3}^{5} \left(2^k - 3\right)$

$= \left(2^3 - 3\right) + \left(2^4 - 3\right) + \left(2^5 - 3\right)$

$= \left(8 - 3\right) + \left(16 - 3\right) + \left(32 - 3\right)$

$= 5 + 13 + 29$

$= 47$

c. $\displaystyle\sum_{i=1}^{5} 4 = 4 + 4 + 4 + 4 + 4 = 20$

6. a. The sum has nine terms, each of the form i^2, starting at $i = 1$ and ending at $i = 9$.

$$1^2 + 2^2 + 3^2 + \cdots + 9^2 = \sum_{i=1}^{9} i^2$$

b. The sum has n terms, each of the form $\frac{1}{2^{i-1}}$, starting at $i = 1$ and ending at $i = n$.

$$1 + \frac{1}{2} + \frac{1}{4} + \frac{1}{8} + \cdots + \frac{1}{2^{n-1}} = \sum_{i=1}^{n} \frac{1}{2^{i-1}}$$

Exercise Set 4.1

1. $a_n = 3n + 2$

$a_1 = 3(1) + 2 = 5$

$a_2 = 3(2) + 2 = 8$

$a_3 = 3(3) + 2 = 11$

$a_4 = 3(4) + 2 = 14$

The first four terms are 5, 8, 11, and 14.

3. $a_n = 3^n$

$a_1 = 3^1 = 3$

$a_2 = 3^2 = 9$

$a_3 = 3^3 = 27$

$a_4 = 3^4 = 81$

The first four terms are 3, 9, 27, and 81.

5. $a_n = (-3)^n$

$a_1 = (-3)^1 = -3$

$a_2 = (-3)^2 = 9$

$a_3 = (-3)^3 = -27$

$a_4 = (-3)^4 = 81$

The first four terms are –3, 9, –27, and 81.

7. $a_n = (-1)^n (n + 3)$

$a_1 = (-1)^1 (1 + 3) = -4$

$a_2 = (-1)^2 (2 + 3) = 5$

$a_3 = (-1)^3 (3 + 3) = -6$

$a_4 = (-1)^4 (4 + 3) = 7$

The first four terms are –4, 5, –6, and 7.

9. $a_n = \dfrac{2n}{n + 4}$

$a_1 = \dfrac{2(1)}{1 + 4} = \dfrac{2}{5}$

$a_2 = \dfrac{2(2)}{2 + 4} = \dfrac{4}{6} = \dfrac{2}{3}$

$a_3 = \dfrac{2(3)}{3 + 4} = \dfrac{6}{7}$

$a_4 = \dfrac{2(4)}{4 + 4} = \dfrac{8}{8} = 1$

The first four terms are $\frac{2}{5}, \frac{2}{3}, \frac{6}{7}$, and 1.

11. $a_n = \dfrac{(-1)^{n+1}}{2^n - 1}$

$a_1 = \dfrac{(-1)^{1+1}}{2^1 - 1} = \dfrac{1}{1} = 1$ $n = 1$

$a_2 = \dfrac{(-1)^{2+1}}{2^2 - 1} = -\dfrac{1}{3}$

$$a_3 = \frac{(-1)^{3+1}}{2^3-1} = \frac{1}{7}$$

$$a_4 = \frac{(-1)^{4+1}}{2^4-1} = -\frac{1}{15}$$

The first four terms are $1, -\frac{1}{3}, \frac{1}{7}$, and $-\frac{1}{15}$.

13. $a_1 = 7$ and $a_n = a_{n-1} + 5$ for $n \ge 2$

$a_2 = a_1 + 5 = 7 + 5 = 12$

$a_3 = a_2 + 5 = 12 + 5 = 17$

$a_4 = a_3 + 5 = 17 + 5 = 22$

The first four terms are 7, 12, 17, and 22.

15. $a_1 = 3$ and $a_n = 4a_{n-1}$ for $n \ge 2$

$a_2 = 4a_1 = 4(3) = 12$

$a_3 = 4a_2 = 4(12) = 48$

$a_4 = 4a_3 = 4(48) = 192$

The first four terms are 3, 12, 48, and 192.

17. $a_1 = 4$ and $a_n = 2a_{n-1} + 3$

$a_2 = 2(4) + 3 = 11$

$a_3 = 2(11) + 3 = 25$

$a_4 = 2(25) + 3 = 53$

The first four terms are 4, 11, 25, and 53.

19. $a_n = \dfrac{n^2}{n!}$

$a_1 = \dfrac{1^2}{1!} = 1$

$a_2 = \dfrac{2^2}{2!} = 2$

$a_3 = \dfrac{3^2}{3!} = \dfrac{9}{6} = \dfrac{3}{2}$

$a_4 = \dfrac{4^2}{4!} = \dfrac{16}{24} = \dfrac{2}{3}$

The first four terms are $1, 2, \frac{3}{2}$, and $\frac{2}{3}$.

21. $a_n = 2(n+1)!$

$a_1 = 2(1+1)! = 2(2) = 4$

$a_2 = 2(2+1)! = 2(6) = 12$

$a_3 = 2(3+1)! = 2(24) = 48$

$a_4 = 2(4+1)! = 2(120) = 240$

The first four terms are 4, 12, 48, and 240.

23. $\dfrac{17!}{15!} = \dfrac{17 \cdot 16 \cdot 15!}{15!} = 17 \cdot 16 = 272$

25. $\dfrac{16!}{2! \cdot 14!} = \dfrac{16 \cdot 15 \cdot 14!}{2! 14!} = \dfrac{16 \cdot 15}{2 \cdot 1} = \dfrac{8 \cdot 15}{1} = 120$

27. $\dfrac{(n+2)!}{n!} = \dfrac{(n+2)(n+1)n!}{n!} = (n+2)(n+1)$

29. $\displaystyle\sum_{i=1}^{6} 5i = 5 \cdot 1 + 5 \cdot 2 + 5 \cdot 3 + 5 \cdot 4 + 5 \cdot 5 + 5 \cdot 6$

$= 5 + 10 + 15 + 20 + 25 + 30$

$= 105$

31. $\displaystyle\sum_{i=1}^{4} 2i^2 = 2 \cdot 1^2 + 2 \cdot 2^2 + 2 \cdot 3^2 + 2 \cdot 4^2$

$= 2 + 8 + 18 + 32$

$= 60$

33.

$\displaystyle\sum_{k=1}^{5} k(k+4) = 1(5) + 2(6) + 3(7) + 4(8) + 5(9)$

$= 5 + 12 + 21 + 32 + 45$

$= 115$

35. $\displaystyle\sum_{i=1}^{4}\left(\dfrac{-1}{2}\right)^{i}$

$=\left(-\dfrac{1}{2}\right)^{1}+\left(-\dfrac{1}{2}\right)^{2}+\left(-\dfrac{1}{2}\right)^{3}+\left(-\dfrac{1}{2}\right)^{4}$

$=-\dfrac{1}{2}+\dfrac{1}{4}+-\dfrac{1}{8}+\dfrac{1}{16}$

$=-\dfrac{5}{16}$

37. $\displaystyle\sum_{i=5}^{9}11=11+11+11+11+11=55$

39. $\displaystyle\sum_{i=0}^{4}\dfrac{(-1)^{i}}{i!}$

$=\dfrac{(-1)^{0}}{0!}+\dfrac{(-1)^{1}}{1!}+\dfrac{(-1)^{2}}{2!}+\dfrac{(-1)^{3}}{3!}+\dfrac{(-1)^{4}}{4!}$

$=1-1+\dfrac{1}{2}-\dfrac{1}{6}+\dfrac{1}{24}$

$=\dfrac{9}{24}=\dfrac{3}{8}$

41. $\displaystyle\sum_{i=1}^{5}\dfrac{i!}{(i-1)!}=\dfrac{1!}{0!}+\dfrac{2!}{1!}+\dfrac{3!}{2!}+\dfrac{4!}{3!}+\dfrac{5!}{4!}$

$=1+2+3+4+5=15$

43. $1^{2}+2^{2}+3^{2}+\cdots+15^{2}=\displaystyle\sum_{i=1}^{15}i^{2}$

45. $2+2^{2}+2^{3}+2^{4}+\cdots+2^{11}=\displaystyle\sum_{i=1}^{11}2^{i}$

47. $1+2+3+\cdots+30=\displaystyle\sum_{i=1}^{30}i$

49. $\dfrac{1}{2}+\dfrac{2}{3}+\dfrac{3}{4}+\cdots+\dfrac{14}{14+1}=\displaystyle\sum_{i=1}^{14}\dfrac{i}{i+1}$

51. $4+\dfrac{4^{2}}{2}+\dfrac{4^{3}}{3}+\cdots+\dfrac{4^{n}}{n}=\displaystyle\sum_{i=1}^{n}\dfrac{4^{i}}{i}$

53. $1+3+5+\cdots+(2n-1)=\displaystyle\sum_{i=1}^{n}(2i-1)$

55. $5+7+9+\cdots+31$

Possible answer: $\displaystyle\sum_{k=1}^{14}(2k+3)$

57. $a+ar+ar^{2}+\cdots+ar^{12}$

Possible answer: $\displaystyle\sum_{k=0}^{12}ar^{k}$

59. $a+(a+d)+(a+2d)+\cdots+(a+nd)$

Possible answer: $\displaystyle\sum_{k=0}^{n}(a+kd)$

61. a. $\displaystyle\sum_{i=1}^{10}a_{i}$

$=333.3+407.5+495.4+662.1+$
$722.9+778.9+753.1+847.0+$
$938.9+942.5=6881.6$
This represents the total number of
CD's sold in the U.S. from 1991 to
2000, in millions.

b. $\dfrac{1}{10}\displaystyle\sum_{i=1}^{10}a_{i}=\dfrac{1}{10}\left(6881.6\right)=688.16$

This represents the average number of
CD's sold each year from 1991 to 2000,
in millions.

63. a. $\displaystyle\sum_{i=1}^{8}a_{i}=14.1+14.2+13.7+12.6+10.9$

$+8.7+7.6+6.5=88.3$
From 1993 through 2000, there were 88.3
million Welfare recipients in the US.

b. $\displaystyle\sum_{n=1}^{8}(-1.23n+16.55)$

$$= (-1.23 \cdot 1 + 16.55) + (-1.23 \cdot 2 + 16.55)$$
$$+ (-1.23 \cdot 3 + 16.55) + (-1.23 \cdot 4 + 16.55)$$
$$+ (-1.23 \cdot 5 + 16.55) + (-1.23 \cdot 6 + 16.55)$$
$$+ (-1.23 \cdot 7 + 16.55) + (-1.23 \cdot 8 + 16.55)$$
$$= 88.12$$

The model is very close to the actual sum.

65. $a_n = 6000\left(1 + \dfrac{0.06}{4}\right)^n, n = 1, 2, 3, \cdots$

$a_{20} = 6000\left(1 + \dfrac{0.06}{4}\right)^{20} \approx 8081.13$

After five years, the balance is \$8081.13.

67.–75. Answers may vary.

77. $\left(\dfrac{300}{20}\right)! = 15! = 1,307,674,368,000$

79. $\dfrac{20!}{(20-3)!} = 6840$

81. Answers may vary.

83. $a_n = \left(1 + \dfrac{1}{n}\right)^n$

$a_{10} = \left(1 + \dfrac{1}{10}\right)^{10} \approx 2.5937$

$a_{100} = \left(1 + \dfrac{1}{100}\right)^{100} \approx 2.7048$

$a_{1000} = \left(1 + \dfrac{1}{1000}\right)^{1000} \approx 2.7169$

$a_{10,000} = \left(1 + \dfrac{1}{10,000}\right)^{10,000} \approx 2.7181$

$a_{100,000} = \left(1 + \dfrac{1}{100,000}\right)^{100,000} \approx 2.7183$

As n gets larger, a_n gets closer to $e \approx 2.7183$.

85. $a_n = \dfrac{100}{n}$

As n gets larger, a_n approaches 0.

87. $a_n = \dfrac{3n^4 + n - 1}{5n^4 + 2n^2 + 1}$

As n gets larger, a_n approaches $\dfrac{3}{5}$.

89. $a_n = \begin{cases} \dfrac{a_{n-1}}{2} & \text{if } a_{n-1} \text{ is even.} \\ 3a_n + 5 & \text{if } a_{n-1} \text{ is odd.} \end{cases}$

$a_1 = 9$

Since 9 is odd, $a_2 = 3(9) + 5 = 32$.

Since 32 is even, $a_3 = \dfrac{32}{2} = 16$.

Similarly, $a_4 = \dfrac{16}{2} = 8$, $a_5 = \dfrac{8}{2} = 4$.

The first five terms of the sequence are 9, 32, 16, 8, and 4.

Section 4.2

Check Point Exercises

1. $a_1 = 51.5$

$a_2 = a_1 + 2.18 = 51.5 + 2.18 = 53.68$

$a_3 = a_2 + 2.18 = 53.68 + 2.18 = 55.86$

$a_4 = a_3 + 2.18 = 55.86 + 2.18 = 58.04$

$a_5 = a_4 + 2.18 = 58.04 + 2.18 = 60.22$

The first five terms are 51.5, 53.68, 55.86, 58.04, and 60.22.

2. $a_1 = 6$, $d = -5$

To find the ninth term, a_9, replace n in the formula with 9, a_1 with 6, and d with -5.

$a_n = a_1 + (n-1)d$

$a_9 = 6 + (9-1)(-5)$

$= 6 + 8(-5)$

$= 6 + (-40)$

$= -34$

3. a. $a_n = a_1 + (n-1)d = 159,000 + (n-1)9700$

b.

a_1 represents 1995 so a_{15} represents 2010.

$a_{15} = 159000 + (15-1)9700 = 294,800$

In 2010, a new one-family house will cost \$294,800.

4. 3, 6, 9, 12, ...

To find the sum of the first 15 terms, S_{15}, replace n in the formuls with 15.

$S_n = \dfrac{n}{2}(a_1 + a_n)$

$S_{15} = \dfrac{15}{2}(a_1 + a_{15})$

Use the formula for the general term of a sequence to find a_{15}. The common difference, d, is 3, and the first term, a_1, is 3.

$a_n = a_1 + (n-1)d$

$a_{15} = 3 + (15-1)(3)$

$= 3 + 14(3)$

$= 3 + 42$

$= 45$

Thus, $S_{15} = \dfrac{15}{2}(3+45) = \dfrac{15}{2}(48) = 360$.

5. $\displaystyle\sum_{i=1}^{30}(6i-11) = (6\cdot1-11) + (6\cdot2-11) +$

$+ (6\cdot3-11) + \ldots + (6\cdot30-11)$

$= -5 + 1 + 7 + \ldots + 169$

So the first term, a_1, is -5; the common difference, d, is $1-(-5) = 6$; the last term, a_{30}, is 169. Substitute $n = 30$, $a_1 = -5$, and $a_{30} = 169$ in the formula $S_n = \dfrac{n}{2}(a_1 + a_n)$.

$S_{30} = \dfrac{30}{2}(-5+169) = 15(164) = 2460$

Thus, $\displaystyle\sum_{i=1}^{30}(6i-11) = 2460$

6. Find the sum of the arithmetic sequence whose first term corresponds to costs in 2001 and whose last term corresponds to costs in 2010. Because the model describes costs n years after 2000, $n = 1$ describes the year 2001 and $n = 10$

179

describes the year 2010.

$a_n = 1800n + 49,730$

$a_1 = 1800 \cdot 1 + 49,730 = 51,530$

$a_{10} = 1800 \cdot 10 + 49,730 = 67,730$

To find the sum of the costs for all 10 years, find the sum of the ten terms of the arithmetic sequence

51,530, 53,330, . . . , 67,730.

There are 10 terms with first term 51,530 and last term 67,730 so $n = 10$, $a_1 = 51,530$, and $a_{10} = 67,730$.

$$S_n = \frac{n}{2}(a_1 + a_n)$$

$$S_{10} = \frac{10}{2}(51,530 + 67,730) = 5(119,260)$$

$$= 596,300$$

The total cost for the ten-year period is $596,300.

Exercise Set 4.2

1. $a_1 = 200, \ d = 20$
The first six terms are 200, 220, 240, 260, 280, and 300.

3. $a_1 = -7, \ d = 4$
The first six terms are –7, –3, 1, 5, 9, and 13.

5. $a_1 = 300, \ d = -90$
The first six terms are 300, 210, 120, 30, –60, and –150.

7. $a_1 = \dfrac{5}{2}, \ d = -\dfrac{1}{2}$

The first six terms are $\dfrac{5}{2}, 2, \dfrac{3}{2}, 1, \dfrac{1}{2},$ and 0.

9. $a_n = a_{n-1} + 6, \ a_1 = -9$
The first six terms are –9, –3, 3, 9, 15, and 21.

11. $a_n = a_{n-1} - 10, \ a_1 = 30$
The first six terms are 30, 20, 10, 0, –10, and –20.

13. $a_n = a_{n-1} - 0.4, \ a_1 = 1.6$
The first six terms are 1.6, 1.2, 0.8, 0.4, 0, and –0.4.

15. $a_1 = 13, \ d = -4$
$a_n = 13 + (n-1)4$
$a_6 = 13 + 5(4) = 13 + 20 = 33$

17. $a_1 = 7, \ d = 5$
$a_n = 7 + (n-1)2$
$a_{50} = 7 + 49(5) = 252$

19. $a_1 = -40, \ d = 5$
$a_n = -40 + (n-1)5$
$a_{200} = -40 + (199)5 = 955$

21. $a_1 = 35, \ d = -3$
$a_n = 35 - 3(n-1)$
$a_{60} = 35 - 3(59) = -142$

23. 1, 5, 9, 13, ...
$d = 5 - 1, \ = 4$
$a_n = 1 + (n-1)4 = 1 + 4n - 4$
$a_n = 4n - 3$
$a_{20} = 4(20) - 3 = 77$

25. 7, 3, –1, –5, ...
$d = 3 - 7 = -4$
$a_n = 7 + (n-1)(-4) = 7 - 4n + 4$
$a_n = 11 - 4n$
$a_{20} = 11 - 4(20) = -69$

27. $a_1 = 9, \ d = 2$
$a_n = 9 + (n-1)(2)$
$a_n = 7 + 2n$
$a_{20} = 7 + 2(20) = 47$

29. $a_1 = -20, \ d = -4$

$a_n = -20 + (n-1)(-4)$

$a_n = -20 - 4n + 4$

$a_n = -16 - 4n$

$a_{20} = -16 - 4(20) = -96$

31. $a_n = a_{n-1} + 3, \ a_1 = 4$

$d = 3$

$a_n = 4 + (n-1)(3)$

$a_n = 1 + 3n$

$a_{20} = 1 + 3(20) = 61$

33. $a_n = a_{n-1} - 10, \ a_1 = 30, \ d = -10$

$a_n = 30 - 10(n-1) = 30 - 10n + 10$

$a_n = 40 - 10n$

$a_{20} = 40 - 10(20) = -160$

35. 4, 10, 16, 22, . . .

$d = 10 - 4 = 6$

$a_n = 4 + (n-1)(6)$

$a_{20} = 4 + (19)(6) = 118$

$S_{20} = \dfrac{20}{2}(4 + 118) = 1220$

37. –10, –6, –2, 2, . . .

$d = -6 - (-10) = -6 + 10 = 4$

$a_n = -10 + (n-1)4$

$a_{50} = -10 + (49)4 = 186$

$S_{50} = \dfrac{50}{2}(-10 + 186) = 4400$

39. $1 + 2 + 3 + 4 + \cdots + 100$

$S_{100} = \dfrac{100}{2}(1 + 100) = 5050$

41. $2 + 4 + 6 + \cdots + 120$

$S_{60} = \dfrac{60}{2}(2 + 120) = 3660$

43. even integers between 21 and 45;

$22 + 24 + 26 + \cdots + 44$

$S_{12} = \dfrac{12}{2}(22 + 44) = 396$

45. $\displaystyle\sum_{i=1}^{17} (5i + 3)$

$= (5 + 3) + (10 + 3) + (15 + 3) + \cdots + (85 + 3)$

$= 8 + 13 + 18 + \cdots + 88$

$S_{17} = \dfrac{17}{2}(8 + 88) = 816$

47. $\displaystyle\sum_{i=1}^{30} (-3i + 5)$

$= (-3 + 5) + (-6 + 5) + (-9 + 5)$

$\quad + \cdots + (-90 + 5)$

$= 2 - 1 - 4 - \cdots - 85$

$S_{30} = \dfrac{30}{2}(2 - 85) = -1245$

49. $\displaystyle\sum_{i=1}^{100} 4i = 4 + 8 + 12 + \cdots + 400$

$S_{100} = \dfrac{100}{2}(4 + 400) = 20,200$

51. a. $a_n = 150 + (n-1)1.7$

  b. $2006 - 1970 = 36, \ n = 36$

   $a_{36} = 150 + (36-1)1.7 = 209.5$

   In 2006, the average American will eat 209.5 pounds of vegetables.

53. a. $a_n = 10 + (n-1)0.66$ (Answers may vary)

  b. $2006 - 1970 = 36, \ n = 36$

   $a_{36} = 10 + (36-1)0.66 = 33.1$

   In 2006, the average American will eat 33.1 pounds of cheese.

55. Company A:
$$a_n = 24,000 + (n-1)(1600)$$
$$a_{10} = 24,000 + 9(1600) = \$38,400$$
Company B:
$$a_n = 28,000 + (n-1)(1000)$$
$$a_{10} = 28,000 + 9(1000) = \$37,000$$
Company A will pay $1400 more.

57. a. $a_1 = 3.78, \ d = 0.576$
$$a_n = 3.78 + (n-1)(0.576)$$
$$a_n = 3.204 + 0.576n$$

b. $a_1 = 3.78$
$$a_{41} = 3.204 + 0.576(41) = 26.82$$
$$S_{41} = \frac{41}{2}(3.78 + 26.82) = 627.3$$
The total amount is 627.3 million tons.

59. $a_n = 33,000 + (n-1)(2500)$
$$a_{10} = 33,000 + 9(2500) = 55,500$$
$$S_n = \frac{10}{2}(33,000 + 55,500) = 442,500$$
The total ten year salary is $442,500.

61. $a_n = 30 + (n-1)2$
$$a_{26} = 30 + (25)2 = 80$$
$$S_{26} = \frac{26}{2}(30 + 80) = 1430$$
The theater has 1430 seats.

63.–69. Answers may vary.

71. 21,700, 23,172, 24,644, 26,166, . . . ,
314,628
$$d = 23,172 - 21,700 = 1472$$
$$314,628 = 1472n + 20,228$$
$$1472n = 294,400$$
$$n = 200$$
It is the 200th term.

73. $1 + 3 + 5 + \cdots + (2n-1)$
$$S_n = \frac{n}{2}(1 + 2n - 1)$$
$$= \frac{n}{2}(2n)$$
$$= n^2$$

Section 4.3

Check Point Exercises

1. $a_1 = 12, \ r = \dfrac{1}{2}$
$$a_2 = 12\left(\frac{1}{2}\right)^1 = 6$$
$$a_3 = 12\left(\frac{1}{2}\right)^2 = \frac{12}{4} = 3$$
$$a_4 = 12\left(\frac{1}{2}\right)^3 = \frac{12}{8} = \frac{3}{2}$$
$$a_5 = 12\left(\frac{1}{2}\right)^4 = \frac{12}{16} = \frac{3}{4}$$
$$a_6 = 12\left(\frac{1}{2}\right)^5 = \frac{12}{32} = \frac{3}{8}$$

The first six terms are
$$12, \ 6, \ 3, \ \frac{3}{2}, \ \frac{3}{4}, \text{and } \frac{3}{8}.$$

2. $a_1 = 5, \ r = -3$
$$a_n = 5r^{n-1}$$
$$a_7 = 5(-3)^{7-1} = 5(-3)^6 = 5(729) = 3645$$
The seventh term is 3645.

3. 3, 6, 12, 24, 48, ...

$$r = \frac{6}{3} = 2, \; a_1 = 3$$

$$a_n = 3(2)^{n-1}$$

$$a_8 = 3(2)^{8-1} = 3(2)^7 = 3(128) = 384$$

The eighth term is 384.

4.
$$a_1 = 2, \; r = \frac{-6}{2} = -3$$

$$S_n = \frac{a_1(1-r^r)}{1-r}$$

$$S_9 = \frac{2\left(1-(-3)^9\right)}{1-(-3)} = \frac{2(19,684)}{4} = 9842$$

The sum of the first nine terms is 9842.

5. $\displaystyle\sum_{i=1}^{8} 2 \cdot 3^i$

$$a_1 = 2 \cdot (3)^1 = 6, \; r = 3$$

$$S_n = \frac{a_1(1-r^n)}{1-r}$$

$$S_8 = \frac{6\left(1-3^8\right)}{1-3} = \frac{6(-6560)}{-2} = 19,680$$

Thus, $\displaystyle\sum_{i=1}^{8} 2 \cdot 3^i = 19,680.$

6. $a_1 = 30,000, \; r = 1.06$

$$S_n = \frac{a_1(1-r^n)}{1-r}$$

$$S_{30} = \frac{30,000\left(1-(1.06)^{30}\right)}{1-1.06} \approx 2,371,746$$

The total lifetime salary is $2,371,746.

7. $A = P\dfrac{\left(1+\frac{r}{n}\right)^{nt} - 1}{\frac{r}{n}}$

$$P = 3000, \; r = 0.10, \; n = 1, \; t = 40$$

$$A = 3000\frac{(1+0.10)^{40} - 1}{0.10} \approx 1,327,778$$

The value of the IRA will be $1,327,778.

8. $3 + 2 + \dfrac{4}{3} + \dfrac{8}{9} + \cdots$

$$a_1 = 3, \; r = \frac{2}{3}$$

$$S = \frac{a_1}{1-r}$$

$$S = \frac{3}{1-\frac{2}{3}} = \frac{3}{\frac{1}{3}} = 9$$

The sum of this infinite geometric series is 9.

9. $0.\overline{9} = 0.9999\cdots = \dfrac{9}{10} + \dfrac{9}{100} + \dfrac{9}{1000} + \cdots$

$$a_1 = \frac{9}{10}, r = \frac{1}{10}$$

$$S = \frac{\frac{9}{10}}{1-\frac{1}{10}} = \frac{\frac{9}{10}}{\frac{9}{10}} = 1$$

An equivalent fraction for $0.\overline{9}$ is 1.

10. $a_1 = 1000(0.8) = 800, \; r = 0.8$

$$S = \frac{800}{1-0.8} = 4000$$

The total amount spent is $4000.

Exercise Set 4.3

1. $a_1 = 5, \; r = 3$

The first five terms are 5, 15, 45, 135, and 405.

3. $a_1 = 20, \ r = \dfrac{1}{2}$

The first five terms are $20, \ 10, \ 5, \ \dfrac{5}{2}$,

and $\dfrac{5}{4}$.

5. $a_n = -4a_{n-1}, \ a_1 = 10$
The first five terms are $10, -40, 160, -640$, and 2560.

7. $a_n = -5a_{n-1}, \ a_1 = -6$
The first five terms are $-6, 30, -150, 750$, and -3750.

9. $a_1 = 6, \ r = 2$

$a_n = 6 \cdot 2^{n-1}$

$a_8 = 6 \cdot 2^7 = 768$

11. $a_1 = 5, \ r = -2$

$a_n = 5 \cdot (-2)^{n-1}$

$a_{12} = 5 \cdot (-2)^{11} = -10,240$

13.

$a_1 = 1000, \ r = -\dfrac{1}{2}$

$a_n = 1000 \left(-\dfrac{1}{2}\right)^{n-1}$

$a_{40} = 1000 \left(-\dfrac{1}{2}\right)^{39}$

≈ 0.000000002

15. $a_1 = 1,000,000, \ r = 0.1$

$a_n = 1,000,000(0.1)^{n-1}$

$a_8 = 1,000,000(0.1)^7 = 0.1$

17. $3, 12, 48, 192, \ldots$

$r = \dfrac{12}{3} = 4$

$a_n = 3(4)^{n-1}$

$a_7 = 3(4)^6 = 12,288$

19. $19, 6, 2, \dfrac{2}{3}, \cdots$ $r = \dfrac{6}{18} = \dfrac{1}{3}$

$a_n = 18\left(\dfrac{1}{3}\right)^{n-1}$

$a_7 = 18\left(\dfrac{1}{3}\right)^6 = \dfrac{2}{81}$

21. $1.5, -3, 6, -12, \ldots$

$r = \dfrac{6}{-3} = -2$

$a_n = 1.5(-2)^{n-1}$

$a_7 = 1.5(-2)^6 = 96$

23. $0.0004, -0.004, 0.04, -0.4, \ldots$

$r = \dfrac{-0.004}{0.0004} = -10$

$a_n = 0.0004(-10)^{n-1}$

$a_7 = 0.0004(-10)^6 = 400$

25. $2, 6, 18, 54, \ldots$

$r = \dfrac{6}{2} = 3$

$S_{12} = \dfrac{2\left(1 - 3^{12}\right)}{1 - 3} = \dfrac{2(-531,440)}{-2} = 531,440$

27. $3, -6, 12, -24, \ldots$

$r = \dfrac{-6}{3} = -2$

$S_{11} = \dfrac{3\left[1 - (-2)^{11}\right]}{1 - (-2)} = \dfrac{3(2049)}{3} = 2049$

29. $-\dfrac{3}{2}, 3, -6, 12, \cdots$

$r = \dfrac{3}{\frac{-3}{2}} = -2$

$S_{14} = \dfrac{-\frac{3}{2}\left[1-(-2)^{14}\right]}{1-(-2)} = \dfrac{-\frac{3}{2}(-16{,}383)}{3} = \dfrac{16{,}383}{2}$

31. $\displaystyle\sum_{i=1}^{8} 3^i$

$r = 3, \quad a_1 = 3$

$S_8 = \dfrac{3\left(1-3^8\right)}{1-3} = \dfrac{3(-6560)}{-2} = 9840$

33. $\displaystyle\sum_{i=1}^{10} 5\cdot 2^i$

$r = 2, \quad a_1 = 10$

$S_{10} = \dfrac{10\left(1-2^{10}\right)}{1-2} = \dfrac{10(-1023)}{-1} = 10{,}230$

35. $\displaystyle\sum_{i=1}^{6} \left(\dfrac{1}{2}\right)^{i+1}$

$r = \dfrac{1}{2}, \quad a_1 = \dfrac{1}{4}$

$S_6 = \dfrac{\dfrac{1}{4}\left(1-\left(\dfrac{1}{2}\right)^6\right)}{1-\dfrac{1}{2}} = \dfrac{\dfrac{1}{4}\left(\dfrac{63}{64}\right)}{\dfrac{1}{2}} = \dfrac{63}{128}$

37. $r = \dfrac{1}{3}$

$S_\infty = \dfrac{1}{1-\frac{1}{3}} = \dfrac{1}{\frac{2}{3}} = \dfrac{3}{2}$

39. $r = \dfrac{1}{4}$

$S_\infty = \dfrac{3}{1-\frac{1}{4}} = \dfrac{3}{\frac{3}{4}} = 4$

41. $r = -\dfrac{1}{2}$

$S_\infty = \dfrac{1}{1-\left(-\dfrac{1}{2}\right)} = \dfrac{1}{\frac{3}{2}} = \dfrac{2}{3}$

43. $r = -0.3$

$S_\infty = \dfrac{8}{1-(-0.3)} = \dfrac{8}{1.3} \approx 6.15385$

45. $r = \dfrac{1}{10}$

$S_\infty = \dfrac{\frac{5}{10}}{1-\frac{1}{10}} = \dfrac{\frac{5}{10}}{\frac{9}{10}} = \dfrac{5}{9}$

47. $r = \dfrac{1}{100}$

$S_\infty = \dfrac{\frac{47}{100}}{1-\frac{1}{100}} = \dfrac{\frac{47}{100}}{\frac{99}{100}} = \dfrac{47}{99}$

49. $0.\overline{257} = \dfrac{257}{1000} + \dfrac{257}{10^6} + \dfrac{257}{10^9} + \cdots$

$r = \dfrac{1}{1000}$

$S_\infty = \dfrac{\frac{257}{1000}}{1-\frac{1}{1000}} = \dfrac{\frac{257}{1000}}{\frac{999}{1000}} = \dfrac{257}{999}$

51. $a_n = n + 5$
arithmetic, $d = 1$

53. $a_n = 2^n$
geometric, $r = 2$

55. $a_n = n^2 + 5$
neither

57. $1, 2, 4, 8, \ldots$
$r = 2$
$a_n = 2^{n-1}$
$a_{15} = 2^{14} = \$16,384$

59. $a_1 = 3,000,000$
$r = 1.04$
$a_n = 3,000,000(1.04)^{n-1}$
$a_7 = 3,000,000(1.04)^6 = \$3,795,957$

61. a. $\dfrac{30.15}{29.76} \approx 1.013$

$\dfrac{30.54}{30.15} \approx 1.013$

$\dfrac{30.94}{30.54} \approx 1.013$

The population is increasing geometrically with $r \approx 1.013$.

b. $a_n = 29.76 \cdot 1.013^{n-1}$

c. $2000 - 1989 = 11$
$a_{11} = 29.76 \cdot 1.013^{11-1} = 33.86$
In 2000, the model predicts California population will be 33.86. This is very close to the actual population.

63. $1, 2, 4, 8, \ldots$
$r = 2$
$S_{15} = \dfrac{1(1 - 2^{15})}{1 - 2} = 32,767$
The total savings is \$32,767.

65. $a_1 = 24,000, \; r = 1.05$
$S_{20} = \dfrac{24,000\left[1 - (1.05)^{20}\right]}{1 - 1.05} = 793,582.90$
The total salary is \$793,583.

67. $r = 0.9$
$S_{10} = \dfrac{20(1 - 0.9^{10})}{1 - 0.9} \approx 130.26$
The total length is 130.26 inches.

69. $A = 2500 \dfrac{\left(1 + 0.09\right)^{40} - 1}{0.09} \approx 844,706.11$
In 40 years, the value is \$844,706.

71. $A = 600 \dfrac{\left(1 + \frac{0.08}{4}\right)^{72} - 1}{\frac{0.08}{4}} \approx 94,834.21$
After 18 years, the value is \$94,834.

73. $r = 0.6$
$S_\infty = \dfrac{6(0.6)}{1 - 0.6} = 9$
The total economic impact is \$9 million.

75. $r = \frac{1}{4}$
$S_\infty = \dfrac{\frac{1}{4}}{1 - \frac{1}{4}} = \dfrac{1}{4} \cdot \dfrac{4}{3} = \dfrac{1}{3}$

77.–85. Answers may vary.

87. $f(x) = \dfrac{2\left[1-\left(\frac{1}{3}\right)^x\right]}{1-\frac{1}{3}}$

Horizontal asymptote at $y = 3$

$$\sum_{n=0}^{\infty} 2\left(\tfrac{1}{3}\right)^n = \frac{2}{1-\frac{1}{3}} = 3$$

89. a. False; there is no common ratio.

    b. False; the sum can be calculated exactly, since the series is geometric $\left(r = \tfrac{1}{2}\right)$.

    c. False; $10 - 5 + \dfrac{5}{2} - \dfrac{5}{4} \cdots = \dfrac{10}{1 + \dfrac{1}{2}}$

    d. True; $r = 0.5 = \tfrac{1}{2}$

    (d) is true.

91. $1{,}000{,}000 = P \dfrac{\left(1 + \dfrac{0.1}{12}\right)^{360} - 1}{\dfrac{0.1}{12}}$

$1{,}000{,}000 \approx 2260.49P$

$P \approx 442.38$

You must deposit \$442 monthly.

Section 4.4

Check Point Exercises

1. We use the Fundamental Counting Principal to find the number of ways a one-topping pizza can be ordered. Multiply the number of choices for each of the three groups.
$3 \cdot 4 \cdot 6 = 72$ pizzas
There are 72 different ways of ordering a one-topping pizza.

2. We use the Fundamental Counting Principal to find the number of ways we can answer the questions. Multiply the number of choices, 3, for each of the six questions.
$3 \cdot 3 \cdot 3 \cdot 3 \cdot 3 \cdot 3 = 3^6 = 729$ ways
There are 729 ways of answering the questions.

3. We use the Fundamental Counting Principal to find the number of different license plates that can be manufactured. Multiply the number of different letters, 26, for the first two places and the number of different digits, 10, for the next three places.
$26 \cdot 26 \cdot 10 \cdot 10 \cdot 10 = 26^2 \cdot 1000 = 676,000$ plates
There are 676,000 different license plates possible.

4. Your group is choosing $r = 4$ officers from a group of $n = 7$ people. The order in which the officers
are chosen matters because the four officers to be chosen have different responsibilities. Thus, we are looking for the number of permutations of 7 things taken 4 at a time.

We use the formula $_nP_r = \dfrac{n!}{(n-r)!}$ with $n =$

7 and $r = 4$. $_7P_4 = \dfrac{7!}{(7-4)!} = \dfrac{7!}{3!} = 840.$

Thus, there are 840 different ways of filling the four offices.

5. Because you are using all six of your books in every possible arrangement, you are arranging $r = 6$ books from a group of $n = 6$ books. Thus, we are looking for the number of permutations of 6 things taken 6 at a time. We use the formula

$_nP_r = \dfrac{n!}{(n-r)!}$ with $n = 6$ and $r = 6$.

$_6P_6 = \dfrac{6!}{(6-6)!} = \dfrac{6!}{0!} = 6! = 720.$

There are 720 different possible permutations. Thus, you can arrange the books in 720 ways.

6. **a.** The order does not matter; this is a combination.

   b. Since what place each runner finishes matters, this is a permutation.

7. The order in which the four people are selected does not matter. This is a problem of selecting $r = 4$ people from a group of $n = 10$ people. We are looking for the number of combinations of 10 things taken 4 at a time. We use the formula

$_nC_r = \dfrac{n!}{(n-r)!\ r!}$ with $n = 10$ and $r = 4$.

$_{10}C_4 = \dfrac{10!}{(10-4)!\,4!} = \dfrac{10!}{6!\,4!} = \dfrac{10 \cdot 9 \cdot 8 \cdot 7 \cdot 6!}{6! \cdot 4 \cdot 3 \cdot 2 \cdot 1}$

$= \dfrac{10 \cdot 9 \cdot 8 \cdot 7}{4 \cdot 3 \cdot 2 \cdot 1} = 210$

Thus, 210 committees of 4 people each can be found from 10 people at the conference on acupuncture.

8. Because the order in which the 4 cards are dealt does not matter, this is a problem involving combinations. We are looking for the number of combinations of $n = 16$ cards drawn $r = 4$ at a time. We use the formula

$$_nC_r = \frac{n!}{(n-r)!\ r!} \text{ with } n = 16 \text{ and } r = 4.$$

$$_{16}C_4 = \frac{16!}{(16-4)!\,4!} = \frac{16!}{12!\,4!} = \frac{16\cdot15\cdot14\cdot13\cdot12!}{12!\cdot4\cdot3\cdot2\cdot1}$$
$$= 1820$$

Thus, there are 1820 different 4-card hands possible.

Exercise Set 4.4

1. $_9P_4 = \dfrac{9!}{5!} = 3024$

3. $_8P_5 = \dfrac{8!}{3!} = 8\cdot7\cdot6\cdot5\cdot4 = 6720$

5. $_6P_6 = \dfrac{6!}{0!} = 720$

7. $_8P_0 = \dfrac{8!}{8!} = 1$

9. $_9C_5 = \dfrac{9!}{4!5!} = \dfrac{9\cdot8\cdot7\cdot6}{4\cdot3\cdot2\cdot1} = \dfrac{3\cdot7\cdot6}{1} = 126$

11. $_{11}C_4 = \dfrac{11!}{7!4!} = \dfrac{11\cdot10\cdot9\cdot8}{4\cdot3\cdot2\cdot1} = \dfrac{11\cdot10\cdot3}{1} = 330$

13. $_7C_7 = \dfrac{7!}{0!\,7!} = 1$

15. $_5C_0 = \dfrac{5!}{5!\,0!} = 1$

17. combination; The order in which the volunteers are chosen does not matter.

19. permutation; The order of the letters matters because ABCD is not the same as BADC.

21. $9\cdot3 = 27$ ways

23. $2\cdot4\cdot5 = 40$ ways

25. $3^5 = 243$ ways

27. $8\cdot2\cdot9 = 144$ area codes

29. $5\cdot4\cdot3\cdot2\cdot1\cdot1 = 120$ ways

31. $1\cdot3\cdot2\cdot1\cdot1 = 6$ paragraphs

33. $_{10}P_3 = \dfrac{10!}{7!3!} = 10\cdot9\cdot8 = 720$ ways

35. $_{13}P_7 = \dfrac{13!}{6!} = 13\cdot12\cdot11\cdot10\cdot9\cdot8\cdot7$
$= 8,648,640$ ways

37. $_6P_3 = \dfrac{6!}{3!} = 6\cdot5\cdot4 = 120$ ways

39. $_9P_5 = \dfrac{9!}{4!} = 9\cdot8\cdot7\cdot6\cdot5 = 15,120$ lineups

41. $_6C_3 = \dfrac{6!}{3!3!} = \dfrac{6\cdot5\cdot4}{3\cdot2\cdot1} = 20$ ways

43. $_{12}C_4 = \dfrac{12!}{8!4!} = \dfrac{12\cdot11\cdot10\cdot9}{4\cdot3\cdot2\cdot1}$
$= 495$ collections

45. $_{17}C_8 = \dfrac{17!}{9!8!} = \dfrac{17\cdot16\cdot15\cdot14\cdot13\cdot12\cdot11\cdot10}{8\cdot7\cdot6\cdot5\cdot4\cdot3\cdot2\cdot1}$
$= 24,310$ groups

47. $_{53}C_6 = \dfrac{53!}{47!6!} = 22,957,480$ selections

49. $_6P_4 = \dfrac{6!}{2!} = 6\cdot5\cdot4\cdot3 = 360$ ways

51. $_{13}C_6 = \dfrac{13!}{7!6!} = \dfrac{13\cdot12\cdot11\cdot10\cdot9\cdot8}{6\cdot5\cdot4\cdot3\cdot2\cdot1}$
$= 1716$ ways

53. $_{20}C_3 = \dfrac{20!}{17!3!} = \dfrac{20\cdot19\cdot18}{3\cdot2\cdot1} = 1140$ ways

55. $_7P_4 = \dfrac{7!}{3!} = 840$ passwords

57. $_{15}P_3 = \dfrac{15!}{12!} = 15 \cdot 14 \cdot 13 = 2730$ cones

59.–67. Answers may vary.

69. a. False; the number of ways is $_{10}C_4$.

b. False;
$$_nP_r = \frac{n!}{(n-r)!} > \frac{n!}{(n-r)!\,r!} =_n C_{r \text{ if } r>1}.$$

c. True; $_7P_3 = \dfrac{7!}{4!} = 3! \dfrac{7!}{4!\,3!} = 3!_7 C_3$

d. False;
the number of ways is $20 \cdot 19 =_{20} P_2$.
(c) is true.

71. $2 \cdot 6 \cdot 6 \cdot 2 = 144$ numbers

Section 4.5

Check Point Exercises

1. $\dfrac{.69}{3.00} = 0.23 = 23\%$
The empirical probability of randomly selecting an Arab American who is a Muslim is 23%.

2. The sample space of equally likely outcomes is $S = \{1, 2, 3, 4, 5, 6\}$. There are six outcomes in the sample space, so $n(S) = 6$. The event of getting a number greater than 4 can be represented by $E = \{5, 6\}$. There are two outcomes in this event, so $n(E) = 2$. The probability of rolling a number greater than 4 is
$$P(E) = \frac{n(E)}{n(S)} = \frac{2}{6} = \frac{1}{3}.$$

3. We have $n(S) = 36$. The phrase "getting a sum of 5" describes the event $E = \{(1,4),(2,3),(3,2),(4,1)\}$. This event has 4 outcomes, so $n(E) = 4$. Thus, the probability of getting a sum of 5 is
$$P(E) = \frac{n(E)}{n(S)} = \frac{4}{36} = \frac{1}{9}.$$

4. Let E be the event of being dealt a king. Because there are 4 kings in the deck, the event of being dealt a king can occur in 4 ways, i.e., $n(E) = 4$. With 52 cards in the deck, $n(S) = 52$. The probability of being

dealt a king is $P(E) = \dfrac{n(E)}{n(S)} = \dfrac{4}{52} = \dfrac{1}{13}$.

5. Because the order of the six numbers does not matter, this is a situation involving combinations. With one lottery ticket, there is only one way of winning so $n(E) = 1$. Using the combinations formula

$_nC_r = \dfrac{n!}{(n-r)!\,r!}$ to find the number of

outcomes in the sample space, we are selecting $r = 6$ numbers from a collection of $n = 49$ numbers.

$_{49}C_6 = \dfrac{49!}{43! \cdot 6!} = 13{,}983{,}816$

So $n(S) = 13{,}983{,}816$.

If a person buys one lottery ticket, the probability of winning is

$P(E) = \dfrac{n(E)}{n(S)} = \dfrac{1}{13{,}983{,}816}$

The probability of winning the state lottery is 0.0000000715.

6. $P(\text{not dying})$

$= 1 - P(\text{dying}) = 1 - \dfrac{1}{1000} = \dfrac{999}{1000}$

The probability of not dying is 0.999

7. We find the probability that either of these mutually exclusive events will occur by adding their individual probabilities.
$P(4 \text{ or } 5) = P(4) + P(5)$

$= \dfrac{1}{6} + \dfrac{1}{6} = \dfrac{2}{6} = \dfrac{1}{3}$

The probability of selecting a 4 or a 5 is $\dfrac{1}{3}$.

8. It is possible for the pointer to land on a number that is odd and less than 5. Two of the numbers , 1 and 3, are odd and less than 5. These events are not mutually exclusive. The probability of landing on a number that is odd and less than 5 is
P (odd or less than 5)
$= P$ (odd) $+ P$ (less than 5)
$- P$ (odd and less than 5)

$= \dfrac{4}{8} + \dfrac{4}{8} - \dfrac{2}{8}$

$= \dfrac{6}{8} = \dfrac{3}{4}$

The probability that the pointer will stop on

an odd number or a number less than 5 is $\dfrac{3}{4}$.

9. $P(\text{Muslim or African American})$
$= P(\text{Muslim}) + P(\text{African American}) - P(\text{both})$

$\dfrac{20}{40} + \dfrac{26}{40} - \dfrac{14}{40} = \dfrac{32}{40} = \dfrac{4}{5}$

10. The wheel has 38 equally likely outcomes and 2 are green. Thus, the probability of a

green occurring on a play is $\dfrac{2}{38}$, or $\dfrac{1}{19}$. The

result that occurs on each play is independent of all previous results. Thus,
P (green and green)
$= P$ (green) $\cdot P$ (green)

$= \dfrac{1}{19} \cdot \dfrac{1}{19} = \dfrac{1}{361}$

$\approx 0.003.$

The probability of green occurring on two

consecutive plays is $\dfrac{1}{361}$.

11. If two or more events are independent, we can find the probability of them all occurring by multiplying the probabilities.

The probability of a baby boy is $\frac{1}{2}$, so the probability of having four boys in a row is P (4 boys in a row)

$$= \frac{1}{2} \cdot \frac{1}{2} \cdot \frac{1}{2} \cdot \frac{1}{2}$$

$$= \frac{1}{16}.$$

Exercise Set 4.5

1. $P(\text{weight training}) = \dfrac{320}{2000} = \dfrac{4}{25} = 0.16$

3. $P(\text{biking}) = \dfrac{240}{2000} = \dfrac{3}{25} = 0.12$

5. $P(\text{African}) = \dfrac{784,400,000}{6,054,900,000} \approx 0.13$

7. $P(\text{North American}) = \dfrac{309,600,000}{6,054,900,000} \approx 0.051$

9. $P(R) = \dfrac{n(E)}{n(S)} = \dfrac{1}{6}$

11. $P(E) = \dfrac{n(E)}{n(S)} = \dfrac{3}{6} = \dfrac{1}{2}$

13. $P(E) = \dfrac{n(E)}{n(S)} = \dfrac{2}{6} = \dfrac{1}{3}$

15. $P(E) = \dfrac{n(E)}{n(S)} = \dfrac{4}{52} = \dfrac{1}{13}$

17. $P(E) = \dfrac{n(E)}{n(S)} = \dfrac{12}{52} = \dfrac{3}{13}$

19. $P(E) = \dfrac{n(E)}{n(S)} = \dfrac{1}{4}$

21. $P(E) = \dfrac{n(E)}{n(S)} = \dfrac{7}{8}$

23. $P(E) = \dfrac{n(E)}{n(S)} = \dfrac{3}{36} = \dfrac{1}{12}$

25. Buying 1 ticket:

$$P(E) = \dfrac{n(E)}{n(S)} = \dfrac{1}{{}_{51}C_6} = \dfrac{1}{18,009,460}$$

Buying 100 tickets:

$$P(E) = \dfrac{100}{18,009,460} = \dfrac{5}{900,473}$$

27. $0.00140 \times 18,009,460 = 25,213$ A 20-year old male is 25,213 times more likely to die than to win the lottery.

29. a. $\quad {}_{52}C_5 = \dfrac{52!}{47!\,5!}$

$$= \dfrac{52 \cdot 51 \cdot 50 \cdot 49 \cdot 48}{5 \cdot 4 \cdot 3 \cdot 2 \cdot 1} = 2,598,960$$

b. $\quad {}_{13}C_5 = \dfrac{13!}{8!\,5!} = \dfrac{13 \cdot 12 \cdot 11 \cdot 10 \cdot 9}{5 \cdot 4 \cdot 3 \cdot 2 \cdot 1} = 1287$

c. $\quad P(E) = \dfrac{n(E)}{n(S)} = \dfrac{1287}{2,598,960} \approx 0.0005$

31. a. 0.1

b. $1 - 0.1 = 0.9$

33. $\dfrac{4}{52} + \dfrac{4}{52} = \dfrac{8}{52} = \dfrac{2}{13} \approx 0.154$

35. $\dfrac{2}{52} + \dfrac{2}{52} = \dfrac{4}{52} = \dfrac{1}{13} \approx 0.076$

37. $P(E) = P(\text{even}) + P(\text{less than 5})$
$\qquad - P(\text{even and less than 5})$
$\quad = \dfrac{3}{6} + \dfrac{4}{6} - \dfrac{2}{6} = \dfrac{5}{6}$

39. $P(E) = P(7) + P(\text{red}) - P(\text{red 7})$
$\quad = \dfrac{4}{52} + \dfrac{26}{52} - \dfrac{2}{52} = \dfrac{28}{52} = \dfrac{7}{13}$

41. $P(E) = P(\text{odd}) + P(\text{less than 6})$
$\qquad - P(\text{odd and less than 6})$
$\quad = \dfrac{4}{8} + \dfrac{5}{8} - \dfrac{3}{8} = \dfrac{6}{8} = \dfrac{3}{4}$

43. $P(E)$
$= P(\text{professor}) + P(\text{male}) - P(\text{male professor})$
$\quad = \dfrac{19}{40} + \dfrac{22}{40} - \dfrac{8}{40} = \dfrac{33}{40}$

45. $P(E) = P(2) \cdot P(3) = \dfrac{1}{6} \cdot \dfrac{1}{6} = \dfrac{1}{36}$

47. $P(E) = P(\text{even}) \cdot P(\text{greater than 2})$
$\quad = \dfrac{3}{6} \cdot \dfrac{4}{6} = \dfrac{1}{2} \cdot \dfrac{2}{3} = \dfrac{1}{3}$

49. $P(E) = \left(\dfrac{1}{2}\right)^{6} = \dfrac{1}{64}$

51. $0.22^{4} \approx 0.00234$

53. a. $P(E) = \dfrac{1}{16} \cdot \dfrac{1}{16} = \dfrac{1}{256}$

  b. $P(E) = \left(\dfrac{1}{16}\right)^{3} = \dfrac{1}{4096}$

  c. $P(E) = \left(\dfrac{15}{16}\right)^{10}$

  d. $1 - \left(\dfrac{15}{16}\right)^{10}$

55.–65. Answers may vary.

Review Exercises

1. $a_n = 7n - 4$
$a_1 = 7 - 4 = 3$
$a_2 = 14 - 4 = 10$
$a_3 = 21 - 4 = 17$
$a_4 = 28 - 4 = 24$
The first four terms are 3, 10, 17, and 24.

2. $a_n = (-1)^{n}\,\dfrac{n+2}{n+1}$
$a_1 = (-1)^{1}\,\dfrac{1+2}{1+1} = -\dfrac{3}{2}$
$a_2 = (-1)^{2}\,\dfrac{2+2}{2+1} = \dfrac{4}{3}$
$a_3 = (-1)^{3}\,\dfrac{3+2}{3+1} = -\dfrac{5}{4}$
$a_4 = (-1)^{4}\,\dfrac{4+2}{4+1} = \dfrac{6}{5}$
The first four terms are
$-\dfrac{3}{2}, \dfrac{4}{3}, -\dfrac{5}{4}, \text{ and } \dfrac{6}{5}.$

3. $a_n = \dfrac{1}{(n-1)!}$
$a_1 = \dfrac{1}{0!} = 1$
$a_2 = \dfrac{1}{1!} = 1$
$a_3 = \dfrac{1}{2!} = \dfrac{1}{2}$
$a_4 = \dfrac{1}{3!} = \dfrac{1}{6}$
The first four terms are $1, 1, \dfrac{1}{2}, \text{ and } \dfrac{1}{6}.$

4. $a_n = \dfrac{(-1)^{n+1}}{2^n}$

$a_1 = \dfrac{(-1)^2}{2^1} = \dfrac{1}{2}$

$a_2 = \dfrac{(-1)^3}{2^2} = -\dfrac{1}{4}$

$a_3 = \dfrac{(-1)^4}{2^3} = \dfrac{1}{8}$

$a_4 = \dfrac{(-1)^5}{2^4} = -\dfrac{1}{16}$

The first four terms are

$\dfrac{1}{2}, -\dfrac{1}{4}, \dfrac{1}{8},$ and $-\dfrac{1}{16}.$

5. $a_1 = 9$ and $a_n = \dfrac{2}{3a_{n-1}}$

$a_1 = 9$

$a_2 = \dfrac{2}{3 \cdot 9} = \dfrac{2}{27}$

$a_3 = \dfrac{2}{3} \cdot \dfrac{27}{2} = \dfrac{54}{6} = 9$

$a_4 = \dfrac{2}{3 \cdot 9} = \dfrac{2}{27}$

The first four terms are $9, \dfrac{2}{27}, 9,$ and $\dfrac{2}{27}.$

6. $a_1 = 4$ and $a_n = 2a_{n-1} + 3$

$a_1 = 4$

$a_2 = 2 \cdot 4 + 3 = 8 + 3 = 11$

$a_3 = 2 \cdot 11 + 3 = 22 + 3 = 25$

$a_4 = 2 \cdot 25 + 3 = 50 + 3 = 53$

The first four terms are 4, 11, 25, and 53.

7. $\dfrac{40!}{4! \cdot 38!} = \dfrac{40 \cdot 39 \cdot 38!}{4 \cdot 3 \cdot 2 \cdot 1 \cdot 38!} = 65$

8. $\displaystyle\sum_{i=1}^{5}\left(2i^2-3\right)=\left(2-3\right)+\left(2\cdot 2^2-3\right)+\left(2\cdot 3^2-3\right)+\left(2\cdot 4^2-3\right)+\left(2\cdot 5^2-3\right)$

$$=-1+5+15+29+47$$
$$=95$$

9. $\displaystyle\sum_{i=0}^{4}(-1)^{i+1}i!=(-1)^1 0!+(-1)^2 1!+(-1)^3 3!+(-1)^4 4!$

$$=-1+1-2+6-24$$
$$=-20$$

10. $\displaystyle\frac{1}{3}+\frac{2}{4}+\frac{3}{5}+\cdots+\frac{15}{17}=\sum_{i=1}^{15}\frac{i}{i+2}$

11. $\displaystyle 4^3+5^3+6^3+\cdots+13^3=\sum_{i=1}^{10}\left(i+3\right)^3$

12. $a_1=7,\ d=4$
The first six terms are 7, 11, 15, 19, 23, and 27.

13. $a_1=-4,\ d=-5$
The first six terms are $-4,\ -9,\ -14,\ -19,\ -24,$ and -29.

14. $a_1=\dfrac{3}{2},\ d=-\dfrac{1}{2}$

The first six terms are $\dfrac{3}{2},\ 1,\ \dfrac{1}{2},\ 0,\ -\dfrac{1}{2},$ and -1.

15. $a_{n+1}=a_n+5,\ a_1=-2$
The first six terms are -2, 3, 8, 13, 18, and 23.

16. $a_1=5,\ d=3$
$a_n=5+\left(n-1\right)3$
$a_6=5+\left(5\right)3=20$

17. $a_1=-8,\ d=-2$
$a_n=-8+\left(n-1\right)\left(-2\right)$
$a_{12}=-8+11\left(-2\right)=-30$

18. $a_1=14,\ d=-4$
$a_n=14+\left(n-1\right)\left(-4\right)$
$a_{14}=14+\left(13\right)\left(-4\right)=-38$

19. −7, −3, 1, 5, …
$$d = -3 - (-7) = 4$$

$$a_n = -7 + (n-1)(4)$$
$$a_n = 4n - 11$$
$$a_{20} = 4(20) - 11$$
$$a_{20} = 69$$

20. $a_1 = 200, d = -20$
$$a_n = 200 + (n-1)(-20)$$
$$a_n = 220 - 20n$$
$$a_{20} = 220 - 20(20)$$
$$a_{20} = -180$$

25. $\displaystyle\sum_{i=1}^{16}(3i+2)$
$$a_1 = 3 + 2 = 5$$
$$a_{16} = 3(16) + 2 = 50$$
$$S_{16} = \frac{16}{2}(5 + 50) = 440$$

21. $a_n = a_{n-1} - 5, a_1 = 3$
$$d = -5$$
$$a_n = 3 + (n-1)(-5) = 3 - 5n + 5$$
$$a_n = 8 - 5n$$
$$a_{20} = 8 - 5(20) = -92$$

26. $\displaystyle\sum_{i=1}^{25}(-2i+6)$
$$a_1 = -2 + 6 = 4$$
$$a_{25} = -2(25) + 6 = -44$$
$$S_{25} = \frac{25}{2}(4 - 44) = -500$$

22. 5, 12, 19, 26, …
$$d = 7$$
$$a_n = 5 + (n-1)(7)$$
$$a_{22} = 5 + 21(7) = 152$$
$$S_{22} = \frac{22}{2}(5 + 152) = 1727$$

27. $\displaystyle\sum_{i=1}^{30} -5i$
$$a_1 = -5$$
$$a_{30} = -5(30) = -150$$
$$S_{30} = \frac{30}{2}(-5 - 150) = -2325$$

23. −6, −3, 0, 3, …
$$d = 3$$
$$a_n = -6 + (n-1)3$$
$$a_{15} = -6 + (14)3 = 36$$
$$S_{15} = \frac{15}{2}(-6 + 36) = 225$$

28. a. $a_n = 20 + 0.52(n-1)$

b. $n = 2010 - 1900 = 110$
$$a_{110} = 20 + 0.52(109) = 76.68$$
In 2010, 76.68% of the labor force will be white-collar.

24. 3 + 6 + 9 + . . . + 300
$$S_{100} = \frac{100}{2}(3 + 300) = 15,150$$

29. $a_n = 31{,}500 + (n-1)2300$

$a_{10} = 31{,}500 + (9)2300 = 52{,}200$

$S_{10} = \dfrac{10}{2}(31{,}500 + 52{,}200) = 418{,}500$

The total salary is \$418, 500.

30. $a_n = 25 + (n-1)$

$a_{35} = 25 + 34 = 59$

$S_{35} = \dfrac{35}{2}(25 + 59) = 1470$

There are 1470 seats.

31. $a_1 = 3,\ r = 2$

The first five terms are 3, 6, 12, 24, and 48.

32. $a_1 = \dfrac{1}{2},\ r = \dfrac{1}{2}$

The first five terms are

$\dfrac{1}{2},\ \dfrac{1}{4},\ \dfrac{1}{8},\ \dfrac{1}{16},$ and $\dfrac{1}{32}.$

33. $a_1 = 16,\ r = -\dfrac{1}{2}$

The first five terms are
16, -8, 4, -2, and 1.

34. $a_n = -5a_{n-1},\ a_1 = -1$

The first five terms are -1, 5, -25, 125, and -625.

35. $a_1 = 2,\ r = 3$

$a_n = 2 \cdot 3^{n-1}$

$a_7 = 2 \cdot 3^6 = 1458$

36. $a_1 = 16,\ r = \dfrac{1}{2}$

$a_n = 16\left(\dfrac{1}{2}\right)^{n-1}$

$a_6 = 16\left(\dfrac{1}{2}\right)^5 = \dfrac{16}{32} = \dfrac{1}{2}$

37. $a_1 = -3,\ r = 2$

$a_n = -3 \cdot 2^{n-1}$

$a_5 = -3 \cdot 2^4 = -48$

38. 1, 2, 4, 8, ...

$a_1 = 1,\ r = \dfrac{2}{1} = 2$

$a_n = 2^{n-1}$

$a_8 = 2^7 = 128$

39. 100, 10, 1, $\dfrac{1}{10}$, ...

$a_1 = 100,\ r = \dfrac{10}{100} = \dfrac{1}{10}$

$a_n = 100\left(\dfrac{1}{10}\right)^{n-1}$

$a_8 = 100\left(\dfrac{1}{10}\right)^7 = \dfrac{1}{100{,}000}$

40. $12, -4, \dfrac{4}{3}, -\dfrac{4}{9} \cdots$

$a_1 = 12,\ r = -\dfrac{4}{12} = -\dfrac{1}{3}$

$a_n = 12\left(-\dfrac{1}{3}\right)^{n-1}$

$a_8 = 12\left(-\dfrac{1}{3}\right)^7 = -\dfrac{4}{729}$

41. $5, -15, 45, -135, \ldots$

$$r = \frac{-15}{5} = -3$$

$$S_{15} = \frac{5\left[1 - (-3)^{15}\right]}{1 - (-3)} = 17{,}936{,}135$$

42. $r = \frac{1}{2}, a_1 = 8$

$$S_{78} = \frac{8\left[1 - \left(\frac{1}{2}\right)^7\right]}{1 - \frac{1}{2}} = -16\left(1 - \frac{1}{128}\right)$$

$$= -16\left(-\frac{127}{128}\right) = \frac{127}{8} = 15\frac{7}{8}$$

43. $S_6 = \frac{5\left(1 - 5^6\right)}{1 - 5} = \frac{5(-15624)}{-4} = 19{,}530$

44. $\displaystyle\sum_{i=1}^{7} 3(-2)^i$

$a_1 = -6, r = -2$

$$S_7 = \frac{-6\left[1 - (-2)^7\right]}{1 - (-2)} = \frac{-6(129)}{3} = -258$$

45. $\displaystyle\sum_{i=1}^{5} 2\left(\tfrac{1}{4}\right)^{i-1}$

$a_1 = 2, r = \frac{1}{4}$

$$S_5 = \frac{2\left[1 - \left(\tfrac{1}{4}\right)^5\right]}{1 - \tfrac{1}{4}} = \frac{2\left(\tfrac{1023}{1024}\right)}{\tfrac{3}{4}} = \frac{341}{128}$$

46. $a_1 = 9, r = \frac{1}{3}$

$$S_\infty = \frac{9}{1 - \frac{1}{3}} = \frac{9}{\frac{2}{3}} = 9 \cdot \frac{3}{2} = \frac{27}{2}$$

47. $a_1 = 2, r = -\frac{1}{2}$

$$S_\infty = \frac{2}{1 - \left(-\frac{1}{2}\right)} = \frac{2}{\frac{3}{2}} = \frac{4}{3}$$

48. $a_1 = -6, r = -\frac{2}{3}$

$$S_\infty = \frac{-6}{1 - \left(-\frac{2}{3}\right)} = \frac{-6}{\frac{5}{3}} = -\frac{18}{5}$$

49. $r = 0.8$

$$S_\infty = \frac{4}{1 - 0.8} = 20$$

50. $0.\overline{6} = 0.6 + 0.06 + 0.006 + \cdots$

$$a_1 = \frac{6}{10}, r = \frac{1}{10}$$

$$S_\infty = \frac{\frac{6}{10}}{1 - \frac{1}{10}} = \frac{\frac{6}{10}}{\frac{9}{10}} = \frac{6}{9} = \frac{2}{3}$$

51. $0.\overline{47} = 0.47 + 0.0047 + 0.000047 + \cdots$

$$a_1 = \frac{47}{100}, r = \frac{1}{100}$$

$$S_\infty = \frac{\frac{47}{100}}{1 - \frac{1}{100}} = \frac{\frac{47}{100}}{\frac{99}{100}} = \frac{47}{99}$$

52. a. $\dfrac{21.36}{20.6} = 1.04$

$\dfrac{22.19}{21.36} = 1.04$

$\dfrac{23.02}{22.19} = 1.04$

b. $a_n = 20.6 + (n-1)1.04$

c. $a_{11} = 20.6 + (11-1)1.04 = 31$
Iraq's population will be approximately 31 million in 2005.

53. $a_1 = 32,000, \ r = 1.06$

$a_6 = 32,000(1.06)^5 \approx 42,823.22$
The sixth year salary is $42,823.22.

$S_6 = \dfrac{32,000\left(1-1.06^6\right)}{1-1.06}$

$= \dfrac{32,000\left(1-1.06^6\right)}{-0.06}$

$\approx 223,210.19$

The total salary paid is $223,210.

54. $A = 200 \dfrac{\left(1+\frac{0.1}{12}\right)^{18\cdot12} - 1}{\frac{0.1}{12}} \approx 120,112.64$

You will save $120,112.64.

55. $4(0.7) + 4(0.7)^2 + \cdots; \ r = 0.7$

$S_\infty = \dfrac{4(0.7)}{1-0.7} = 9.\overline{3}$

The total spending is $9\dfrac{1}{3}$ million.

56. $_8P_3 = \dfrac{8!}{5!} = 8 \cdot 7 \cdot 6 = 336$

57. $_9P_5 = \dfrac{9!}{4!} = 9 \cdot 8 \cdot 7 \cdot 6 \cdot 5 = 15,120$

58. $_8C_3 = \dfrac{8!}{5!\,3!} = \dfrac{8 \cdot 7 \cdot 6}{3 \cdot 2 \cdot 1} = 56$

59. $_{13}C_{11} = \dfrac{13!}{2!\,11!} = \dfrac{13 \cdot 12}{2 \cdot 1} = 78$

60. $4 \cdot 5 = 20$ choices

61. $3^5 = 243$ possibilities

62. $_{15}P_4 = \dfrac{15!}{11!} = 15 \cdot 14 \cdot 13 \cdot 12 = 32,760$ ways

63. $_{20}C_4 = \dfrac{20!}{16!\,4!} = \dfrac{20 \cdot 19 \cdot 18 \cdot 17}{4 \cdot 3 \cdot 2 \cdot 1} = 4845$ ways

64. $_{20}C_3 = \dfrac{20!}{17!\,3!} = \dfrac{20 \cdot 19 \cdot 18}{3 \cdot 2 \cdot 1} = 1140$ sets

65. $_{20}P_4 = \dfrac{20!}{16!}$
$= 20 \cdot 19 \cdot 18 \cdot 17$
$= 116,280$ ways

66. $5! = 120$ ways

67. $P(E) = \dfrac{10,966,556}{33,871,648} \approx 0.324$

68. $P(E) = \dfrac{6,669,666}{20,851,820} \approx 0.320$

69. $P(E) = \dfrac{n(E)}{n(S)} = \dfrac{4}{6} = \dfrac{2}{3}$

70. $P(E) = \dfrac{2}{6} + \dfrac{2}{6} = \dfrac{4}{6} = \dfrac{2}{3}$

71. $P(E) = \dfrac{4}{52} + \dfrac{4}{52} = \dfrac{8}{52} = \dfrac{2}{13}$

72. $P(E) = \dfrac{4}{52} + \dfrac{26}{52} - \dfrac{2}{52} = \dfrac{28}{52} = \dfrac{7}{13}$

73. $P(\text{not yellow}) = 1 - P(\text{yellow}) = 1 - \dfrac{1}{6} = \dfrac{5}{6}$

74. $P(E) = \dfrac{3}{6} + \dfrac{3}{6} - \dfrac{1}{6} = \dfrac{5}{6}$

75. a. $P(E) = \dfrac{n(E)}{n(S)} = \dfrac{1}{_{20}C_5} = \dfrac{1}{15,504}$

b. $P(E) = \dfrac{100}{15,504} = \dfrac{25}{3876}$

76. $P(E) = \dfrac{70}{200} + \dfrac{140}{200} - \dfrac{50}{200} = \dfrac{160}{200} = \dfrac{4}{5}$

77. $P(E) = \dfrac{60}{200} + \dfrac{130}{200} - \dfrac{40}{200} = \dfrac{150}{200} = \dfrac{3}{4}$

78. $0.303 + 0.230 = 0.533$

Chapter 4 Test

1. $a_n = \dfrac{(-1)^{n+1}}{n^2}$

$a_1 = \dfrac{(-1)^2}{1^2} = 1$

$a_2 = \dfrac{(-1)^3}{2^2} = -\dfrac{1}{4}$

$a_3 = \dfrac{(-1)^4}{3^2} = \dfrac{1}{9}$

$a_4 = \dfrac{(-1)^5}{4^2} = -\dfrac{1}{16}$

$a_5 = \dfrac{(-1)^6}{5^2} = \dfrac{1}{25}$

The first five terms are

$1, -\dfrac{1}{4}, \dfrac{1}{9}, -\dfrac{1}{16}$, and $\dfrac{1}{25}$.

2. $\displaystyle\sum_{i=1}^{5}\left(i^2 + 10\right) = 11 + 14 + 19 + 26 + 35 = 105$

3. $\displaystyle\sum_{i=1}^{20}\left(3i - 4\right)$

$a_1 = 3 - 4 = -1$

$d = 3$

$a_n = -1 + (n-1)3$

$a_{20} = -1 + (19)3 = 56$

$S_{20} = \dfrac{20}{2}(-1 + 56) = 550$

4. $\displaystyle\sum_{i=1}^{15}(-2)^i$

$a_1 = -2, \; r = -2$

$S_{15} = \dfrac{-2\left[1 - (-2)^{15}\right]}{1 - (-2)} = -21,846$

5. $\dbinom{9}{2} = \dfrac{9!}{7!\,2!} = \dfrac{9 \cdot 8}{2 \cdot 1} = 36$

6. $_{10}P_3 = \dfrac{10!}{7!} = 10 \cdot 9 \cdot 8 = 720$

7. $_{10}C_3 = \dfrac{10!}{7!\,3!} = \dfrac{10 \cdot 9 \cdot 8}{3 \cdot 2 \cdot 1} = 120$

8. $\dfrac{2}{3} + \dfrac{3}{4} + \dfrac{4}{5} + \cdots + \dfrac{21}{22} = \displaystyle\sum_{i=1}^{20}\dfrac{i+1}{i+2}$

9. $4, 9, 14, 19, \ldots$

$a_1 = 4, \; d = 5$

$a_n = 4 + (n-1) \cdot 5 = 4 + 5n - 1$

$a_n = 5n - 1$

$a_{12} = 5(12) - 1 = 59$

10.　16, 4, 1, $\dfrac{1}{4}$, $\cdots$

$\quad a_1 = 16,\ r = \dfrac{1}{4}$

$\quad a_n = 16\left(\dfrac{1}{4}\right)^{n-1}$

$\quad a_{12} = 16\left(\dfrac{1}{4}\right)^{11} = \dfrac{1}{262{,}144}$

11.　7, –14, 28, –56, . . .

$\quad a_1 = 7,\ r = -2$

$\quad S_{10} = \dfrac{7\left[1 - \left(-2\right)^{10}\right]}{1 - \left(-2\right)} = \dfrac{7(-1023)}{3} = -2387$

12.　–7, –14, –21, –28, . . .

$\quad a_1 = -7,\ d = -7$

$\quad a_n = -7 + \left(n-1\right)\left(-7\right)$

$\quad a_{10} = -7 + 9\left(-7\right) = -70$

$\quad S_{10} = \dfrac{10}{2}\left(-7 - 70\right) = -385$

13.　$4 + \dfrac{4}{2} + \dfrac{4}{2^2} + \dfrac{4}{2^3} + \cdots$

$\quad r = \dfrac{1}{2}$

$\quad S_\infty = \dfrac{4}{1 - \dfrac{1}{2}} = 8$

14.　$a_1 = 30{,}000,\ r = 1.04$

$\quad S_8 = \dfrac{30{,}000\left[1 - \left(1.04\right)^8\right]}{1 - 1.04} \approx 276{,}426.79$

　　The total salary is \$276,427.

15. $S_1 : 1 = \dfrac{1\left[3(1)-1\right]}{2}$

$1 = \dfrac{2}{2}$

$1 = 1$ is true.

$S_k : 1 + 4 + 7 + \cdots + (3k-2) = \dfrac{k(3k-1)}{2}$

$S_{k+1} : 1 + 4 + 7 + \cdots + (3k-2) + (3k+1) = \dfrac{(k+1)(3k+2)}{2}$

Add $(3k+1)$ to both sides of S_k:

$1 + 4 + 7 + \cdots + (3k-2) + (3k+1) = \dfrac{k(3k-1)}{2} + (3k+1)$

Simplify the right-hand side:

$\dfrac{k(3k-1)}{2} + (3k+1) = \dfrac{k(3k-1) + 2(3k+1)}{2}$

$= \dfrac{3k^2 + 5k + 2}{2}$

$= \dfrac{(k+1)(3k+2)}{2}$

If S_k is true, then S_{k+1} is true. The statement is true for all n.

16. $\left(x^2 - 1\right)^5 = \binom{5}{0}\left(x^2\right)^5 + \binom{5}{1}\left(x^2\right)^4(-1) + \binom{5}{2}\left(x^2\right)^3(-1)^2 + \binom{5}{3}\left(x^2\right)^2(-1)^3 + \binom{5}{4}x^2(-1)^4 + \binom{5}{5}(-1)^5$

$= x^{10} - 5x^8 + 10x^6 - 10x^4 + 5x^2 - 1$

17. ${}_{11}P_3 = \dfrac{11!}{8!} = 11 \cdot 10 \cdot 9 = 990$ ways

21. $P(E) = \dfrac{26}{52} + \dfrac{12}{52} - \dfrac{6}{52} = \dfrac{32}{52} = \dfrac{8}{13}$

18. ${}_{10}C_4 = \dfrac{10!}{6!\,4!} = \dfrac{10 \cdot 9 \cdot 8 \cdot 7}{4 \cdot 3 \cdot 2 \cdot 1} = 210$ sets

22. $P(E) = \dfrac{25}{50} + \dfrac{20}{50} - \dfrac{15}{50} = \dfrac{30}{50} = \dfrac{3}{5}$

19. Four digits are open: $10^4 = 10,000$

20. ${}_{15}C_6 = \dfrac{15!}{9!\,6!} = \dfrac{15 \cdot 14 \cdot 13 \cdot 12 \cdot 11 \cdot 10}{6 \cdot 5 \cdot 4 \cdot 3 \cdot 2} = 5005$

$P(E) = \dfrac{50}{5005} = \dfrac{10}{1001}$